Ultimate Family Puzzles

NUMBERS

igloo

igloo

Published in 2006
by Igloo Books Ltd
Cottage Farm,
Sywell,
NN6 0BJ.
www.igloo-books.com

10 9 8 7 6 5 4 3 2

ISBN 978 1 84561 3815

Project Management by Metro Media Ltd
Production: Cecilia Thom
Text design & layout: Kurt Young, Richard Reid
Cover design: Dan Tyler & Kurt Young
Puzzles created by: Puzzlecraft and Puzzle Press

Printed in China

Welcome to
Ultimate Family Puzzles
NUMBERS

All the family can enjoy *Ultimate Family Puzzles: Numbers*, as it has something to suit everyone. It contains popular puzzles such as Sudoku, Kakuro, Number Sequences, Magic Squares and many more.

There are three levels of difficulty in this book. Easy puzzles are marked with one star and, as the name suggests, are the most simple puzzles to do. These are suitable for the youngest child or the puzzle beginner. The moderate puzzles are that little bit harder, and have been highlighted with two stars for those who feel that the easy puzzles do not provide enough of a challenge.

Then finally there are the challenging puzzles, which are marked with three stars. These are for serious puzzlers only and represent the peak of difficulty. So, something for all the family to sit down together and enjoy!

EASY ☆

MODERATE ☆☆

CHALLENGING ☆☆☆

DOMINO PLACEMENT

A standard set of dominoes has been laid out, using only the dominoes shown below each puzzle. Can you draw in the edges of them all? The check-box is provided as an aid, and in some puzzles, a starting domino has been placed, which will get you on your way.

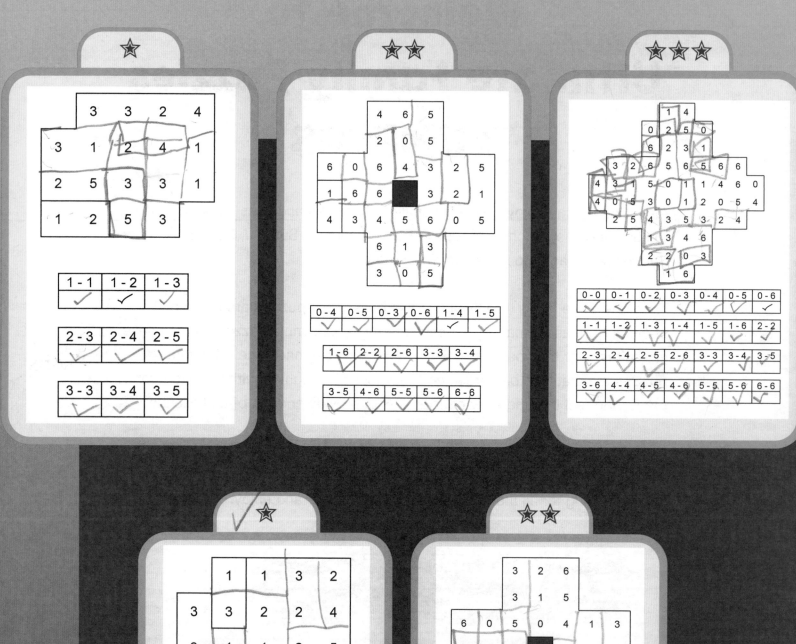

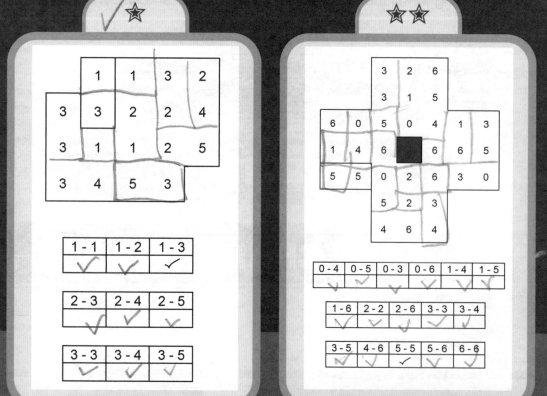

★

	3	3	2	4
3	1	2	4	1
2	5	3	3	1
1	2	5	3	

1 - 1	1 - 2	1 - 3
✓	✓	✓

2 - 3	2 - 4	2 - 5
✓	✓	✓

3 - 3	3 - 4	3 - 5
✓	✓	✓

★★

		4	6	5		
		2	0	5		
6	0	6	4	3	2	5
1	6	6	■	3	2	1
4	3	4	5	6	0	5
		6	1	3		
		3	0	5		

0 - 4	0 - 5	0 - 3	0 - 6	1 - 4	1 - 5
✓	✓	✓	✓	✓	✓

1 - 6	2 - 2	2 - 6	3 - 3	3 - 4
✓	✓	✓	✓	✓

3 - 5	4 - 6	5 - 5	5 - 6	6 - 6
✓	✓	✓	✓	✓

★★★

				1	4				
			0	2	5	0			
			6	2	3	1			
	3	2	6	5	6	5	6	6	
4	3	1	5	0	1	1	4	6	0
4	0	5	3	0	1	2	0	5	4
	2	5	4	3	5	3	2	4	
			1	3	4	6			
			2	2	0	3			
				1	6				

0 - 0	0 - 1	0 - 2	0 - 3	0 - 4	0 - 5	0 - 6
✓	✓	✓	✓	✓	✓	✓

1 - 1	1 - 2	1 - 3	1 - 4	1 - 5	1 - 6	2 - 2
✓	✓	✓	✓	✓	✓	✓

2 - 3	2 - 4	2 - 5	2 - 6	3 - 3	3 - 4	3 - 5
✓	✓	✓	✓	✓	✓	✓

3 - 6	4 - 4	4 - 5	4 - 6	5 - 5	5 - 6	6 - 6
✓	✓	✓	✓	✓	✓	✓

★

	1	1	3	2
3	3	2	2	4
3	1	1	2	5
3	4	5	3	

1 - 1	1 - 2	1 - 3
✓	✓	✓

2 - 3	2 - 4	2 - 5
✓	✓	✓

3 - 3	3 - 4	3 - 5
✓	✓	✓

★★

		3	2	6		
		3	1	5		
6	0	5	0	4	1	3
1	4	6	■	6	6	5
5	5	0	2	6	3	0
		5	2	3		
		4	6	4		

0 - 4	0 - 5	0 - 3	0 - 6	1 - 4	1 - 5
✓	✓	✓	✓	✓	✓

1 - 6	2 - 2	2 - 6	3 - 3	3 - 4
✓	✓	✓	✓	✓

3 - 5	4 - 6	5 - 5	5 - 6	6 - 6
✓	✓	✓	✓	✓

Turn to page 196 for the solutions

DOMINO PLACEMENT

★★★

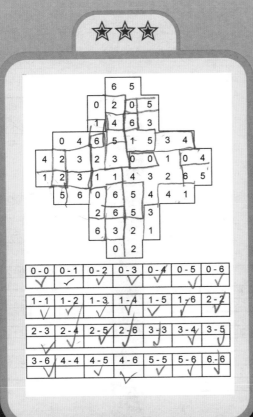

				6	5				
			0	2	0	5			
			1	4	6	3			
	0	4	6	5	1	5	3	4	
4	2	3	2	3	0	0	1	0	4
1	2	3	1	1	4	3	2	6	5
	5	6	0	6	5	4	4	1	
			2	6	5	3			
			6	3	2	1			
				0	2				

0 - 0	0 - 1	0 - 2	0 - 3	0 - 4	0 - 5	0 - 6
✓	✓	✓	✓	✓	✓	✓

1 - 1	1 - 2	1 - 3	1 - 4	1 - 5	1 - 6	2 - 2
✓	✓	✓	✓	✓	✓	✓

2 - 3	2 - 4	2 - 5	2 - 6	3 - 3	3 - 4	3 - 5
✓	✓	✓	✓	✓	✓	✓

3 - 6	4 - 4	4 - 5	4 - 6	5 - 5	5 - 6	6 - 6
✓		✓	✓	✓	✓	✓

★

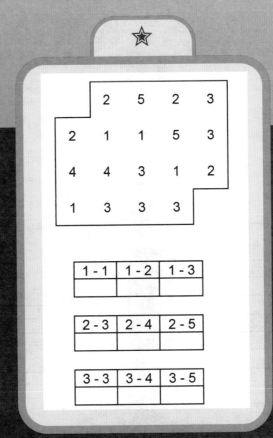

	2	5	2	3
2	1	1	5	3
4	4	3	1	2
1	3	3	3	

1 - 1	1 - 2	1 - 3

2 - 3	2 - 4	2 - 5

3 - 3	3 - 4	3 - 5

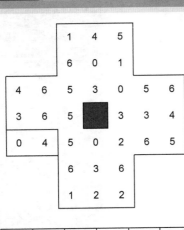

★★

		1	4	5		
		6	0	1		
4	6	5	3	0	5	6
3	6	5	■	3	3	4
0	4	5	0	2	6	5
		6	3	6		
		1	2	2		

0 - 4	0 - 5	0 - 3	0 - 6	1 - 4	1 - 5
✓					

1 - 6	2 - 2	2 - 6	3 - 3	3 - 4

3 - 5	4 - 6	5 - 5	5 - 6	6 - 6

★★★

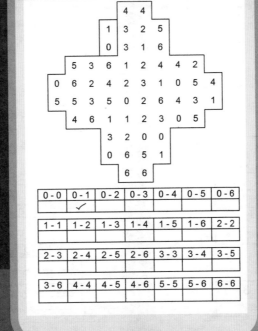

				4	4				
			1	3	2	5			
			0	3	1	6			
	5	3	6	1	2	4	4	2	
0	6	2	4	2	3	1	0	5	4
5	5	3	5	0	2	6	4	3	1
	4	6	1	1	2	3	0	5	
			3	2	0	0			
			0	6	5	1			
				6	6				

0 - 0	0 - 1	0 - 2	0 - 3	0 - 4	0 - 5	0 - 6
	✓					

1 - 1	1 - 2	1 - 3	1 - 4	1 - 5	1 - 6	2 - 2

2 - 3	2 - 4	2 - 5	2 - 6	3 - 3	3 - 4	3 - 5

3 - 6	4 - 4	4 - 5	4 - 6	5 - 5	5 - 6	6 - 6

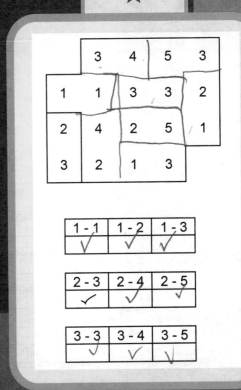

★

	3	4	5	3
1	1	3	3	2
2	4	2	5	1
3	2	1	3	

1 - 1	1 - 2	1 - 3
✓	✓	✓

2 - 3	2 - 4	2 - 5
✓	✓	✓

3 - 3	3 - 4	3 - 5
✓	✓	✓

Turn to page 196 for the solutions

DOMINO PLACEMENT

A standard set of dominoes has been laid out, using only the dominoes shown below each puzzle. Can you draw in the edges of them all? The check-box is provided as an aid, and in some puzzles, a starting domino has been placed, which will get you on your way.

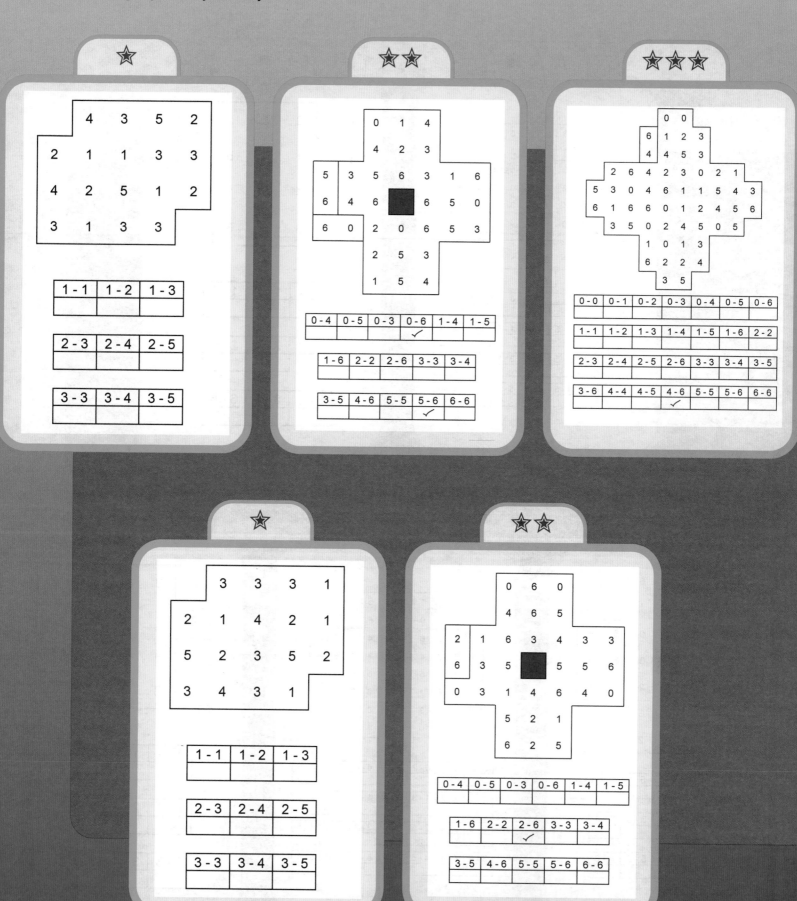

★

	4	3	5	2
2	1	1	3	3
4	2	5	1	2
3	1	3	3	

1 - 1	1 - 2	1 - 3

2 - 3	2 - 4	2 - 5

3 - 3	3 - 4	3 - 5

★★

		0	1	4		
		4	2	3		
5	3	5	6	3	1	6
6	4	6	■	6	5	0
6	0	2	0	6	5	3
		2	5	3		
		1	5	4		

0 - 4	0 - 5	0 - 3	0 - 6	1 - 4	1 - 5
			✓		

1 - 6	2 - 2	2 - 6	3 - 3	3 - 4

3 - 5	4 - 6	5 - 5	5 - 6	6 - 6
			✓	

★★★

				0	0				
			6	1	2	3			
			4	4	5	3			
	2	6	4	2	3	0	2	1	
5	3	0	4	6	1	1	5	4	3
6	1	6	6	0	1	2	4	5	6
	3	5	0	2	4	5	0	5	
			1	0	1	3			
			6	2	2	4			
				3	5				

0 - 0	0 - 1	0 - 2	0 - 3	0 - 4	0 - 5	0 - 6

1 - 1	1 - 2	1 - 3	1 - 4	1 - 5	1 - 6	2 - 2

2 - 3	2 - 4	2 - 5	2 - 6	3 - 3	3 - 4	3 - 5

3 - 6	4 - 4	4 - 5	4 - 6	5 - 5	5 - 6	6 - 6
			✓			

★

	3	3	3	1
2	1	4	2	1
5	2	3	5	2
3	4	3	1	

1 - 1	1 - 2	1 - 3

2 - 3	2 - 4	2 - 5

3 - 3	3 - 4	3 - 5

★★

		0	6	0		
		4	6	5		
2	1	6	3	4	3	3
6	3	5	■	5	5	6
0	3	1	4	6	4	0
		5	2	1		
		6	2	5		

0 - 4	0 - 5	0 - 3	0 - 6	1 - 4	1 - 5

1 - 6	2 - 2	2 - 6	3 - 3	3 - 4
		✓		

3 - 5	4 - 6	5 - 5	5 - 6	6 - 6

 Turn to page 196 for the solutions

DOMINO PLACEMENT

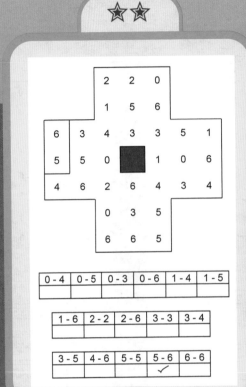

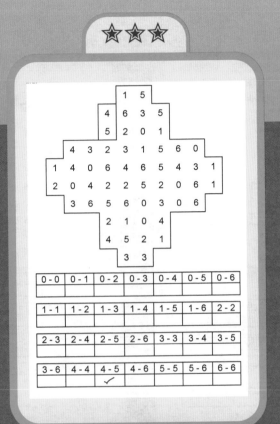

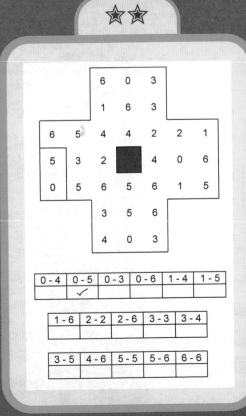

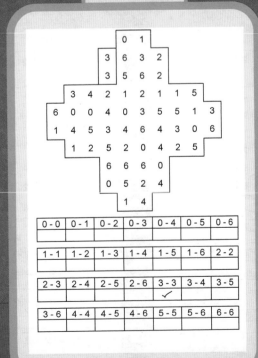

★★★

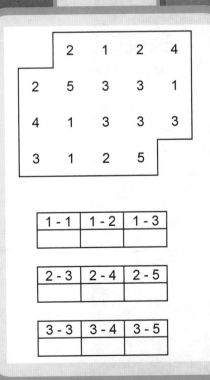

				1	5				
			4	6	3	5			
			5	2	0	1			
	4	3	2	3	1	5	6	0	
1	4	0	6	4	6	5	4	3	1
2	0	4	2	2	5	2	0	6	1
	3	6	5	6	0	3	0	6	
			2	1	0	4			
			4	5	2	1			
				3	3				

0 - 0	0 - 1	0 - 2	0 - 3	0 - 4	0 - 5	0 - 6

1 - 1	1 - 2	1 - 3	1 - 4	1 - 5	1 - 6	2 - 2

2 - 3	2 - 4	2 - 5	2 - 6	3 - 3	3 - 4	3 - 5

3 - 6	4 - 4	4 - 5	4 - 6	5 - 5	5 - 6	6 - 6
		✓				

★★

		2	2	0		
		1	5	6		
6	3	4	3	3	5	1
5	5	0	■	1	0	6
4	6	2	6	4	3	4
		0	3	5		
		6	6	5		

0 - 4	0 - 5	0 - 3	0 - 6	1 - 4	1 - 5

1 - 6	2 - 2	2 - 6	3 - 3	3 - 4

3 - 5	4 - 6	5 - 5	5 - 6	6 - 6
			✓	

★★

		6	0	3		
		1	6	3		
6	5	4	4	2	2	1
5	3	2	■	4	0	6
0	5	6	5	6	1	5
		3	5	6		
		4	0	3		

0 - 4	0 - 5	0 - 3	0 - 6	1 - 4	1 - 5
	✓				

1 - 6	2 - 2	2 - 6	3 - 3	3 - 4

3 - 5	4 - 6	5 - 5	5 - 6	6 - 6

★★★

				0	1				
			3	6	3	2			
			3	5	6	2			
	3	4	2	1	2	1	1	5	
6	0	0	4	0	3	5	5	1	3
1	4	5	3	4	6	4	3	0	6
	1	2	5	2	0	4	2	5	
			6	6	6	0			
			0	5	2	4			
				1	4				

0 - 0	0 - 1	0 - 2	0 - 3	0 - 4	0 - 5	0 - 6

1 - 1	1 - 2	1 - 3	1 - 4	1 - 5	1 - 6	2 - 2

2 - 3	2 - 4	2 - 5	2 - 6	3 - 3	3 - 4	3 - 5
				✓		

3 - 6	4 - 4	4 - 5	4 - 6	5 - 5	5 - 6	6 - 6

★

	2	1	2	4
2	5	3	3	1
4	1	3	3	3
3	1	2	5	

1 - 1	1 - 2	1 - 3

2 - 3	2 - 4	2 - 5

3 - 3	3 - 4	3 - 5

Turn to page 196 for the solutions

DOMINO PLACEMENT

A standard set of dominoes has been laid out, using only the dominoes shown below each puzzle. Can you draw in the edges of them all? The check-box is provided as an aid, and in some puzzles, a starting domino has been placed, which will get you on your way.

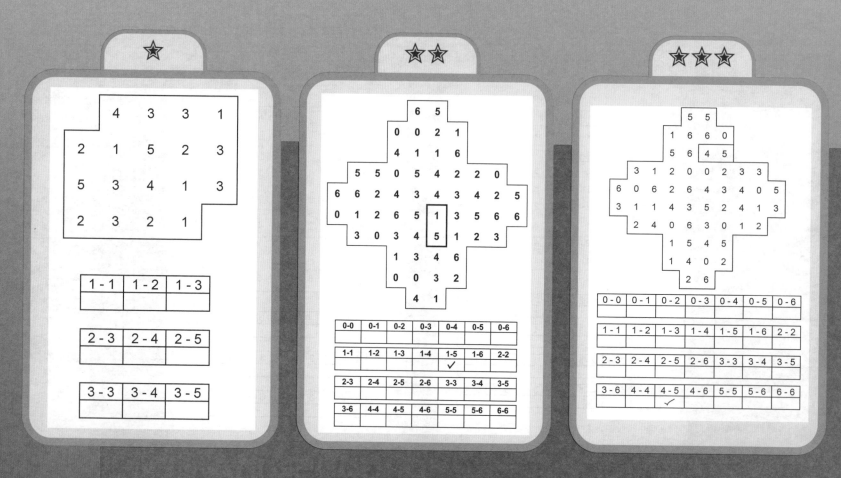

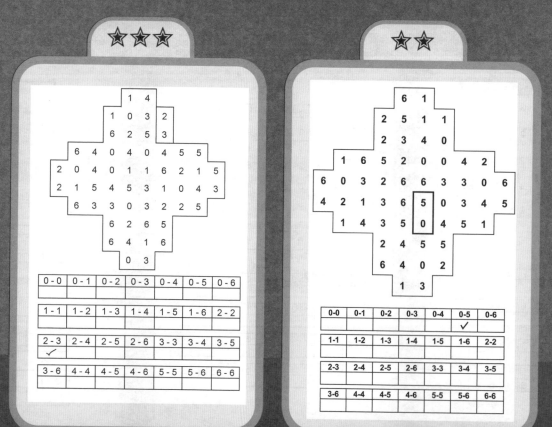

★

	4	3	3	1
2	1	5	2	3
5	3	4	1	3
2	3	2	1	

1 - 1	1 - 2	1 - 3

2 - 3	2 - 4	2 - 5

3 - 3	3 - 4	3 - 5

★★

				6	5				
			0	0	2	1			
			4	1	1	6			
	5	5	0	5	4	2	2	0	
6	6	2	4	3	4	3	4	2	5
0	1	2	6	5	1	3	5	6	6
	3	0	3	4	5	1	2	3	
			1	3	4	6			
			0	0	3	2			
				4	1				

0-0	0-1	0-2	0-3	0-4	0-5	0-6

1-1	1-2	1-3	1-4	1-5	1-6	2-2
				✓		

2-3	2-4	2-5	2-6	3-3	3-4	3-5

3-6	4-4	4-5	4-6	5-5	5-6	6-6

★★★

				5	5				
			1	6	6	0			
			5	6	4	5			
	3	1	2	0	0	2	3	3	
6	0	6	2	6	4	3	4	0	5
3	1	1	4	3	5	2	4	1	3
	2	4	0	6	3	0	1	2	
			1	5	4	5			
			1	4	0	2			
				2	6				

0 - 0	0 - 1	0 - 2	0 - 3	0 - 4	0 - 5	0 - 6

1 - 1	1 - 2	1 - 3	1 - 4	1 - 5	1 - 6	2 - 2

2 - 3	2 - 4	2 - 5	2 - 6	3 - 3	3 - 4	3 - 5

3 - 6	4 - 4	4 - 5	4 - 6	5 - 5	5 - 6	6 - 6
		✓				

★★★

				1	4				
			1	0	3	2			
			6	2	5	3			
	6	4	0	4	0	4	5	5	
2	0	4	0	1	1	6	2	1	5
2	1	5	4	5	3	1	0	4	3
	6	3	3	0	3	2	2	5	
			6	2	6	5			
			6	4	1	6			
				0	3				

0 - 0	0 - 1	0 - 2	0 - 3	0 - 4	0 - 5	0 - 6

1 - 1	1 - 2	1 - 3	1 - 4	1 - 5	1 - 6	2 - 2

2 - 3	2 - 4	2 - 5	2 - 6	3 - 3	3 - 4	3 - 5
✓						

3 - 6	4 - 4	4 - 5	4 - 6	5 - 5	5 - 6	6 - 6

★★

				6	1				
			2	5	1	1			
			2	3	4	0			
	1	6	5	2	0	0	4	2	
6	0	3	2	6	6	3	3	0	6
4	2	1	3	6	5	0	3	4	5
	1	4	3	5	0	4	5	1	
			2	4	5	5			
			6	4	0	2			
				1	3				

0-0	0-1	0-2	0-3	0-4	0-5	0-6
					✓	

1-1	1-2	1-3	1-4	1-5	1-6	2-2

2-3	2-4	2-5	2-6	3-3	3-4	3-5

3-6	4-4	4-5	4-6	5-5	5-6	6-6

Turn to page 196 for the solutions

DOMINO PLACEMENT

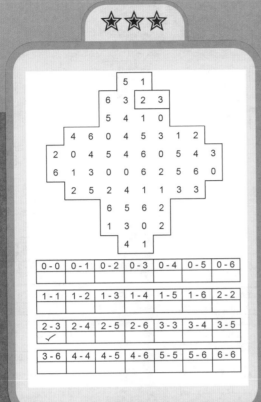

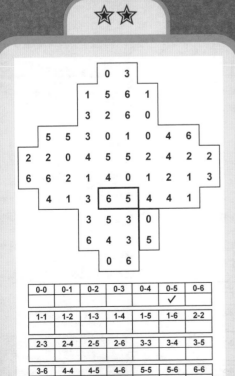

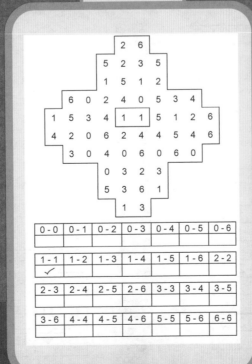

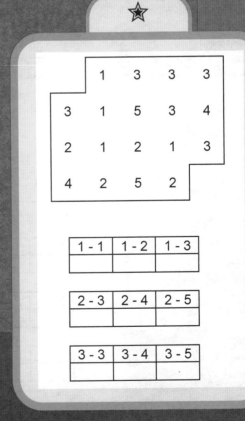

★★★

				5	1				
			6	3	2	3			
			5	4	1	0			
	4	6	0	4	5	3	1	2	
2	0	4	5	4	6	0	5	4	3
6	1	3	0	0	6	2	5	6	0
	2	5	2	4	1	1	3	3	
			6	5	6	2			
			1	3	0	2			
				4	1				

0 - 0	0 - 1	0 - 2	0 - 3	0 - 4	0 - 5	0 - 6

1 - 1	1 - 2	1 - 3	1 - 4	1 - 5	1 - 6	2 - 2

2 - 3	2 - 4	2 - 5	2 - 6	3 - 3	3 - 4	3 - 5
✓						

3 - 6	4 - 4	4 - 5	4 - 6	5 - 5	5 - 6	6 - 6

★

	3	3	2	3
1	4	5	1	4
2	2	2	1	3
1	3	5	3	

1 - 1	1 - 2	1 - 3

2 - 3	2 - 4	2 - 5

3 - 3	3 - 4	3 - 5

★★

				0	3				
			1	5	6	1			
			3	2	6	0			
	5	5	3	0	1	0	4	6	
2	2	0	4	5	5	2	4	2	2
6	6	2	1	4	0	1	2	1	3
	4	1	3	6	5	4	4	1	
			3	5	3	0			
			6	4	3	5			
				0	6				

0-0	0-1	0-2	0-3	0-4	0-5	0-6
					✓	

1-1	1-2	1-3	1-4	1-5	1-6	2-2

2-3	2-4	2-5	2-6	3-3	3-4	3-5

3-6	4-4	4-5	4-6	5-5	5-6	6-6
					✓	

★★★

				2	6				
			5	2	3	5			
			1	5	1	2			
	6	0	2	4	0	5	3	4	
1	5	3	4	1	1	5	1	2	6
4	2	0	6	2	4	4	5	4	6
	3	0	4	0	6	0	6	0	
			0	3	2	3			
			5	3	6	1			
				1	3				

0 - 0	0 - 1	0 - 2	0 - 3	0 - 4	0 - 5	0 - 6

1 - 1	1 - 2	1 - 3	1 - 4	1 - 5	1 - 6	2 - 2
✓						

2 - 3	2 - 4	2 - 5	2 - 6	3 - 3	3 - 4	3 - 5

3 - 6	4 - 4	4 - 5	4 - 6	5 - 5	5 - 6	6 - 6

★

	1	3	3	3
3	1	5	3	4
2	1	2	1	3
4	2	5	2	

1 - 1	1 - 2	1 - 3

2 - 3	2 - 4	2 - 5

3 - 3	3 - 4	3 - 5

Turn to page 196 for the solutions

DOMINO PLACEMENT

A standard set of dominoes has been laid out, using only the dominoes shown below each puzzle. Can you draw in the edges of them all? The check-box is provided as an aid, and in some puzzles, a starting domino has been placed, which will get you on your way.

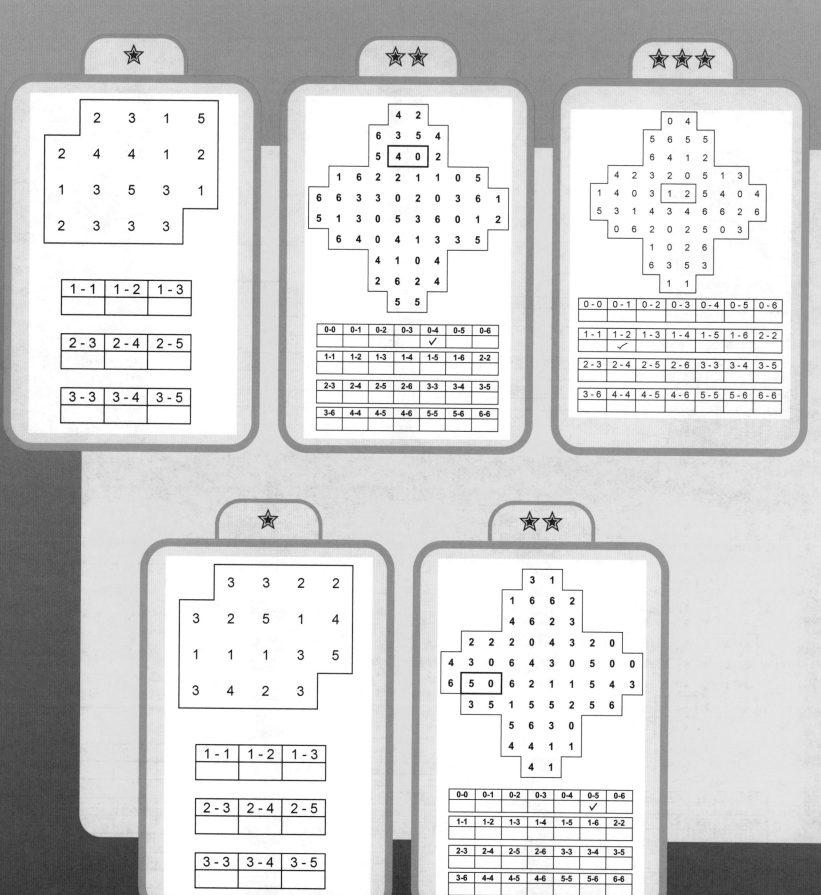

★

	2	3	1	5
2	4	4	1	2
1	3	5	3	1
2	3	3	3	

1 - 1	1 - 2	1 - 3
2 - 3	2 - 4	2 - 5
3 - 3	3 - 4	3 - 5

★★

				4	2				
			6	3	5	4			
			5	**4**	**0**	2			
	1	6	2	2	1	1	0	5	
6	6	3	3	0	2	0	3	6	1
5	1	3	0	5	3	6	0	1	2
	6	4	0	4	1	3	3	5	
			4	1	0	4			
			2	6	2	4			
				5	5				

0-0	0-1	0-2	0-3	0-4	0-5	0-6
				✓		
1-1	1-2	1-3	1-4	1-5	1-6	2-2
2-3	2-4	2-5	2-6	3-3	3-4	3-5
3-6	4-4	4-5	4-6	5-5	5-6	6-6

★★★

				0	4				
			5	6	5	5			
			6	4	1	2			
	4	2	3	2	0	5	1	3	
1	4	0	3	**1**	**2**	5	4	0	4
5	3	1	4	3	4	6	6	2	6
	0	6	2	0	2	5	0	3	
			1	0	2	6			
			6	3	5	3			
				1	1				

0 - 0	0 - 1	0 - 2	0 - 3	0 - 4	0 - 5	0 - 6
1 - 1	1 - 2	1 - 3	1 - 4	1 - 5	1 - 6	2 - 2
	✓					
2 - 3	2 - 4	2 - 5	2 - 6	3 - 3	3 - 4	3 - 5
3 - 6	4 - 4	4 - 5	4 - 6	5 - 5	5 - 6	6 - 6

★

	3	3	2	2
3	2	5	1	4
1	1	1	3	5
3	4	2	3	

1 - 1	1 - 2	1 - 3
2 - 3	2 - 4	2 - 5
3 - 3	3 - 4	3 - 5

★★

				3	1				
			1	6	6	2			
			4	6	2	3			
	2	2	2	0	4	3	2	0	
4	3	0	6	4	3	0	5	0	0
6	**5**	**0**	6	2	1	1	5	4	3
	3	5	1	5	5	2	5	6	
			5	6	3	0			
			4	4	1	1			
				4	1				

0-0	0-1	0-2	0-3	0-4	0-5	0-6
					✓	
1-1	1-2	1-3	1-4	1-5	1-6	2-2
2-3	2-4	2-5	2-6	3-3	3-4	3-5
3-6	4-4	4-5	4-6	5-5	5-6	6-6

Turn to page 196 for the solutions

DOMINO PLACEMENT

★★★

				2	2				
			4	0	1	3			
			6	2	6	4			
	1	6	6	0	0	4	2	4	
3	5	3	2	4	6	2	0	5	1
1	2	0	5	1	1	4	3	4	5
	3	6	2	3	5	6	0	6	
			1	0	1	5			
			3	3	4	0			
				5	5				

0 - 0	0 - 1	0 - 2	0 - 3	0 - 4	0 - 5	0 - 6
		✓				

1 - 1	1 - 2	1 - 3	1 - 4	1 - 5	1 - 6	2 - 2

2 - 3	2 - 4	2 - 5	2 - 6	3 - 3	3 - 4	3 - 5

3 - 6	4 - 4	4 - 5	4 - 6	5 - 5	5 - 6	6 - 6
			✓			

★

	2	1	2	5
2	4	3	3	1
3	1	4	5	3
3	1	3	2	

1 - 1	1 - 2	1 - 3
		✓

2 - 3	2 - 4	2 - 5

3 - 3	3 - 4	3 - 5

★★

				0	3				
			1	1	6	0			
			6	3	3	0			
	3	1	2	3	1	2	4	4	
1	1	5	4	5	6	6	2	3	0
4	6	5	3	4	0	0	3	2	4
	5	1	5	2	2	4	5	6	
			0	5	1	0			
			5	6	4	6			
				2	2				

0-0	0-1	0-2	0-3	0-4	0-5	0-6
					✓	

1-1	1-2	1-3	1-4	1-5	1-6	2-2

2-3	2-4	2-5	2-6	3-3	3-4	3-5

3-6	4-4	4-5	4-6	5-5	5-6	6-6

★★★

				2	1				
			5	4	5	3			
			5	2	6	4			
	3	0	2	0	1	1	0	1	
4	3	0	5	2	3	2	2	3	6
6	2	1	1	6	0	4	6	3	6
	2	5	6	1	3	5	0	5	
			4	0	1	4			
			3	6	0	5			
				4	4				

0 - 0	0 - 1	0 - 2	0 - 3	0 - 4	0 - 5	0 - 6
			✓			

1 - 1	1 - 2	1 - 3	1 - 4	1 - 5	1 - 6	2 - 2

2 - 3	2 - 4	2 - 5	2 - 6	3 - 3	3 - 4	3 - 5

3 - 6	4 - 4	4 - 5	4 - 6	5 - 5	5 - 6	6 - 6

★

	4	3	1	1
3	3	2	1	2
3	5	3	3	4
2	2	1	5	

1 - 1	1 - 2	1 - 3

2 - 3	2 - 4	2 - 5

3 - 3	3 - 4	3 - 5

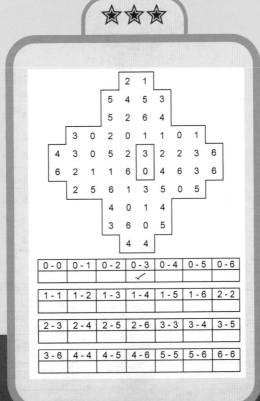

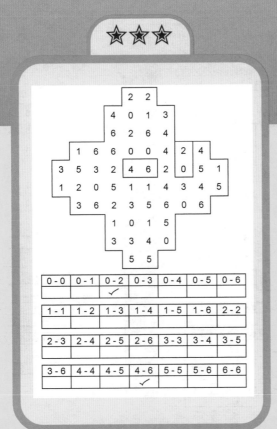

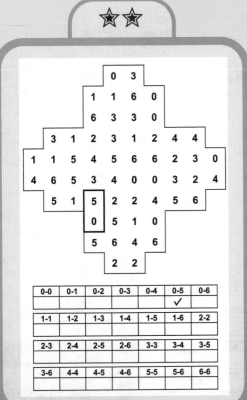

Turn to page 196 for the solutions

DOMINO PLACEMENT

A standard set of dominoes has been laid out, using only the dominoes shown below each puzzle. Can you draw in the edges of them all? The check-box is provided as an aid, and in some puzzles, a starting domino has been placed, which will get you on your way.

★

	2	4	3	4
1	1	3	2	1
2	3	5	3	3
2	5	3	1	

1 - 1	1 - 2	1 - 3
2 - 3	2 - 4	2 - 5
3 - 3	3 - 4	3 - 5

★★

				2	2				
			6	3	5	5			
			6	5	0	3			
	1	5	4	1	0	4	3	2	
3	6	0	6	2	0	3	1	1	0
1	4	1	0	3	3	4	2	0	5
	2	6	2	5	0	4	5	4	
			1	2	6	6			
			3	5	4	1			
				6	4				

0-0	0-1	0-2	0-3	0-4	0-5	0-6
1-1	1-2	1-3	1-4	1-5	1-6	2-2
2-3	2-4	2-5	2-6	3-3	3-4	3-5
					✓	
3-6	4-4	4-5	4-6	5-5	5-6	6-6

★★★

				6	0				
			6	3	1	6			
			5	4	2	3			
	6	3	4	6	0	5	0	4	
5	1	0	1	0	2	6	6	5	2
1	2	5	3	1	3	2	4	0	1
	2	0	0	2	1	6	5	5	
			3	4	1	4			
			3	2	5	4			
				4	3				

0 - 0	0 - 1	0 - 2	0 - 3	0 - 4	0 - 5	0 - 6
1 - 1	1 - 2	1 - 3	1 - 4	1 - 5	1 - 6	2 - 2
2 - 3	2 - 4	2 - 5	2 - 6	3 - 3	3 - 4	3 - 5
						✓
3 - 6	4 - 4	4 - 5	4 - 6	5 - 5	5 - 6	6 - 6

★★★

				2	4				
			5	4	6	3			
			5	0	1	3			
	6	4	1	2	2	5	0	2	
1	6	0	2	6	3	2	3	6	3
1	4	6	4	3	0	5	0	0	1
	0	1	5	1	6	3	2	5	
			4	6	5	1			
			4	3	4	2			
				0	5				

0 - 0	0 - 1	0 - 2	0 - 3	0 - 4	0 - 5	0 - 6
	✓					
1 - 1	1 - 2	1 - 3	1 - 4	1 - 5	1 - 6	2 - 2
2 - 3	2 - 4	2 - 5	2 - 6	3 - 3	3 - 4	3 - 5
3 - 6	4 - 4	4 - 5	4 - 6	5 - 5	5 - 6	6 - 6
✓						

★★

				0	5				
			4	4	2	1			
			5	3	2	3			
	1	1	2	6	6	5	4	1	
2	1	6	0	0	6	5	6	2	5
3	3	5	2	3	5	2	0	0	1
	4	0	5	6	4	3	4	3	
			3	4	0	1			
			6	1	4	2			
				0	6				

0-0	0-1	0-2	0-3	0-4	0-5	0-6
1-1	1-2	1-3	1-4	1-5	1-6	2-2
2-3	2-4	2-5	2-6	3-3	3-4	3-5
✓						
3-6	4-4	4-5	4-6	5-5	5-6	6-6

Turn to page 196 for the solutions

DOMINO PLACEMENT

★★★

				4	2				
			4	6	6	0			
			2	5	1	3			
	4	5	0	3	2	4	5	0	
0	1	2	3	4	0	0	6	5	2
5	2	1	1	4	5	5	4	1	2
	6	3	6	2	3	4	6	6	
			5	3	1	0			
			1	0	3	3			
				6	1				

0 - 0	0 - 1	0 - 2	0 - 3	0 - 4	0 - 5	0 - 6
					✓	

1 - 1	1 - 2	1 - 3	1 - 4	1 - 5	1 - 6	2 - 2

2 - 3	2 - 4	2 - 5	2 - 6	3 - 3	3 - 4	3 - 5

3 - 6	4 - 4	4 - 5	4 - 6	5 - 5	5 - 6	6 - 6

★

	4	3	2	5
2	3	1	3	5
1	3	2	1	3
2	4	3	1	

1 - 1	1 - 2	1 - 3

2 - 3	2 - 4	2 - 5

3 - 3	3 - 4	3 - 5

★★

				5	2				
			0	5	6	5			
			1	1	3	5			
	0	1	4	4	6	5	0	1	
2	0	2	6	1	0	2	2	4	5
6	4	2	0	0	3	6	4	3	1
	6	3	2	2	1	4	0	3	
			3	3	1	3			
			5	6	4	4			
				6	5				

0-0	0-1	0-2	0-3	0-4	0-5	0-6

1-1	1-2	1-3	1-4	1-5	1-6	2-2

2-3	2-4	2-5	2-6	3-3	3-4	3-5

3-6	4-4	4-5	4-6	5-5	5-6	6-6
			✓			

★

	2	5	2	3
2	1	2	4	3
3	3	3	1	4
1	1	3	5	

1 - 1	1 - 2	1 - 3

2 - 3	2 - 4	2 - 5

3 - 3	3 - 4	3 - 5

★★

				0	0				
			6	4	5	1			
			6	6	3	3			
	1	0	6	4	2	4	1	1	
5	6	5	5	4	6	0	0	5	1
2	4	1	3	1	1	2	3	3	2
	2	0	2	4	3	2	2	0	
			3	4	3	0			
			5	6	4	5			
				6	5				

0-0	0-1	0-2	0-3	0-4	0-5	0-6

1-1	1-2	1-3	1-4	1-5	1-6	2-2

2-3	2-4	2-5	2-6	3-3	3-4	3-5
					✓	

3-6	4-4	4-5	4-6	5-5	5-6	6-6

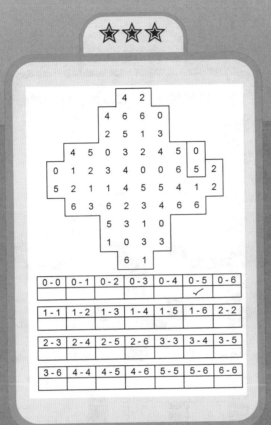

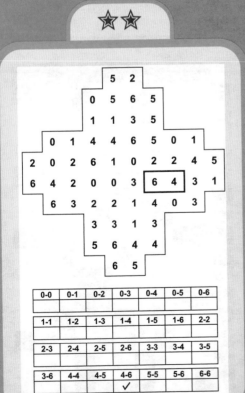

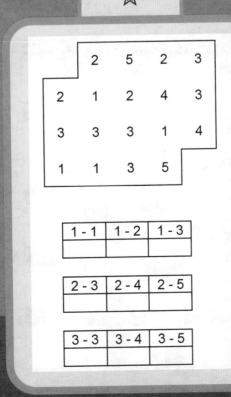

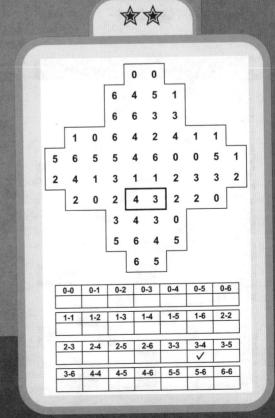

Turn to page 196 for the solutions

KAKURO

In Kakuro the numbers in the black squares refer to the SUMS of the digits which you are to fill into the empty spaces. The number ABOVE the diagonal line refers to the empty spaces directly to the RIGHT of that number. A number BELOW the diagonal line refers to the empty spaces directly BELOW that number. No zeros are used here and a digit can only appear once in any particular digit combination.

 Turn to page 196 for the solutions

KAKURO

Turn to page 196 for the solutions

KAKURO

In Kakuro the numbers in the black squares refer to the SUMS of the digits which you are to fill into the empty spaces. The number ABOVE the diagonal line refers to the empty spaces directly to the RIGHT of that number. A number BELOW the diagonal line refers to the empty spaces directly BELOW that number. No zeros are used here and a digit can only appear once in any particular digit combination.

Turn to page 196 for the solutions

Turn to page 196 for the solutions

KAKURO

In Kakuro the numbers in the black squares refer to the SUMS of the digits which you are to fill into the empty spaces. The number ABOVE the diagonal line refers to the empty spaces directly to the RIGHT of that number. A number BELOW the diagonal line refers to the empty spaces directly BELOW that number. No zeros are used here and a digit can only appear once in any particular digit combination.

 Turn to page 196 for the solutions

KAKURO

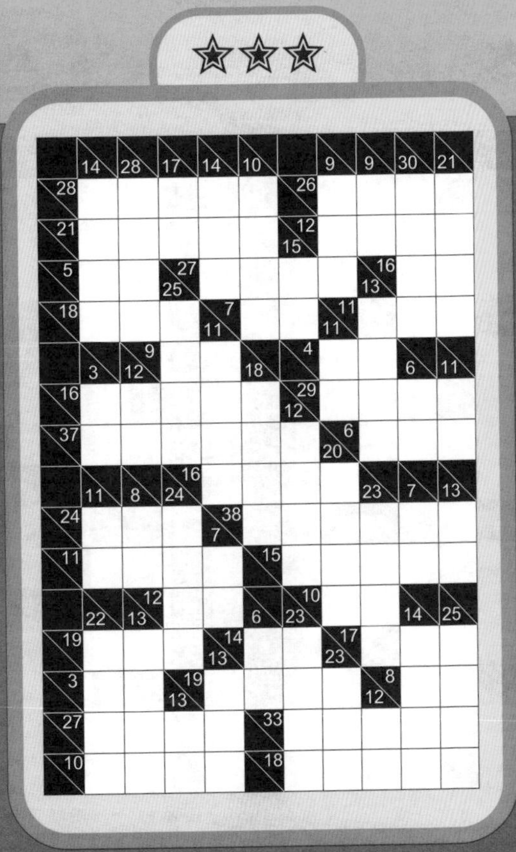

KAKURO

In Kakuro the numbers in the black squares refer to the SUMS of the digits which you are to fill into the empty spaces. The number ABOVE the diagonal line refers to the empty spaces directly to the RIGHT of that number. A number BELOW the diagonal line refers to the empty spaces directly BELOW that number. No zeros are used here and a digit can only appear once in any particular digit combination.

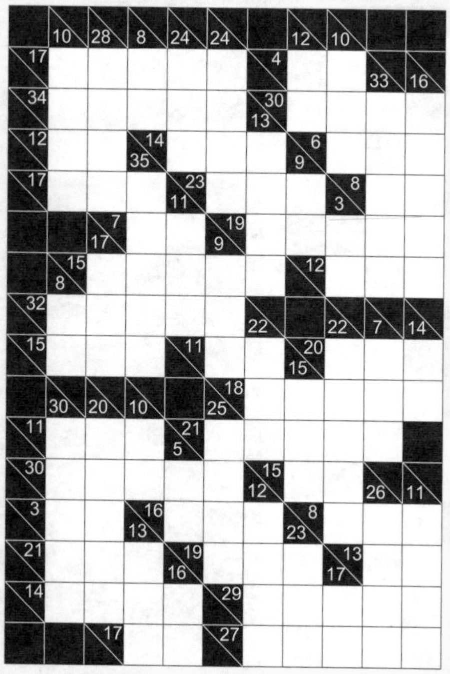

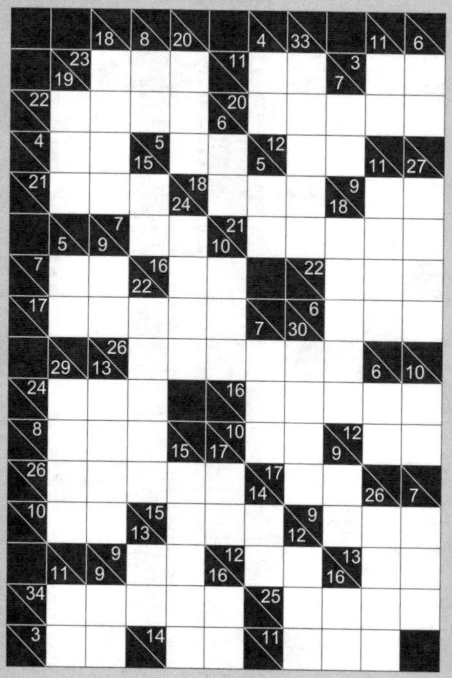

 Turn to page 196 for the solutions

KAKURO

Turn to page 196 for the solutions

KAKURO

In Kakuro the numbers in the black squares refer to the SUMS of the digits which you are to fill into the empty spaces. The number ABOVE the diagonal line refers to the empty spaces directly to the RIGHT of that number. A number BELOW the diagonal line refers to the empty spaces directly BELOW that number. No zeros are used here and a digit can only appear once in any particular digit combination.

 Turn to page 196 for the solutions

KAKURO

WHATEVER NEXT?

★★

20	18
14	12

31	16
8	9

18	16
15	15

?

Which of the three squares below fits most logically into the empty square above?

A

16	11
31	20

B

9	22
18	15

C

17	19
18	15

★

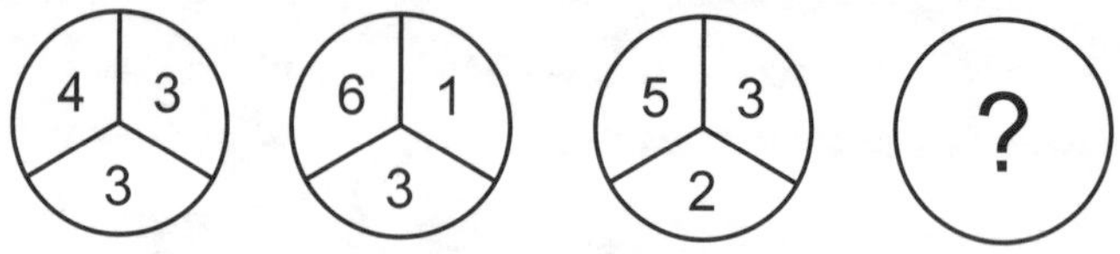

Which of the three circles below fits most logically into the empty circle above?

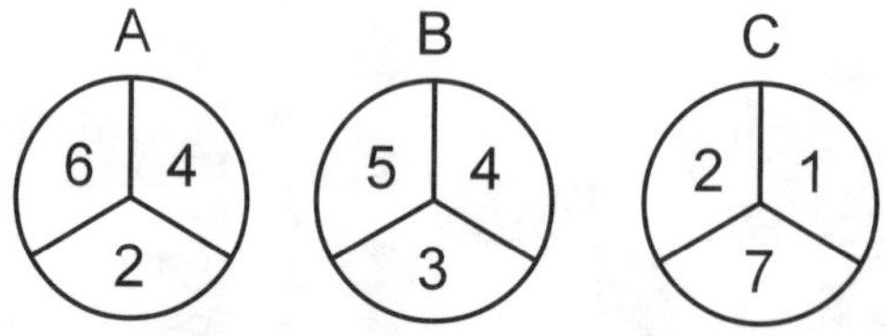

★★★

2	1	4
3	2	1
4	2	6

7	4	5
6	8	3
4	5	8

9	8	6
7	9	8
9	10	9

?

Which of the four squares below fits most logically into the empty square above?

A

9	7	16
18	11	14
8	17	15

B

6	5	9
8	7	4
6	8	5

C

15	11	10
14	9	13
12	7	9

D

21	18	16
14	19	16
20	17	19

★★

13	17
9	13

18	13
11	6

5	8
7	10

?

Which of the three squares below fits most logically into the empty square above?

A

8	10
11	13

B

12	9
8	13

C

14	9
11	13

★

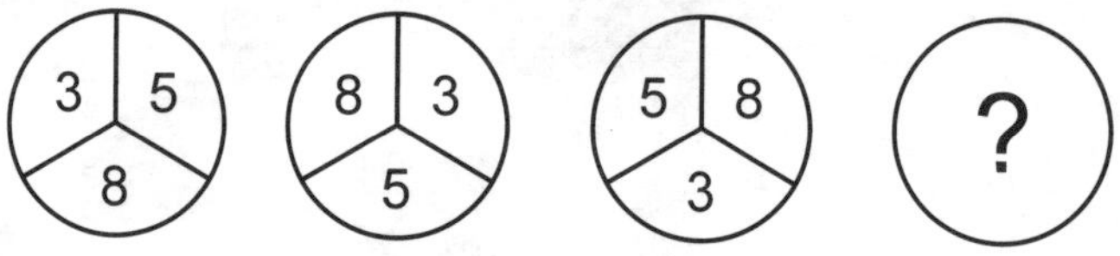

Which of the three circles below fits most logically into the empty circle above?

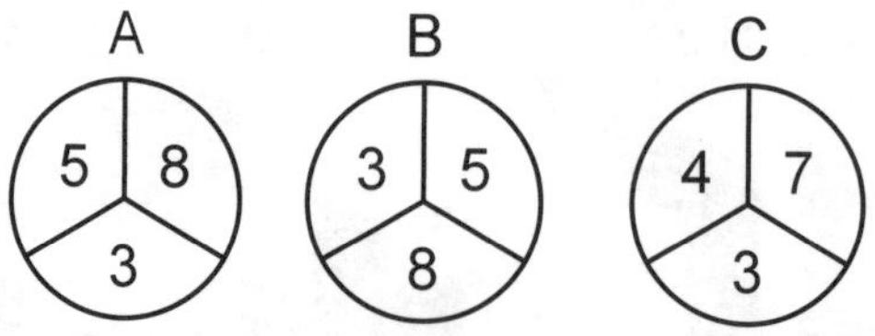

 Turn to page 196 for the solutions

WHATEVER NEXT?

★★★

2	1	4
4	3	2
3	1	1

4	3	6
6	4	4
5	3	3

6	5	8
8	5	6
7	5	5

?

Which of the four squares below fits most logically into the empty square above?

A

7	7	9
8	5	7
7	6	6

B

8	7	10
10	6	8
9	7	7

C

7	8	9
8	5	7
9	7	7

D

7	8	9
9	6	8
7	6	6

★★

5	2
2	5

5	4
5	1

10	2
1	5

?

Which of the three squares below fits most logically into the empty square above?

A

5	8
2	2

B

8	7
2	1

C

1	5
20	1

★

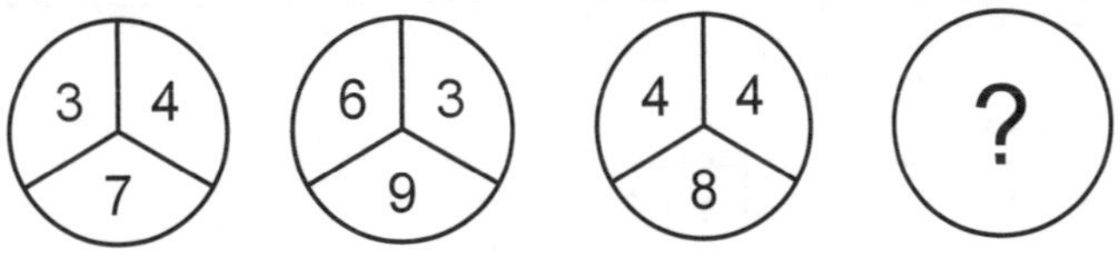

Which of the three circles below fits most logically into the empty circle above?

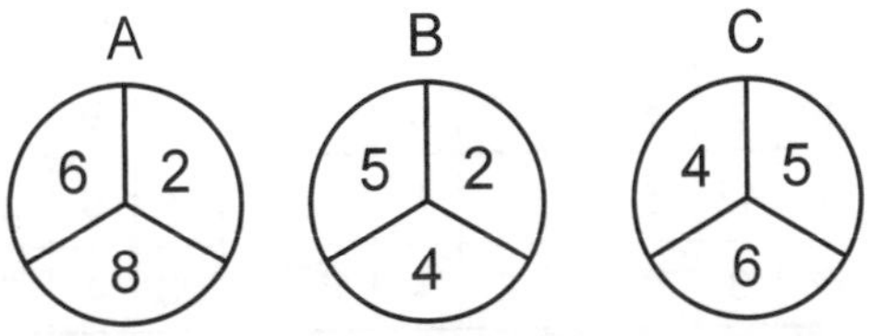

★★

5	4
7	3

6	6
11	6

7	8
15	9

?

Which of the three squares below fits most logically into the empty square above?

A

9	11
18	15

B

8	10
19	12

C

11	10
8	16

★★★

8	1	3
3	6	6
7	4	7

6	2	4
8	3	4
6	6	6

5	6	1
6	5	4
4	9	5

?

Which of the four squares below fits most logically into the empty square above?

A

7	3	2
7	4	4
6	7	5

B

8	1	2
6	4	9
6	6	6

C

6	4	2
8	3	6
7	6	5

D

7	2	3
4	7	4
6	8	7

Turn to page 196 for the solutions

WHATEVER NEXT?

★★

9	8
7	10

11	13
8	16

15	11
19	7

?

Which of the three squares below fits most logically into the empty square above?

A

8	7
10	9

B

12	6
4	10

C

12	6
13	5

★

Which of the three circles below fits most logically into the empty circle above?

A B C

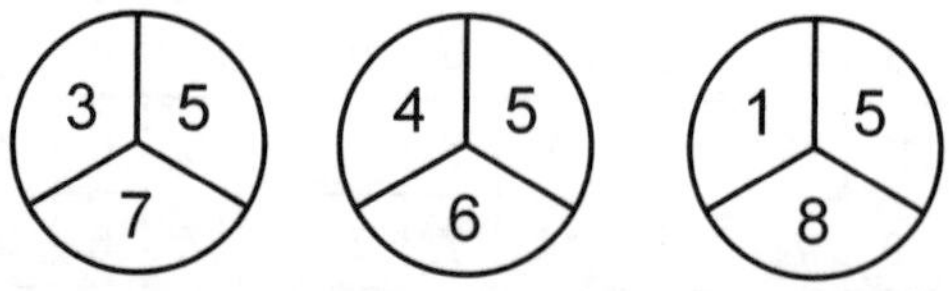

★★★

10	2	5
6	48	8
5	25	5

9	6	54
16	8	2
28	4	7

3	18	6
4	9	36
6	2	3

?

Which of the four squares below fits most logically into the empty square above?

A

6	20	4
5	18	7
38	3	9

B

15	5	3
7	42	6
7	3	21

C

42	4	9
6	6	35
2	4	8

D

9	9	81
3	6	16
28	4	9

★★

8	29
15	22

17	38
24	31

4	25
11	18

?

Which of the three squares below fits most logically into the empty square above?

A

11	31
20	26

B

19	40
26	33

C

7	19
9	11

★

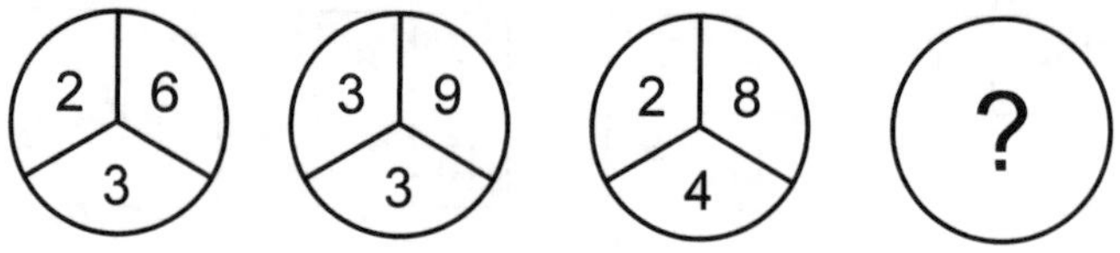

Which of the three circles below fits most logically into the empty circle above?

A B C

 Turn to page 196 for the solutions

★★★

11	8	7
5	3	6
14	12	9

22	4	14
10	6	3
7	6	18

11	2	7
5	3	6
14	3	9

?

Which of the four squares below fits most logically into the empty square above?

A

11	4	7
10	3	6
6	7	18

B

22	8	14
5	6	6
7	6	9

C

22	1	14
10	6	3
7	6	18

D

22	1	14
5	3	3
7	3	18

★

8 8 / 9

8 7 / 10

6 11 / 8

?

Which of the three circles below fits most logically into the empty circle above?

A: 12 6 / 7

B: 8 6 / 9

C: 11 7 / 9

★

4 2 / 6

3 4 / 7

4 1 / 5

?

Which of the three circles below fits most logically into the empty circle above?

A: 5 4 / 6

B: 5 3 / 8

C: 3 6 / 4

★★

17	26
8	62

161	17
71	8

35	116
206	44

?

Which of the three squares below fits most logically into the empty square above?

A

8	62
71	26

B

26	36
7	19

C

181	27
9	62

★★★

9	11	10
4	5	3
6	7	5

8	3	5
2	3	1
4	2	4

9	10	9
3	5	6
7	4	3

?

Which of the four squares below fits most logically into the empty square above?

A

13	12	15
16	6	2
9	3	4

B

9	7	8
4	3	9
6	4	3

C

5	9	2
1	2	2
8	6	4

D

3	12	7
6	3	7
8	7	4

Turn to page 196 for the solutions

WHATEVER NEXT?

★★

4	3
12	5

8	16
6	2

3	11
4	4

?

Which of the three squares below fits most logically into the empty square above?

A

13	8
3	2

B

15	8
4	6

C

6	3
7	14

★

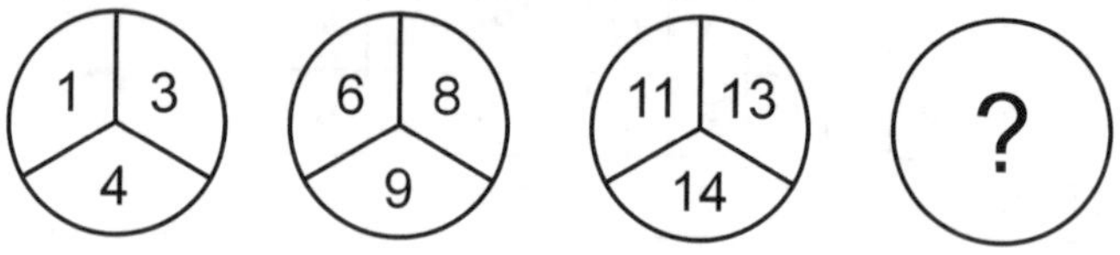

Which of the three circles below fits most logically into the empty circle above?

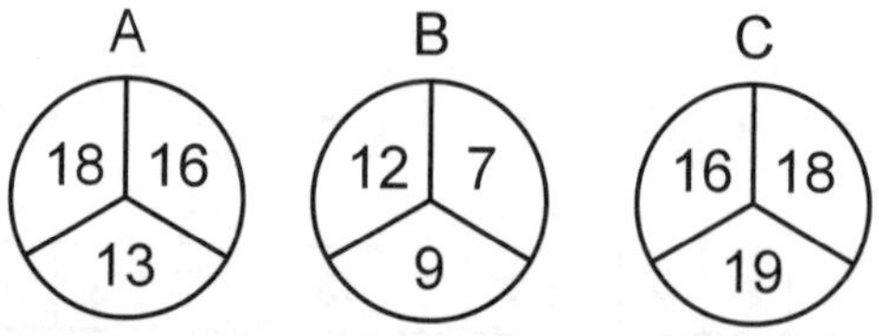

★★★

10	2	18
6	17	11
9	4	30

2	30	9
10	6	11
4	17	18

30	6	9
17	10	2
18	4	11

?

Which of the four squares below fits most logically into the empty square above?

A

4	10	6
30	9	17
2	11	18

B

4	30	6
11	18	9
17	8	4

C

11	4	9
6	17	18
30	12	10

D

9	5	18
30	17	6
11	10	2

★★★

6		
		4
	3	

		6
4		
3		

3		4
		6

?

Which of the four squares below fits most logically into the empty square above?

A

4		
		6
	3	

B

6		
		4
		3

C

3		
4		
6		

D

3		6
	4	

★

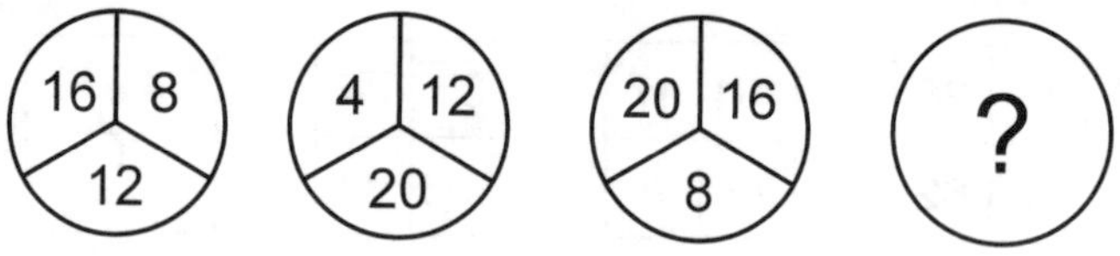

Which of the three circles below fits most logically into the empty circle above?

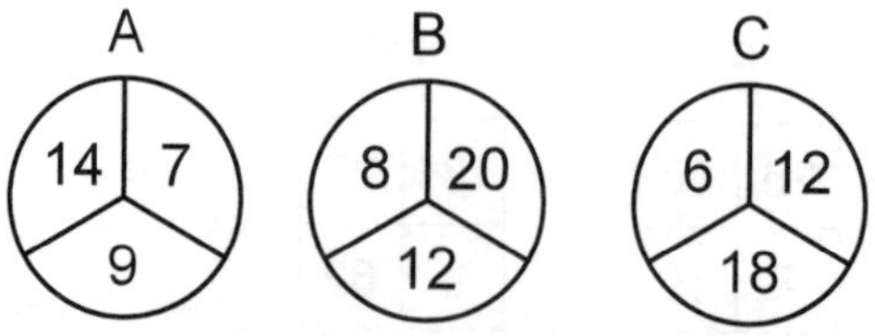

 Turn to page 196 for the solutions

WHATEVER NEXT?

★★★

3	12	2
16	4	8
4	12	3

2	6	1
9	3	3
3	15	5

6	30	7
20	5	35
4	15	3

?

Which of the four squares below fits most logically into the empty square above?

A

4	19	7
12	4	18
6	15	3

B

8	20	9
13	3	18
5	16	4

C

4	20	6
25	5	35
7	25	9

D

9	18	6
10	2	12
5	14	7

★★

13	8
1	20

22	17
10	29

31	26
19	38

?

Which of the three squares below fits most logically into the empty square above?

A

20	33
26	41

B

36	40
26	18

C

40	35
28	47

★

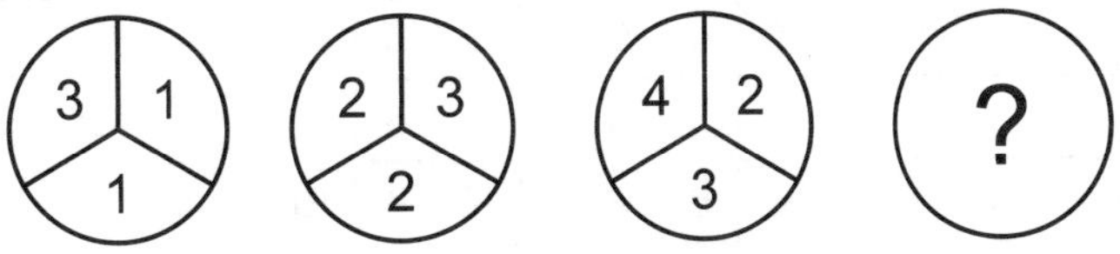

Which of the three circles below fits most logically into the empty circle above?

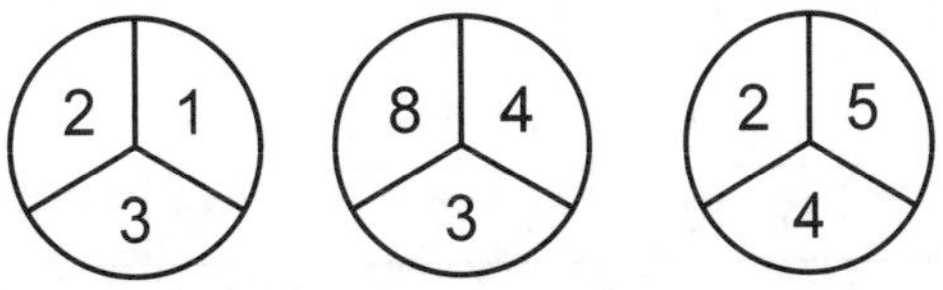

★★

4	2
40	5

6	2
48	4

5	2
60	6

?

Which of the three squares below fits most logically into the empty square above?

A

3	7
29	4

B

3	5
45	3

C

6	2
38	4

★★★

8	2	7
9	4	8
9	4	8

3	2	7
9	6	8
7	4	11

11	2	7
9	5	8
8	4	4

?

Which of the four squares below fits most logically into the empty square above?

A

7	2	4
9	8	8
8	4	5

B

7	2	3
9	6	8
8	4	4

C

2	2	7
9	9	8
4	4	6

D

4	2	6
9	7	8
8	4	4

Turn to page 196 for the solutions

WHATEVER NEXT?

★★

6	12
3	24

14	28
7	56

12	24
6	48

?

Which of the three squares below fits most logically into the empty square above?

A

8	16
4	32

B

5	10
3	18

C

18	24
9	38

★

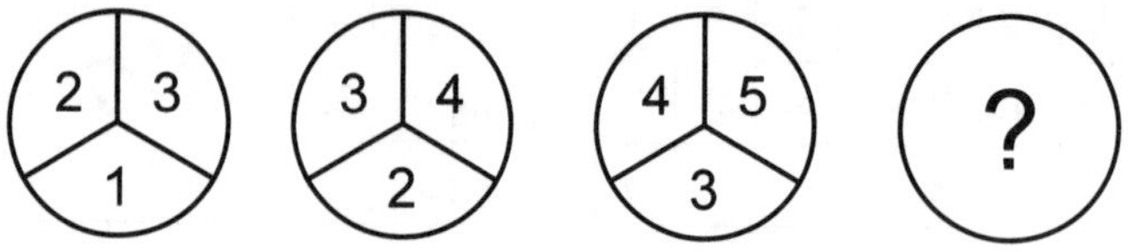

Which of the three circles below fits most logically into the empty circle above?

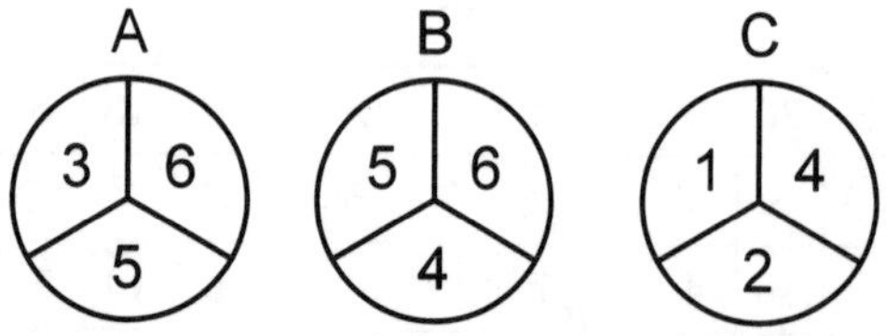

★★★

4	2	6
6	1	3
8	4	4

5	4	9
7	3	6
9	6	7

6	6	12
8	5	9
10	8	10

?

Which of the four squares below fits most logically into the empty square above?

A

3	7	10
6	8	9
4	6	16

B

11	9	17
3	4	11
8	11	13

C

7	8	15
9	7	12
11	10	13

D

6	8	11
3	7	16
11	14	19

★★

1	2
3	4

1	4
12	12

1	8
48	36

?

Which of the three squares below fits most logically into the empty square above?

A

2	16
64	50

B

1	12
64	48

C

1	16
192	108

★

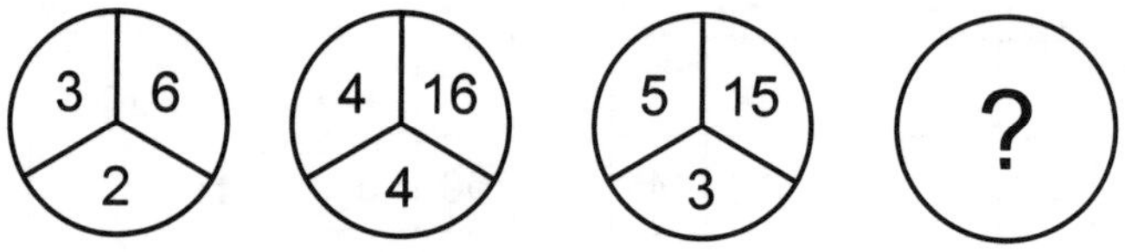

Which of the three circles below fits most logically into the empty circle above?

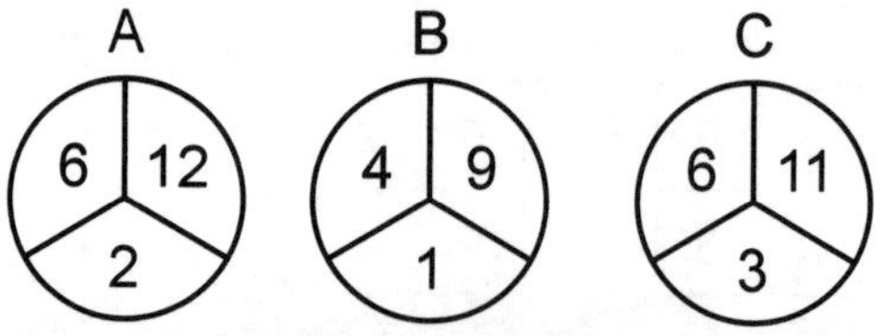

 Turn to page 196 for the solutions

WHATEVER NEXT?

★★★

7	8	9
4	3	6
3	5	3

6	4	5
4	1	3
2	3	2

7	9	8
6	4	7
1	5	1

?

Which of the four squares below fits most logically into the empty square above?

A

6	8	9
4	5	6
3	4	4

B

6	4	8
4	2	7
4	3	2

C

8	4	7
7	3	8
2	1	1

D

6	3	2
4	1	2
2	2	0

★★

7	6
4	9

6	9
7	4

9	4
6	7

?

Which of the three squares below fits most logically into the empty square above?

A

4	7
9	6

B

9	7
4	6

C

6	7
9	4

★

Which of the three circles below fits most logically into the empty circle above?

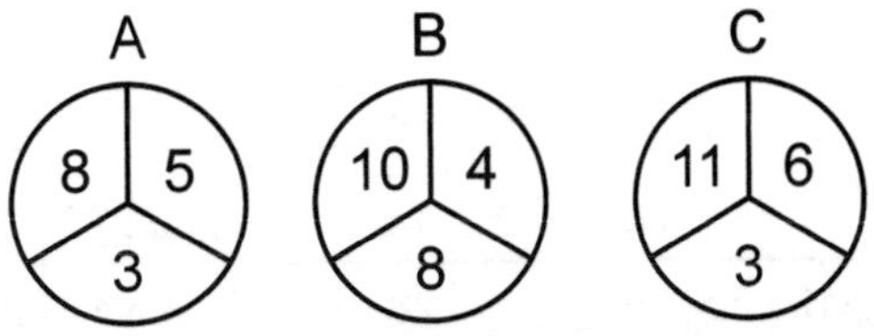

★★

4	6
9	6

8	4
6	12

6	8
4	3

?

Which of the three squares below fits most logically into the empty square above?

A

8	6
7	7

B

20	4
3	15

C

9	5
3	8

★★★

4	5	3
2	6	7
4	9	8

4	2	4
9	6	5
8	7	3

8	9	4
7	6	2
3	5	4

?

Which of the four squares below fits most logically into the empty square above?

A

3	7	8
8	6	4
7	4	2

B

3	7	8
5	5	9
2	4	4

C

5	3	7
4	6	8
2	4	9

D

3	7	8
5	6	9
4	2	4

Turn to page 196 for the solutions

WHATEVER NEXT?

★★

3	4		7	6		11	13		?	
4	4		9	8		10	11			

Which of the three squares below fits most logically into the empty square above?

A

13	14
20	8

B

12	10
8	11

C

17	18
10	15

★

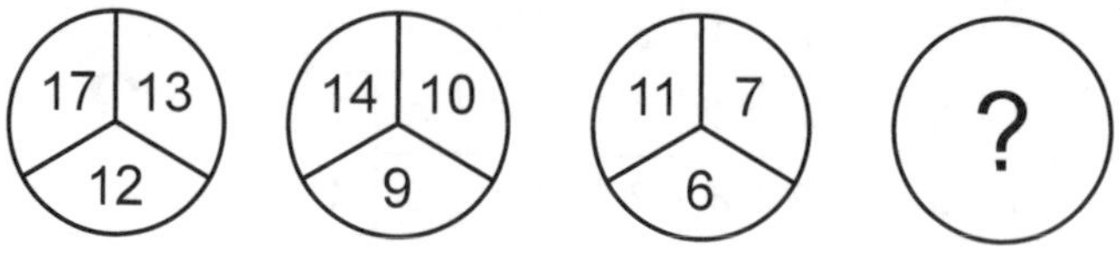

Which of the three circles below fits most logically into the empty circle above?

A

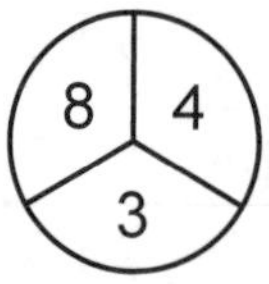

B

C

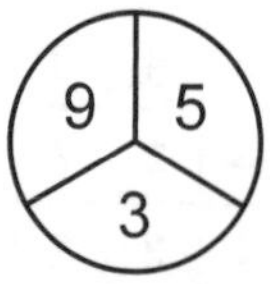

★★★

6	15	24		13	22	31		7	16	25		?	
8	17	26		18	27	36		4	13	22			
11	20	29		12	21	30		15	24	33			

Which of the four squares below fits most logically into the empty square above?

A

6	14	21
8	16	20
14	23	29

B

7	19	21
8	17	30
13	20	25

C

11	20	29
6	15	24
19	28	37

D

9	17	27
20	27	35
8	17	25

★★

3	16		14	3		25	2		?	
14	2		1	10		5	17			

Which of the three squares below fits most logically into the empty square above?

A

10	18
25	3

B

9	34
38	3

C

8	21
60	4

★

Which of the three circles below fits most logically into the empty circle above?

A

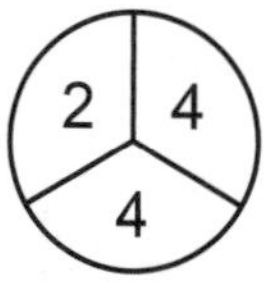

B

C

Turn to page 196 for the solutions

WHATEVER NEXT?

5	4	5
7	3	2
5	4	5

4	5	3
4	1	2
5	4	4

6	5	8
6	3	4
7	7	4

?

Which of the four squares below fits most logically into the empty square above?

A

7	8	8
6	4	6
6	5	4

B

6	8	7
2	3	4
4	3	3

C

8	6	3
9	4	7
2	6	4

D

9	6	2
7	4	3
1	5	6

12	20	11
19	15	14
16	12	22

18	6	19
13	26	20
16	15	8

17	15	14
19	19	16
11	13	17

?

Which of the four squares below fits most logically into the empty space above?

A

17	23	15
18	13	18
11	11	14

B

17	23	15
19	13	18
11	11	14

C

17	22	15
19	13	18
11	11	14

D

17	23	15
19	13	18
14	11	14

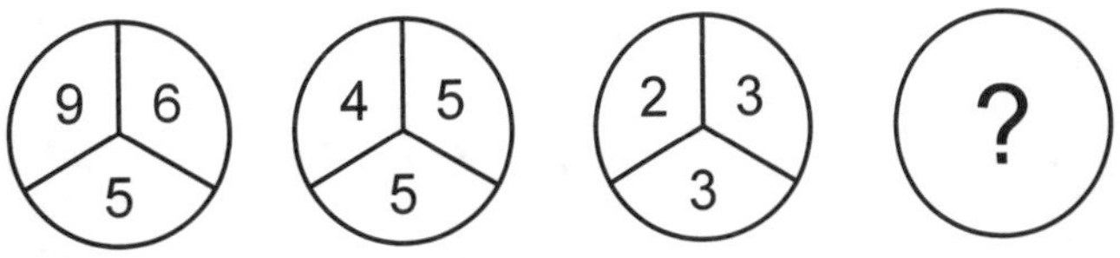

Which of the three circles below fits most logically into the empty circle above?

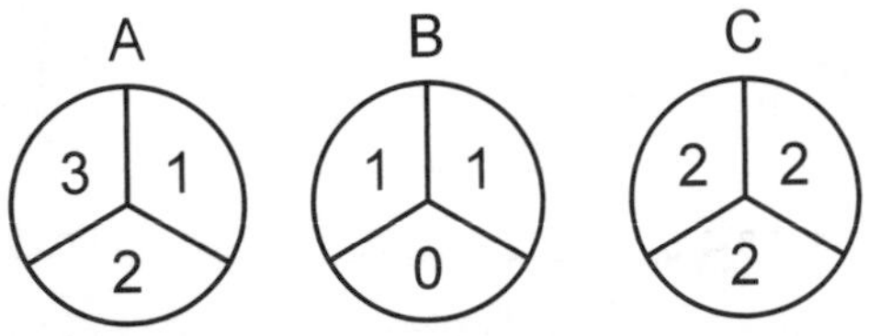

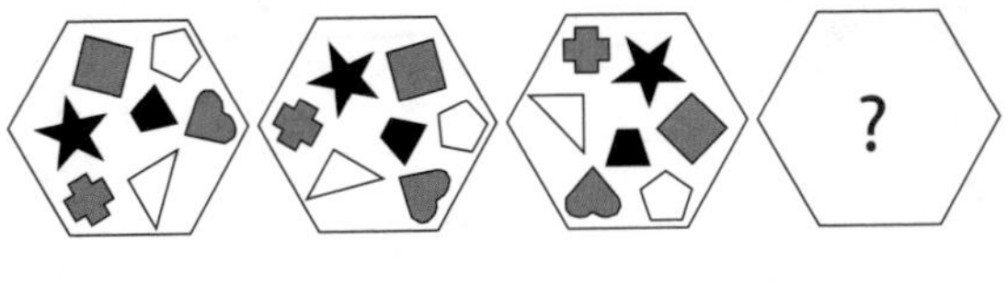

Which figure below continues the sequence above?

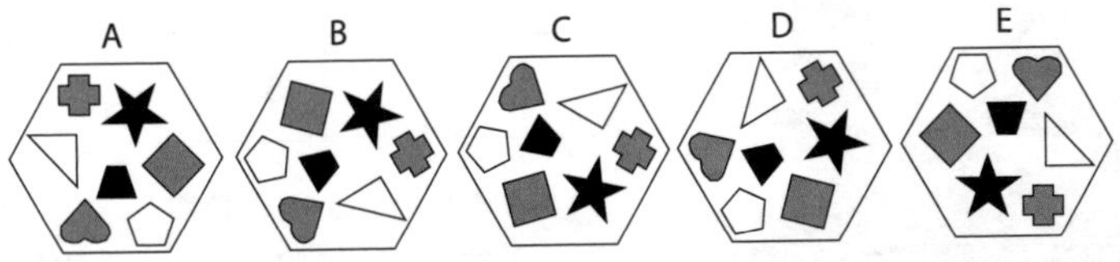

10	10	3
28	2	27
20	26	12

50	47	43
41	5	52
4	5	58

6	17	78
68	61	7
16	70	73

?

Which of the four squares below fits most logically into the empty square above?

A

6	66	7
61	8	76
16	68	60

B

77	68	87
7	17	17
18	70	72

C

9	96	9
92	19	19
91	99	97

D

5	60	40
56	4	55
42	66	5

Turn to page 196 for the solutions

COMBIKU

Each horizontal row and vertical column should contain different colors and different numbers. Every square will contain one number and one colored circle and no combination may be repeated anywhere in the puzzle; so, for instance, if a square contains a 3 surrounded by a red circle, then no other square containing a 3 will have a red circle and no other square with a red circle will contain a 3.

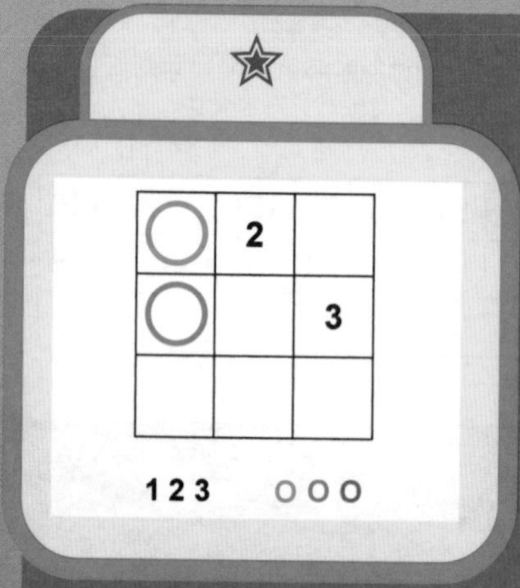

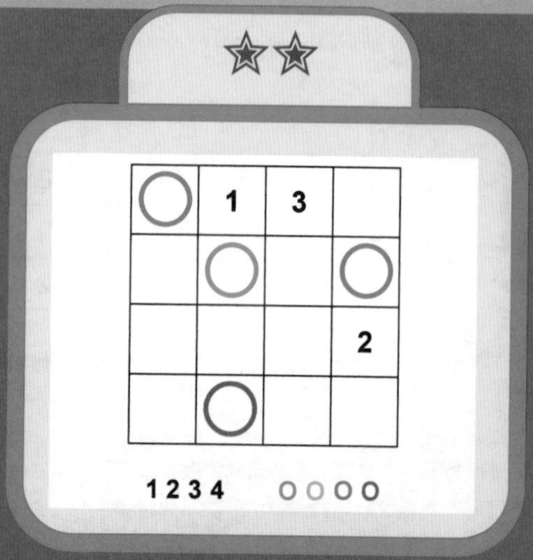

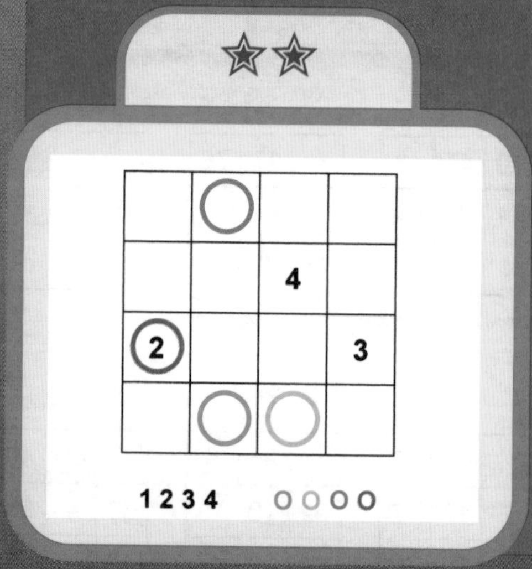

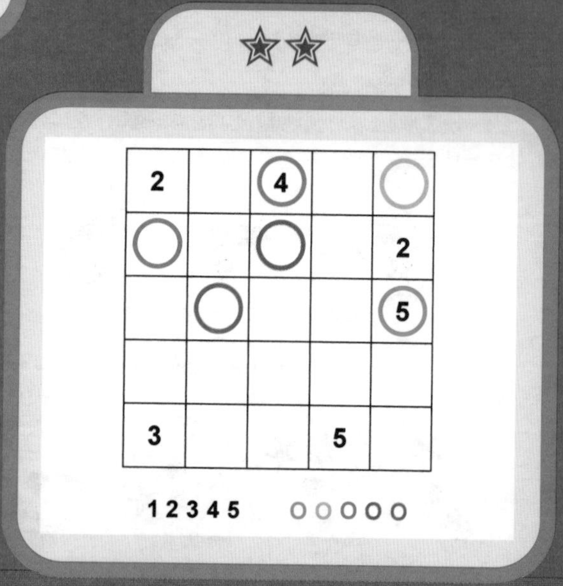

 Turn to page 196 for the solutions

COMBIKU

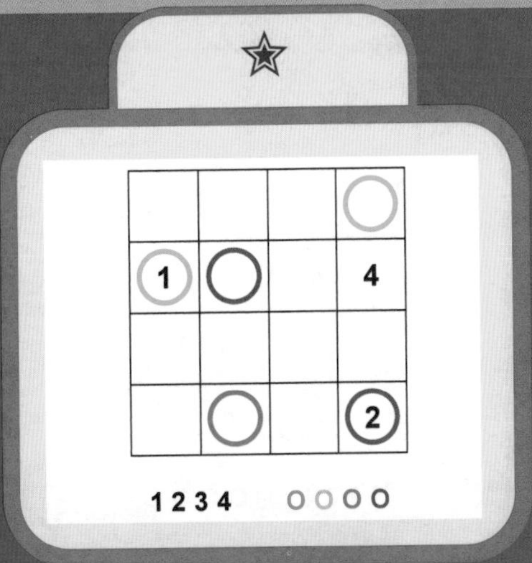

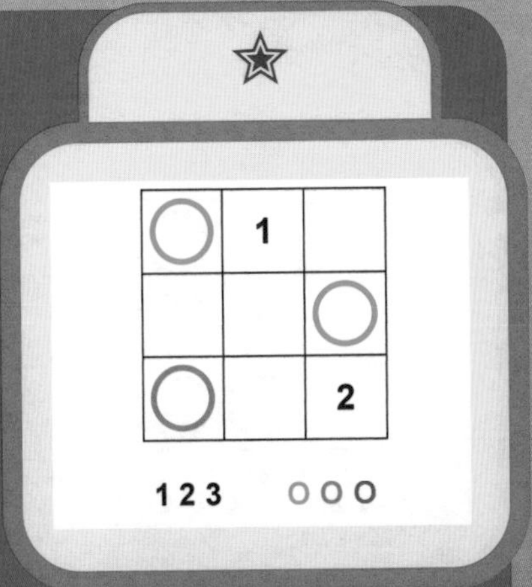

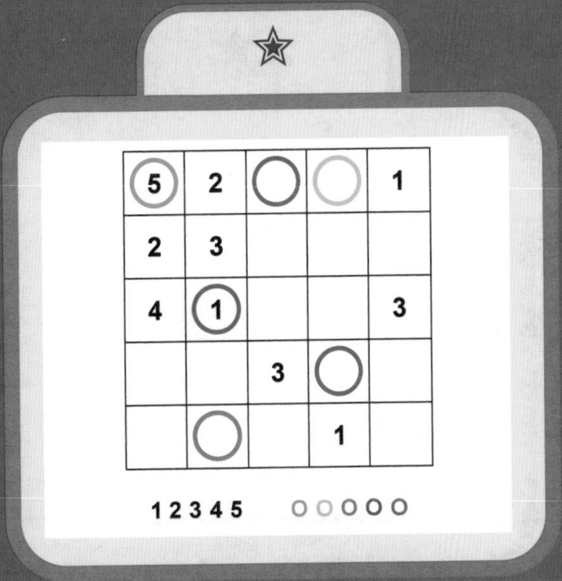

Turn to page 196 for the solutions

COMBIKU

Each horizontal row and vertical column should contain different colors and different numbers. Every square will contain one number and one colored circle and no combination may be repeated anywhere in the puzzle; so, for instance, if a square contains a 3 surrounded by a red circle, then no other square containing a 3 will have a red circle and no other square with a red circle will contain a 3.

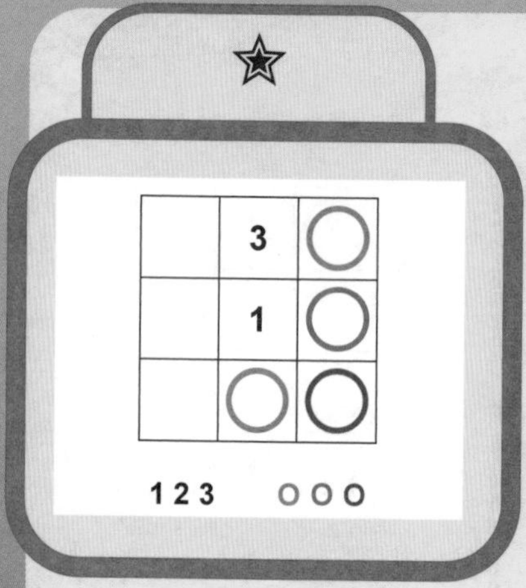

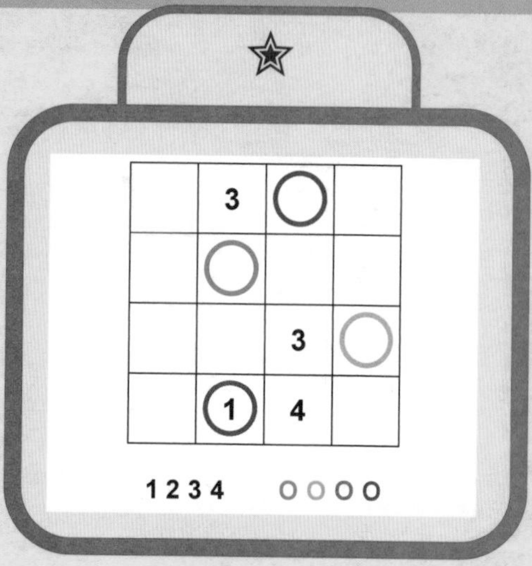

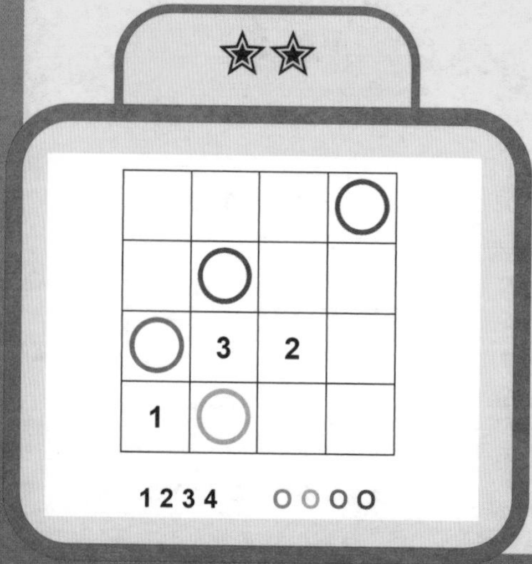

 Turn to page 196 for the solutions

★★

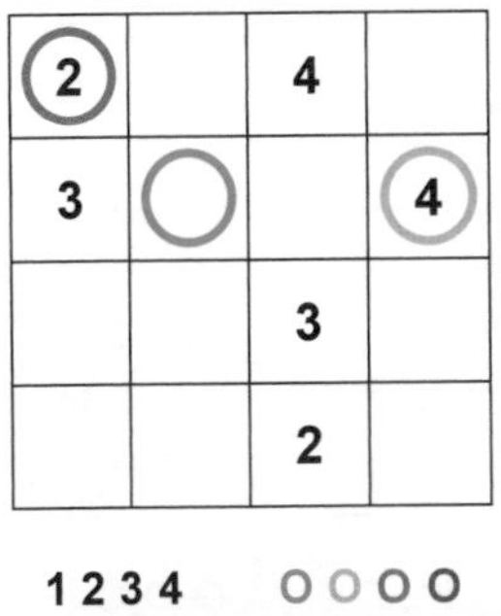

★

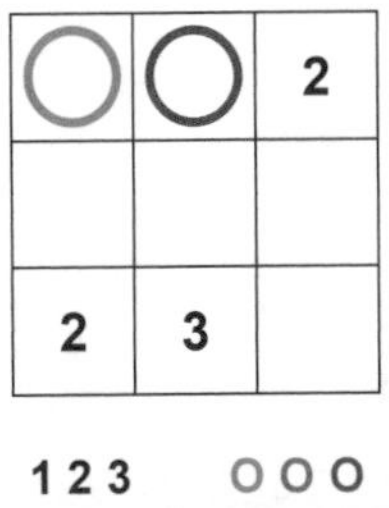

★★★

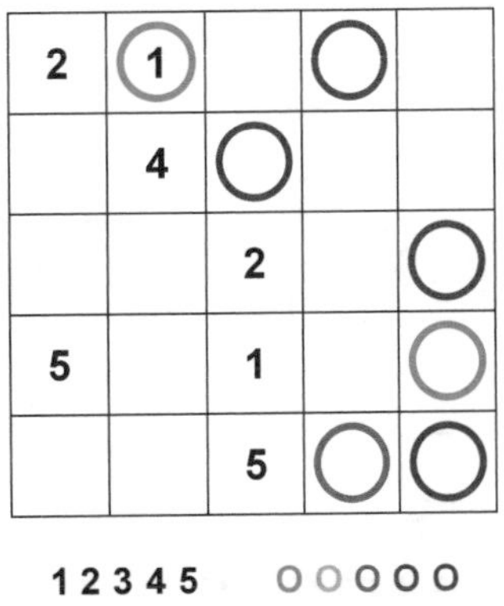

★

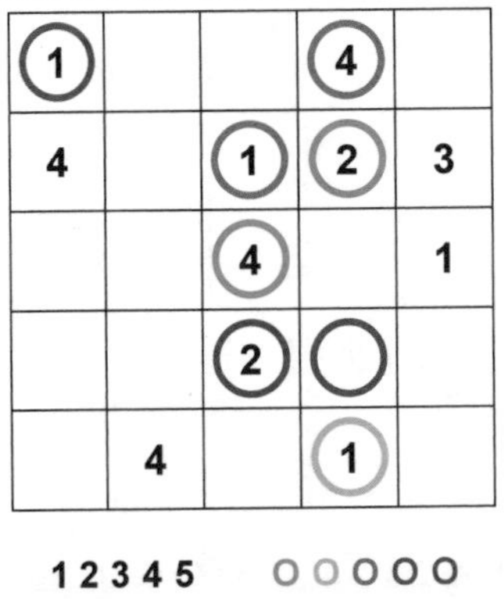

★★

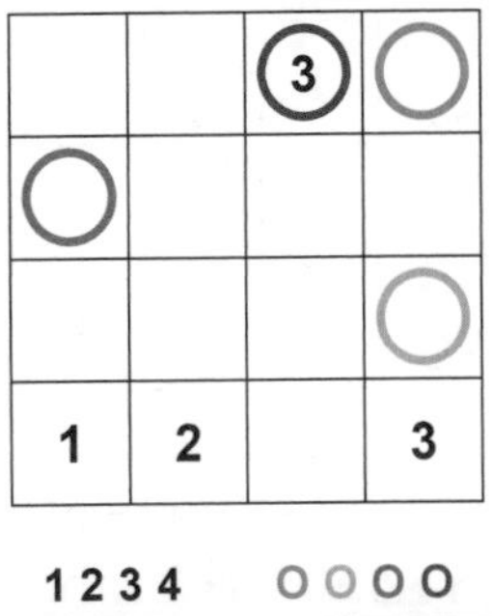

Turn to page 196 for the solutions

COMBIKU

Each horizontal row and vertical column should contain different colors and different numbers. Every square will contain one number and one colored circle and no combination may be repeated anywhere in the puzzle; so, for instance, if a square contains a 3 surrounded by a red circle, then no other square containing a 3 will have a red circle and no other square with a red circle will contain a 3.

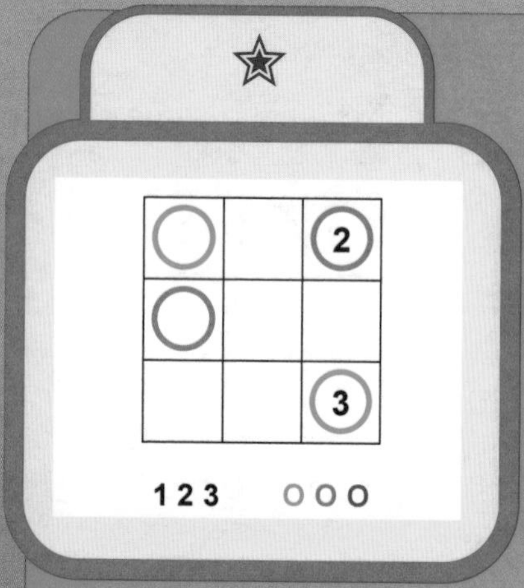

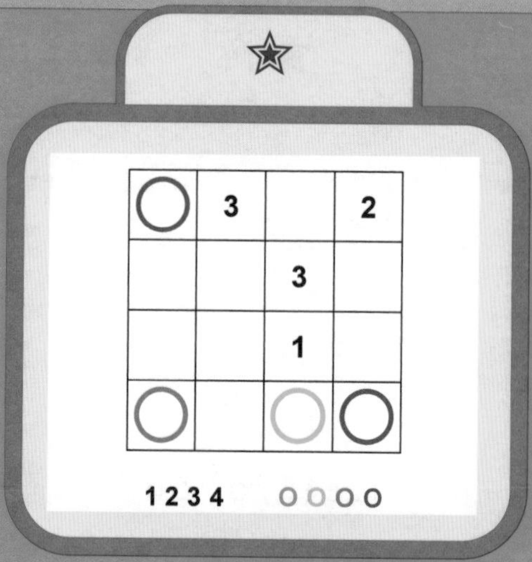

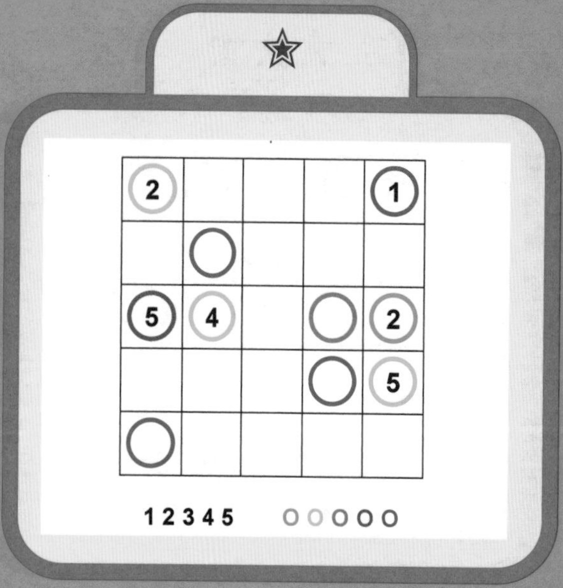

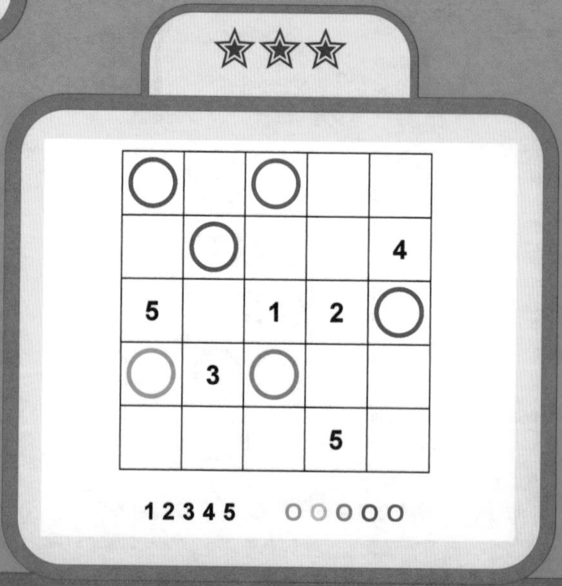

 Turn to page 196 for the solutions

COMBIKU

☆

	(3)	4	○
1	(4)		
3	2		(4)
4		(2)	(3)

1 2 3 4 ○ ○ ○ ○

☆

(3)	○	2
	○	3
	(3)	

1 2 3 ○ ○ ○

☆☆

5	4	○	○	
			○	2
		5	3	1
		(2)		○

1 2 3 4 5 ○ ○ ○ ○ ○

☆☆

	○		2	
(1)		(4)		○
3	2	5		
	○			○

1 2 3 4 5 ○ ○ ○ ○ ○

☆☆

	(4)		○
(2)	○		3
			○

1 2 3 4 ○ ○ ○ ○

Turn to page 196 for the solutions

COMBIKU

Each horizontal row and vertical column should contain different colors and different numbers. Every square will contain one number and one colored circle and no combination may be repeated anywhere in the puzzle; so, for instance, if a square contains a 3 surrounded by a red circle, then no other square containing a 3 will have a red circle and no other square with a red circle will contain a 3.

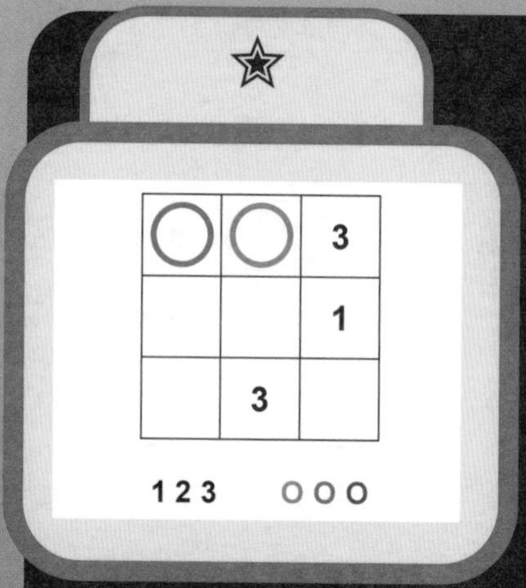

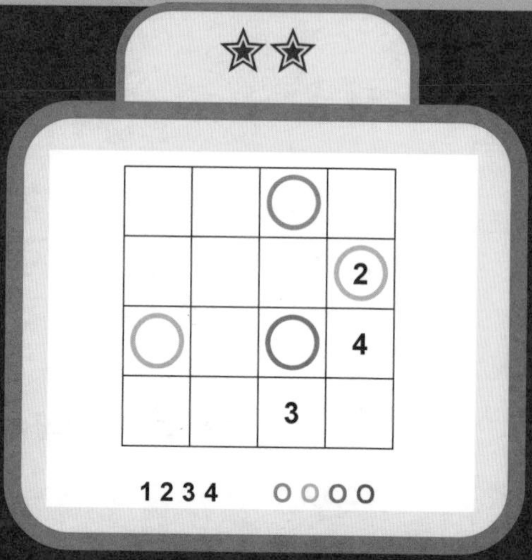

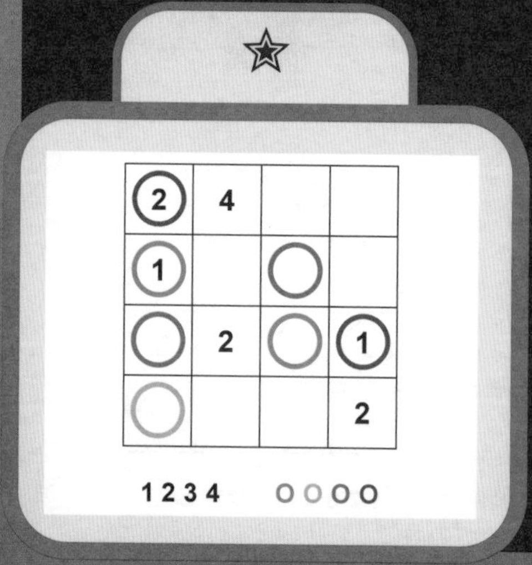

 Turn to page 196 for the solutions

COMBIKU

★★

	2		(4)
4		○	1
○			

1 2 3 4 ○ ○ ○ ○

★

	○	3
		○
○	(1)	2

1 2 3 ○ ○ ○

★

2		○		(1)
(1)	○		○	
	(1)			
○	(5)	4		2
	○			

1 2 3 4 5 ○ ○ ○ ○ ○

★★

	(5)			○
				(3)
○		2		
4		3	5	
		(4)	○	

1 2 3 4 5 ○ ○ ○ ○ ○

★★

	4		(3)
	○		
	(2)		
		4	

1 2 3 4 ○ ○ ○ ○

Turn to page 196 for the solutions

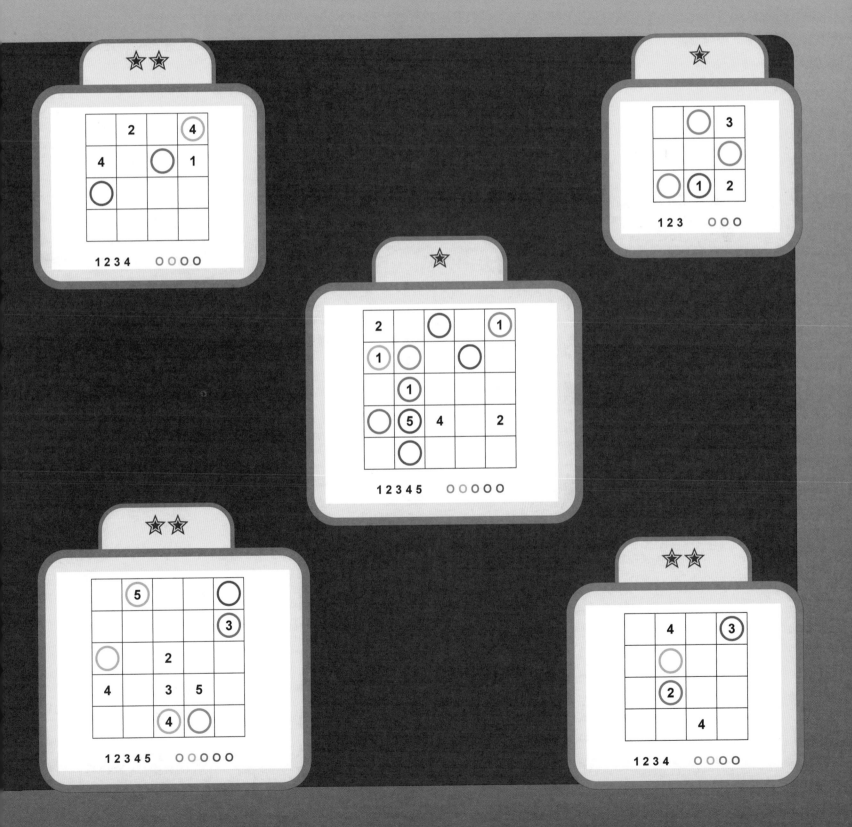

COMBIKU

Each horizontal row and vertical column should contain different colors and different numbers. Every square will contain one number and one colored circle and no combination may be repeated anywhere in the puzzle; so, for instance, if a square contains a 3 surrounded by a red circle, then no other square containing a 3 will have a red circle and no other square with a red circle will contain a 3.

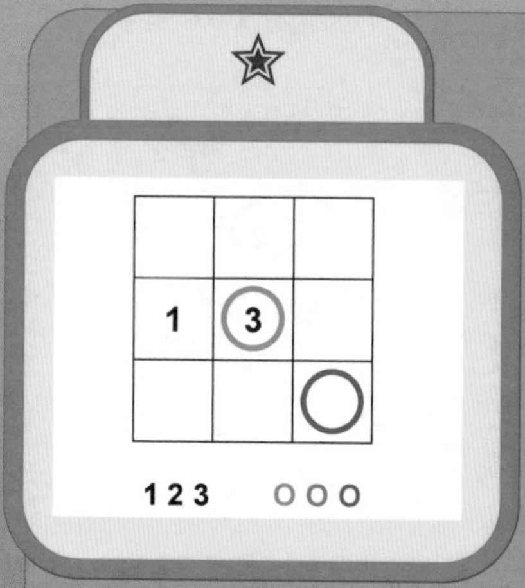

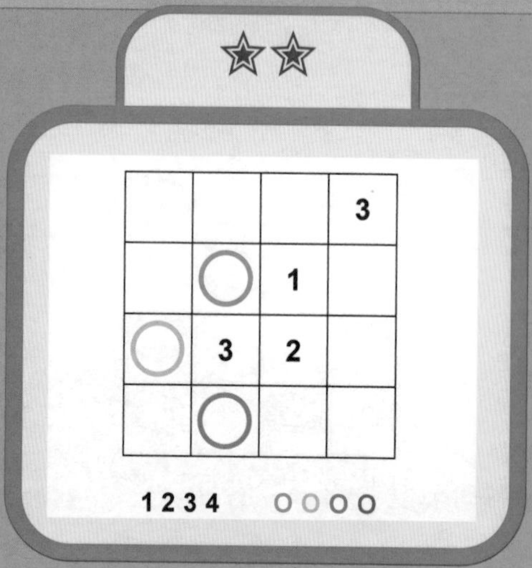

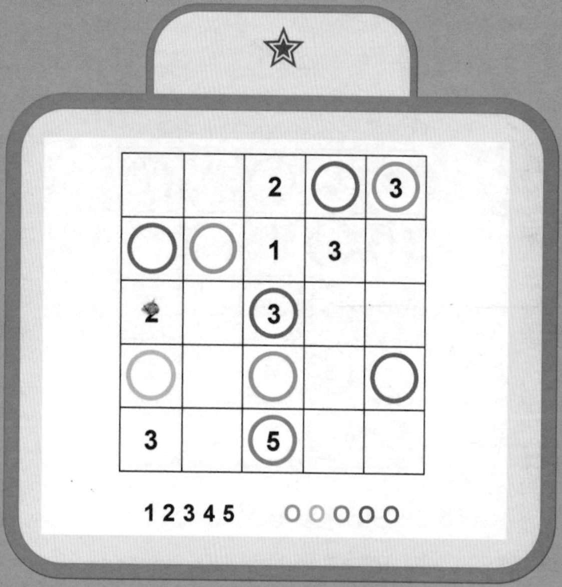

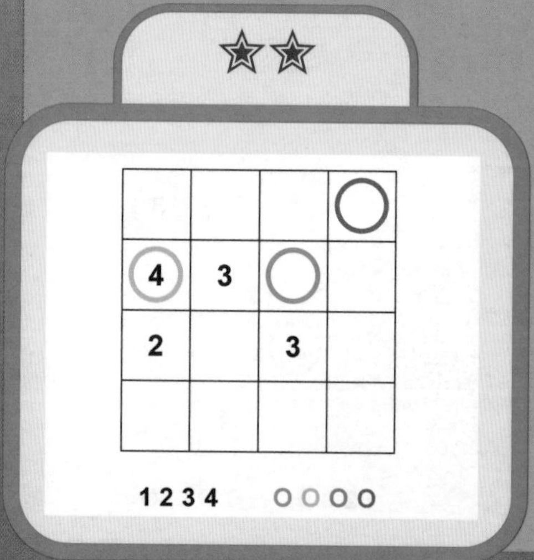

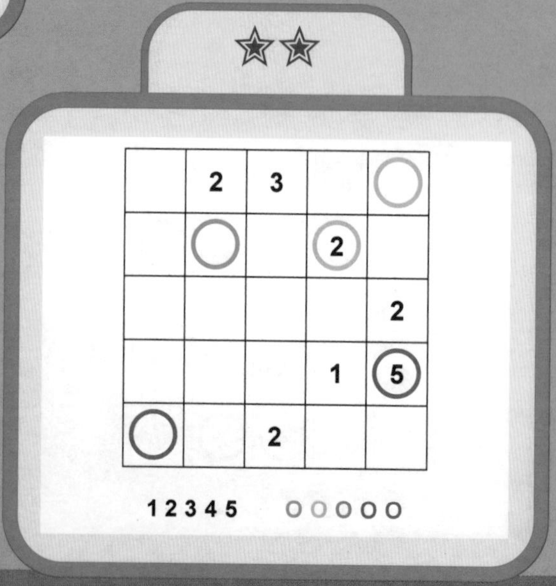

 Turn to page 196 for the solutions

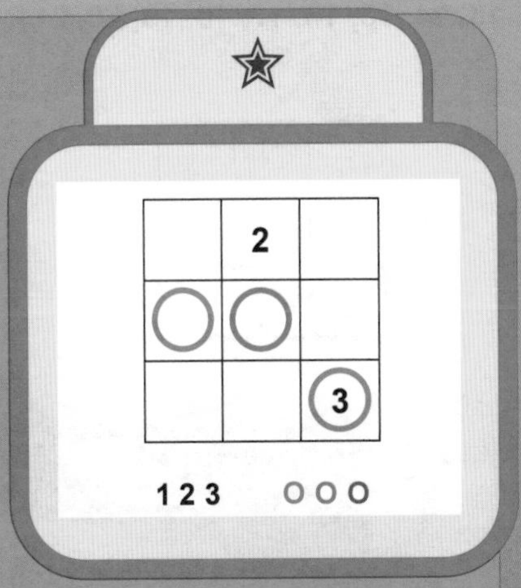

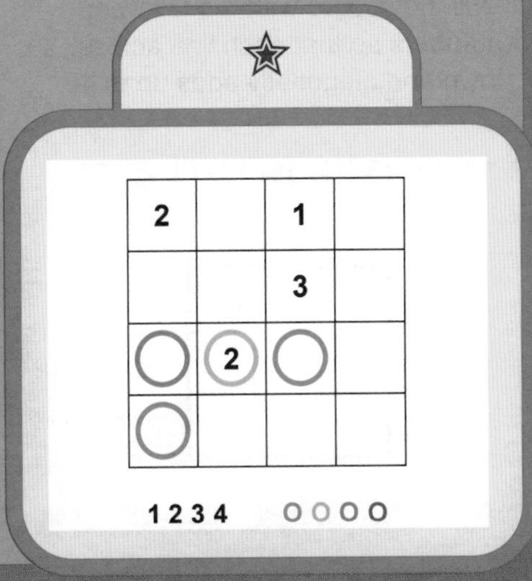

Turn to page 196 for the solutions

MAGIC SQUARE

★

Fill the square with the following numbers so that each line across, down and diagonally adds up to 51.

13, 14, 15, 16, 17, 18, 19, 20, 21

14	21	16
19	17	15
18	13	20

★★

Fill the square with the following numbers so that each line across, down and diagonally adds up to 34. Some numbers are already in place.

2, 4, 8, 9, 10, 13, 14, 15, 16

	11	5	
			3
12	1		6
7			

★

Fill the square with the following numbers to make three three-digit numbers, so that the number in the second row is twice that in the top row and that in the bottom row is three times that in the top row. One number is already in place.

1, 2, 4, 5, 6, 7, 8, 9

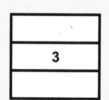

	3	

★★

Fill the square with the following numbers so that each line across, down and diagonally adds up to 48.

11, 12, 13, 15, 16, 17, 19, 20, 21

12	21	15
19	16	13
17	11	20

★★★

The numbers in each line of five squares across, down and diagonally should add up to 65, but in every row across and column down there is one number out of place. Swap these with one another to make the total correct.

8	9	24	17	15
2	25	18	11	10
21	19	12	14	3
20	13	1	4	22
6	7	5	23	16

 Turn to page 196 for the solutions

MAGIC SQUARE

★

Fill the square with the following numbers so that each line across, down and diagonally adds up to 15.

1, 3, 3, 5, 5, 5, 7, 7, 9

3	9	3
5	5	5
7	1	7

★★

Fill the empty squares with numbers so that each line across, down and diagonally adds up to 72.

17		
26	15	

★★★

The numbers in each line of five squares across, down and diagonally should add up to 88, but in every row across and column down there is one number out of place. Swap these with one another to make the total correct.

23	24	8	38	19
9	15	14	19	7
19	9	12	25	22
15	17	20	17	23
21	20	10	13	21

★★

Fill the square with the following numbers so that each line across, down and diagonally adds up to 105.

25, 28, 31, 32, 35, 38, 39, 42, 45

★

Fill the square with the following numbers so that each line across, down and diagonally adds up to 18.

2, 3, 4, 5, 6, 7, 8, 9, 10

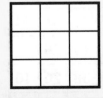

3	10	5
8	6	4
7	2	9

Turn to page 196 for the solutions

MAGIC SQUARE

★

Fill the square with the following numbers so that each line across, down and diagonally adds up to 21.

2, 4, 5, 6, 7, 8, 9, 10, 12

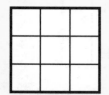

★★

Fill the square with the following numbers so that each line across, down and diagonally adds up to 134. Some numbers are already in place.

17, 22, 24, 26, 27, 31, 34, 39, 45

57			
	33		
	40	22	41
29		49	

★

Fill the square with the following numbers so that each line across, down and diagonally adds up to 36.

7, 9, 10, 11, 12, 13, 14, 15, 17

★★

Fill the square with the following numbers so that each line across, down and diagonally adds up to 65. Some numbers are already in place.

5, 6, 10, 12, 13, 14, 14, 15

		13	29
27		18	
19		20	
	28		17

★★★

The numbers in each line of five squares across, down and diagonally should add up to 100, but in every row across and column down there is one number out of place. Swap these with one another to make the total correct.

27	21	16	15	12
3	5	43	34	14
20	14	10	26	6
17	20	30	20	16
24	39	4	36	28

 Turn to page 196 for the solutions

MAGIC SQUARE

★★

Fill the square with the following numbers so that each line across, down and diagonally adds up to 68. Some numbers are already in place.

6, 18, 20, 22, 24, 26, 28, 30

2		16	
	14		4
	12		
8		10	32

★★

Fill the square with the following numbers so that each line across, down and diagonally adds up to 99. Some numbers are already in place.

10, 16, 23, 23, 24, 28, 35, 37

22			38
	24		
31			21
9		25	30

★★★

The numbers in each line of six squares across, down and diagonally should add up to 113, but in every row across and column down there is one number out of place. Swap these with one another to make the total correct.

15	6	14	27	12	11
32	15	17	7	23	16
29	25	18	16	13	16
12	25	23	24	14	18
9	28	40	31	3	20
22	11	19	12	20	35

★

Fill the square with the following numbers so that each line across, down and diagonally adds up to 30.

2, 3, 4, 9, 10, 11, 16, 17, 18

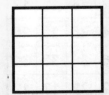

★

Fill the square with the following numbers so that each line across, down and diagonally adds up to 15.

1, 2, 3, 4, 5, 6, 7, 8, 9

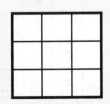

Turn to page 196 for the solutions

MAGIC SQUARE

★

Fill the square with the following numbers so that each line across, down and diagonally adds up to 18.

1, 3, 4, 5, 6, 7, 8, 9, 11

★★

Fill the square with the following numbers so that each line across, down and diagonally adds up to 62. Some numbers are already in place.

9, 13, 15, 15, 15, 16, 18, 20, 22, 23

		17	**12**
		17	
14			**12**
10			

★

Fill the square with the following numbers so that each line across, down and diagonally adds up to 21.

3, 4, 5, 6, 7, 8, 9, 10, 11

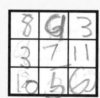

★★

Fill the blank squares in the grid with the following numbers so that each line across, down and diagonally adds up to the totals shown. Every listed number is used just once.

0, 1, 2, 3, 4,
5, 6, 7, 8, 9

		6			=	25
		6			=	16
	9	**5**		**2**	=	16
	7				=	23
=	=	=	=	=	=	
19	30	22	12	16	23	

★★★

The numbers in each line of six squares across, down and diagonally should add up to 134, but in every row across and column down there is one number out of place. Swap these with one another to make the total correct.

20	**24**	**17**	**17**	**25**	**42**
37	**22**	**13**	**20**	**24**	**21**
13	**29**	**22**	**18**	**12**	**19**
15	**39**	**34**	**26**	**10**	**20**
12	**10**	**26**	**34**	**32**	**31**
16	**21**	**32**	**22**	**17**	**12**

 Turn to page 196 for the solutions

MAGIC SQUARE

★

Fill the square with the following numbers so that each line across, down and diagonally adds up to 34. Some numbers are already in place.

1, 2, 6, 7, 9, 10, 13, 14, 16

	12	**8**	
		11	
15			**3**
4		**5**	

★★

Fill the square with the following numbers so that each line across, down and diagonally adds up to 99. Some numbers are already in place.

14, 17, 18, 19, 21, 25, 26, 27, 28, 41

		31	
13	**34**		
			42
	20	**20**	

★

Fill the square with the following numbers so that each line across, down and diagonally adds up to 30.

2, 4, 6, 8, 10, 12, 14, 16, 18

★★★

The numbers in each line of six squares across, down and diagonally should add up to 122, but in every row across and column down there is one number out of place. Swap these with one another to make the total correct.

21	**5**	**14**	**31**	**44**	**15**
30	**29**	**21**	**9**	**22**	**20**
36	**29**	**20**	**10**	**6**	**22**
6	**30**	**22**	**30**	**13**	**17**
10	**26**	**23**	**17**	**12**	**22**
27	**12**	**20**	**13**	**21**	**27**

★★

Fill the blank squares in the grid with the following numbers so that each line across, down and diagonally adds up to the totals shown. Every listed number is used just once.

0, 1, 2, 3, 4,
5, 6, 7, 8, 9

		2			=	21
	9		**3**	**2**	=	17
					=	20
	6			**5**	=	14
=	=	=	=	=	=	
26	19	15	17	21		17

Turn to page 196 for the solutions

MAGIC SQUARE

★★

Fill the square with the following numbers so that each line across, down and diagonally adds up to 83. Some numbers are already in place.

12, 18, 19, 21, 21, 23, 24, 26, 27, 27

26			12
	22		
18		17	
		19	

★

Fill the square with the following numbers so that each line across, down and diagonally adds up to 46. Some numbers are already in place.

4, 6, 7, 9, 11, 14, 15, 16, 17, 19

18		12	
13			8
		5	
		10	

★

Fill the square with the following numbers so that each line across, down and diagonally adds up to 31. Some numbers are already in place.

2, 2, 4, 4, 5, 6, 7, 10, 11

16		8	
			12
	14	0	
6		17	

★★

Fill the square with the following numbers so that each line across, down and diagonally adds up to 43. Some numbers are already in place.

4, 10, 10, 11, 12, 12, 13, 15, 17, 20

	8		4
	6		14
		7	
9			

★★★

The numbers in each line of seven squares across, down and diagonally should add up to 131, but in every row across and column down there is one number out of place. Swap these with one another to make the total correct.

29	28	21	17	15	4	16
27	18	17	22	20	16	17
30	11	33	16	20	20	18
4	17	12	7	36	5	17
1	19	18	14	18	26	16
17	18	41	10	14	20	23
35	38	6	26	14	7	23

 Turn to page 196 for the solutions

MAGIC SQUARE

★

Fill the square with the following numbers so that each line across, down and diagonally adds up to 43. Some numbers are already in place.

4, 6, 7, 9, 11, 12, 13, 15, 15

14			16
		13	10
14			
2			11

★★★

Fill the square with the following numbers so that each line across, down and diagonally adds up to 50. Some numbers are already in place.

8, 11, 11, 13, 13, 13, 13, 14, 14, 18, 19

			12
7			
		10	
16			8

★★★

The numbers in each line of seven squares across, down and diagonally should add up to 123, but in every row across and column down there is one number out of place. Swap these with one another to make the total correct.

31	19	10	13	14	32	15
6	21	17	22	30	17	7
17	30	17	24	17	11	8
7	22	33	13	15	17	11
14	16	21	22	13	11	29
16	13	3	19	12	12	43
27	13	19	13	20	18	11

★★

Fill the square with the following numbers so that each line across, down and diagonally adds up to 67. Some numbers are already in place.

7, 10, 13, 13, 14, 17, 18, 19, 19, 21, 21, 22, 22, 24, 35

		3		
5	5			1
		5		
7			13	
14		3	4	

★

Fill the square with the following numbers so that each line across, down and diagonally adds up to 51. Some numbers are already in place.

3, 9, 12, 13, 14, 15, 16, 17, 21

	8		6
10			
		11	24
	18		7

Turn to page 196 for the solutions

MAGIC SQUARE

★

Fill the square with the following numbers so that each line across, down and diagonally adds up to 77. Some numbers are already in place.

4, 11, 11, 14, 18, 18, 18, 25, 27

34			
21			20
	30	11	
	25		21

★★

Fill the square with the following numbers so that each line across, down and diagonally adds up to 111. Each differently coloured block of four squares contains numbers which are consecutive: some numbers are already in place.

1, 3, 4, 5, 8, 10, 11, 13, 15, 16, 18, 20, 21, 23, 24, 25, 28, 30, 31, 33, 34, 35

32	29				
		2		22	
12	9	17			
			19	26	27
		36			
14				6	7

★

Fill the square with the following numbers so that each line across and down adds up to the totals shown.

3, 4, 5, 7, 8, 9

2			= 14
		6	= 15
	1		= 16
= 14	= 15	= 16	

★★

The numbers in each line of five squares across, down and diagonally should add up to 58, but in every row across and column down there is one number out of place. Swap these with one another to make the total correct.

16	16	11	9	14
17	9	29	13	1
15	5	6	16	15
7	3	17	11	12
14	17	3	8	6

★★★

This grid originally contained all 25 of the numbers listed below, but some have dropped out. Can you discover which are missing and replace them in the grid, so that each line across and down adds up to 95?

1, 1, 5, 5, 9, 11, 13, 14, 15, 16, 16, 18, 19, 20, 22, 22, 23, 24, 25, 27, 29, 33, 33, 37, 37

	16	25		18
14	23			5
1			33	
		1	15	
20		13		11

Turn to page 196 for the solutions

MAGIC SQUARE

★

Fill the star with the following numbers so that each line connects four numbers which total 24 and each of the numbers in the boxes at the five points of the star also total 24. Some numbers are already in place.

4, 5, 6, 8, 9, 12

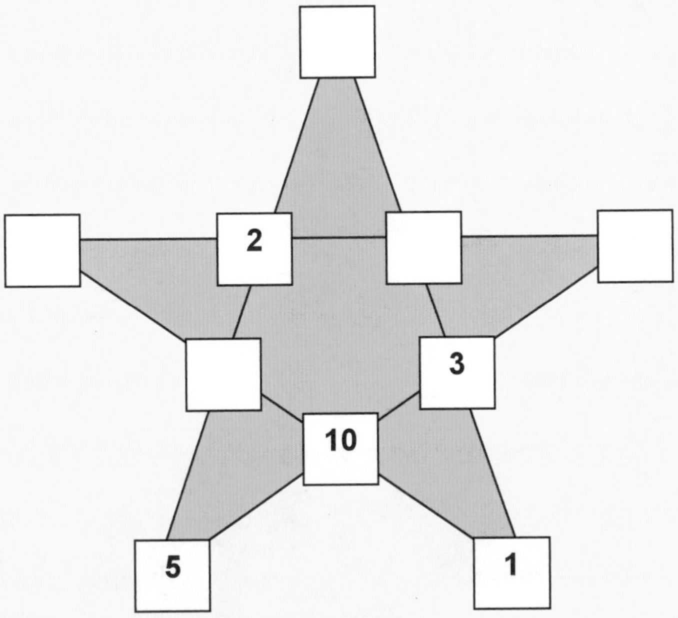

★★

The numbers in each line of five squares across, down and diagonally should add up to 70, but in every row across and column down there is one number out of place. Swap these with one another to make the total correct.

20	10	21	1	13
19	14	12	18	14
3	19	4	5	5
18	14	23	10	11
16	39	17	2	22

★

Fill the empty squares with numbers so that each line across, down and diagonally adds up to 27.

	16	3
15		10

★★★

This grid originally contained all 25 of the numbers listed below, but some have dropped out. Can you discover which are missing and replace them in the grid, so that each line across and down adds up to the totals shown?

5, 6, 7, 8, 9, 9, 11, 12, 13, 13, 14, 16, 16, 18, 19, 20, 21, 22, 23, 23, 24, 25, 25, 28, 28

5			24		= 81
	28	6		18	= 82
12		23		9	= 83
28			16		= 84
	22	25			= 85
= 85	= 84	= 83	= 82	= 81	

★★

The numbers in each line of five squares across, down and diagonally should add up to 83, but in every row across and column down there is one number out of place. Swap these with one another to make the total correct.

20	26	7	11	20
11	18	28	14	16
18	12	13	25	20
14	16	22	20	15
6	16	14	17	16

Turn to page 196 for the solutions

WHAT'S IT WORTH?

Each symbol stands for a different number. In order to reach the correct total at the end of each row and column, what is the value of the triangle, star, circle and pentagon?

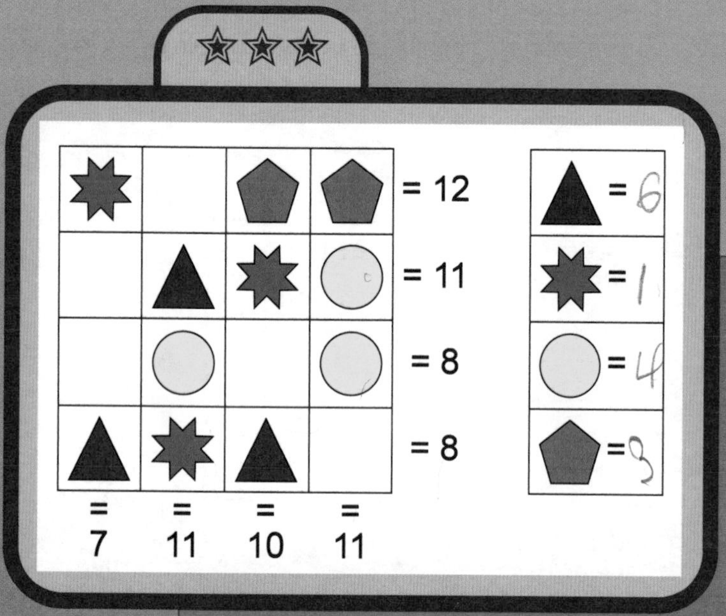

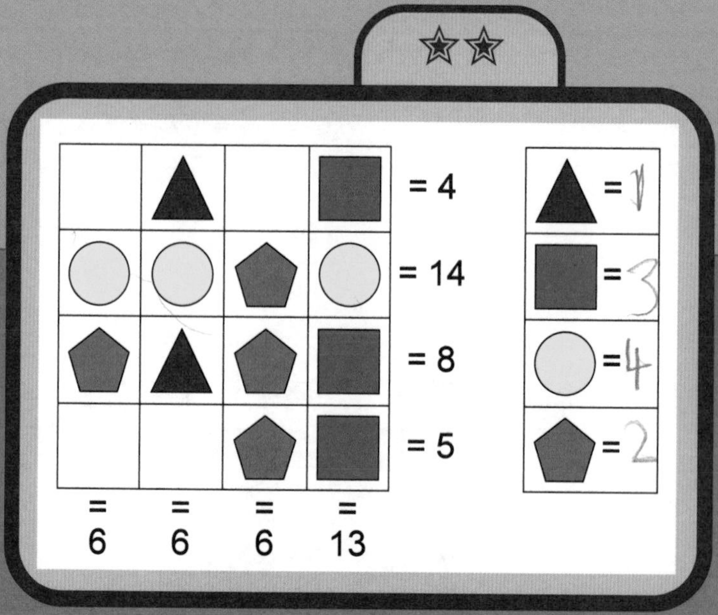

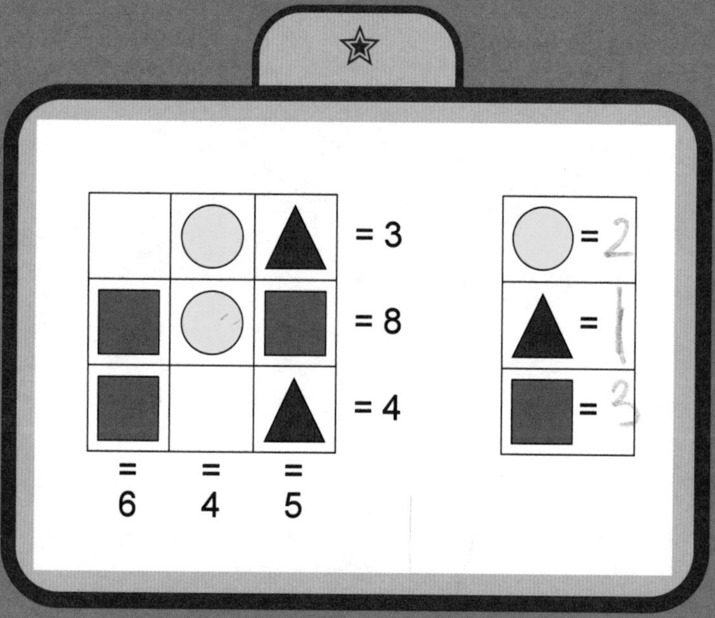

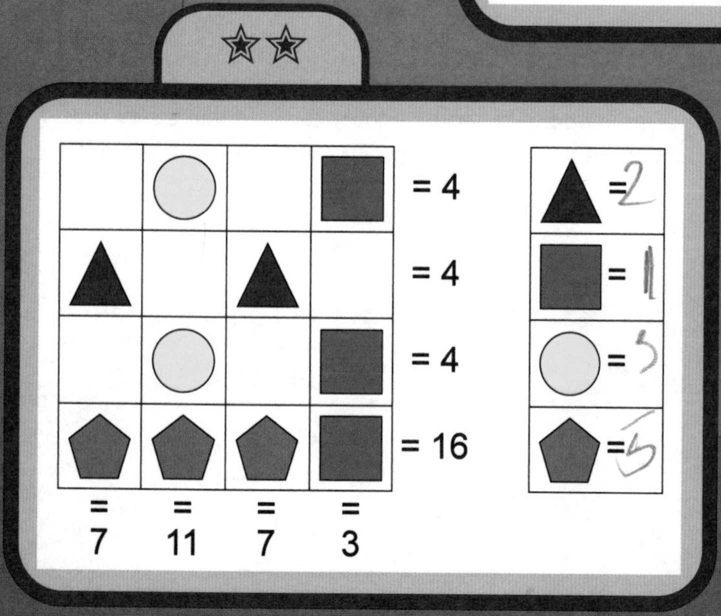

 Turn to page 196 for the solutions

WHAT'S IT WORTH?

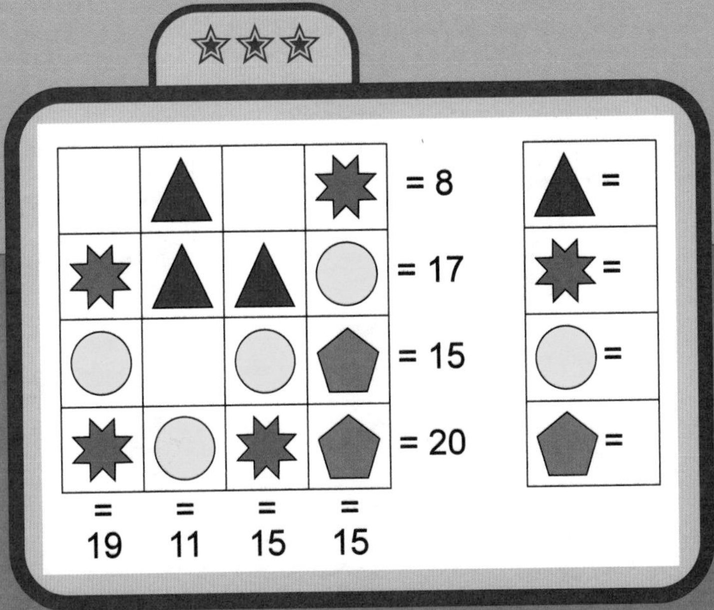

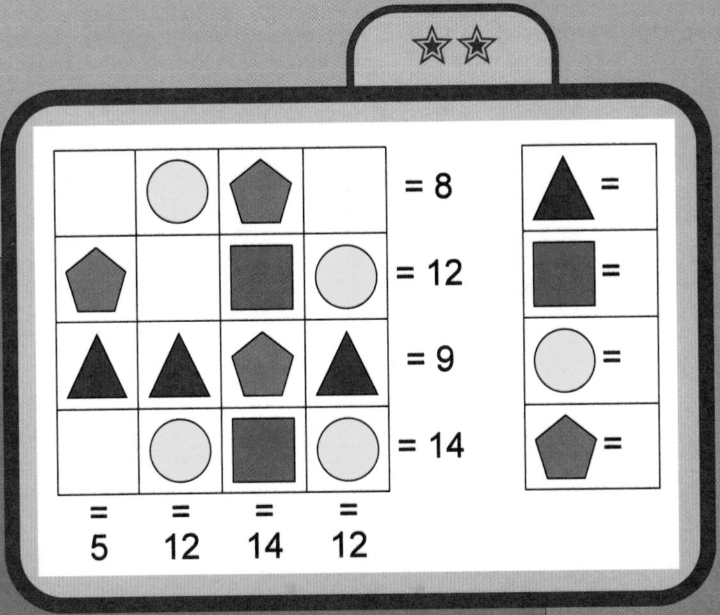

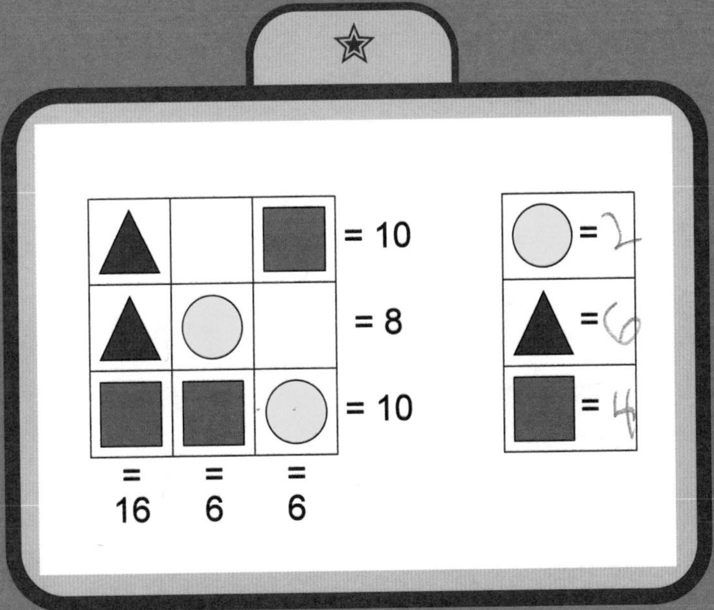

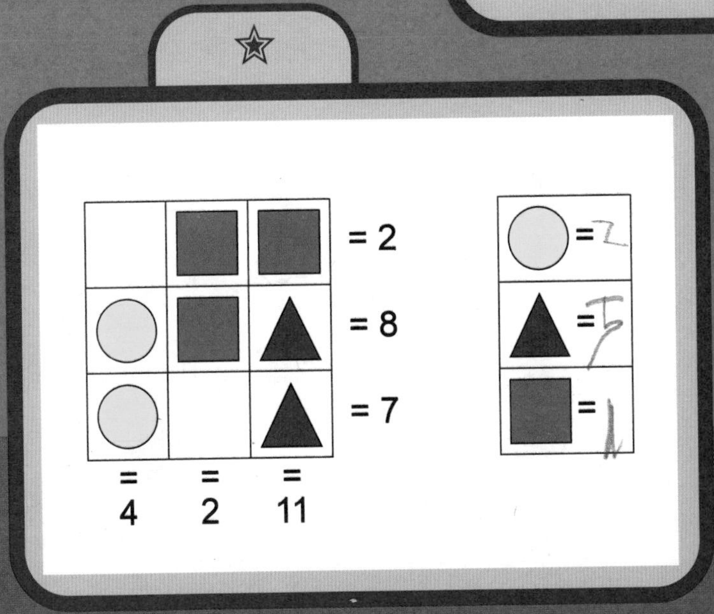

Turn to page 196 for the solutions

WHAT'S IT WORTH?

Each symbol stands for a different number. In order to reach the correct total at the end of each row and column, what is the value of the triangle, star, circle and pentagon?

★★★

	⬟	○	⬟	= 9
▲	▲	▲	○	= 31
	✷		▲	= 11
⬟	✷	⬟	○	= 12
= 9	= 15	= 16	= 23	

▲ =
✷ =
○ =
⬟ =

★★

■	▲			= 6
○	▲	○		= 6
	▲	■	■	= 8
■	⬟	⬟	⬟	= 11
= 5	= 15	= 6	= 5	

▲ =
■ =
○ =
⬟ =

★

▲	○	○	= 8
	■	▲	= 3
■	■	▲	= 4
= 3	= 5	= 7	

○ =
▲ =
■ =

★★

	▲	○	⬟	= 10
	○	⬟	■	= 8
○	⬟	■	■	= 10
⬟	▲		■	= 7
= 6	= 14	= 8	= 7	

▲ =
■ =
○ =
⬟ =

★★★

▲	⬟	▲	▲	= 14
○	○	⬟	▲	= 22
✷	✷	✷	○	= 26
○	⬟	✷		= 16
= 26	= 18	= 18	= 16	

▲ =
✷ =
○ =
⬟ =

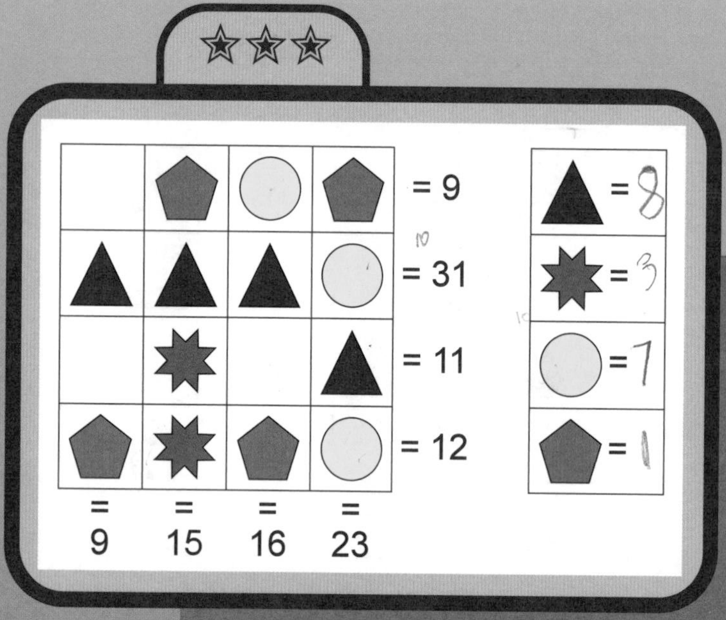

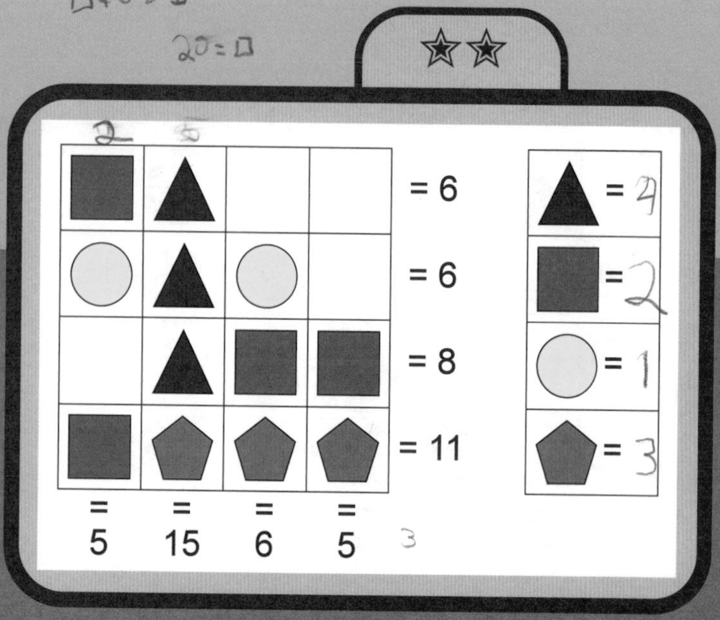

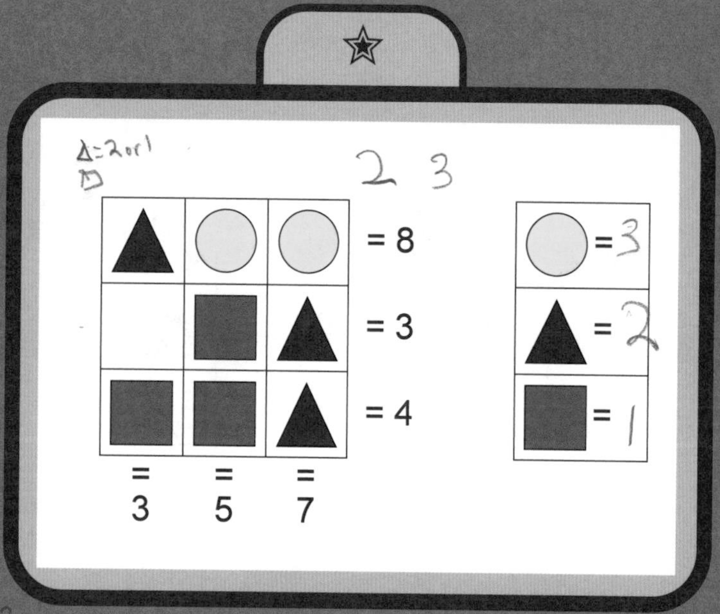

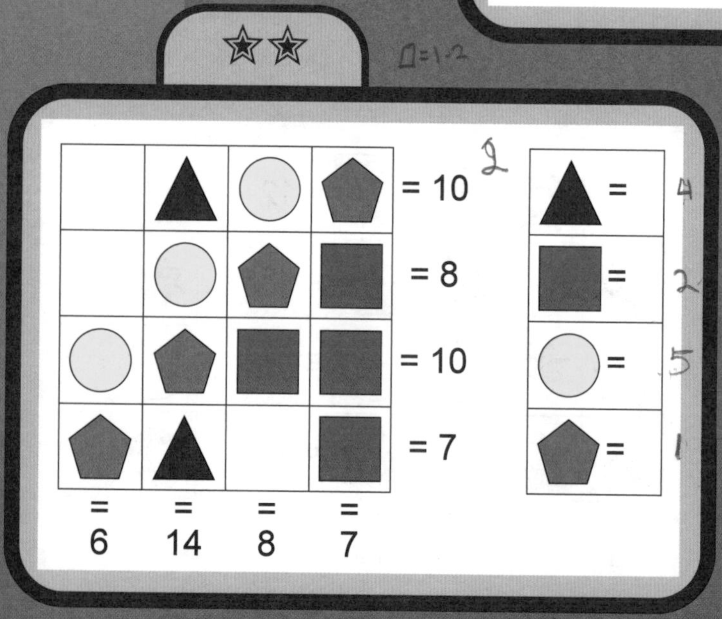

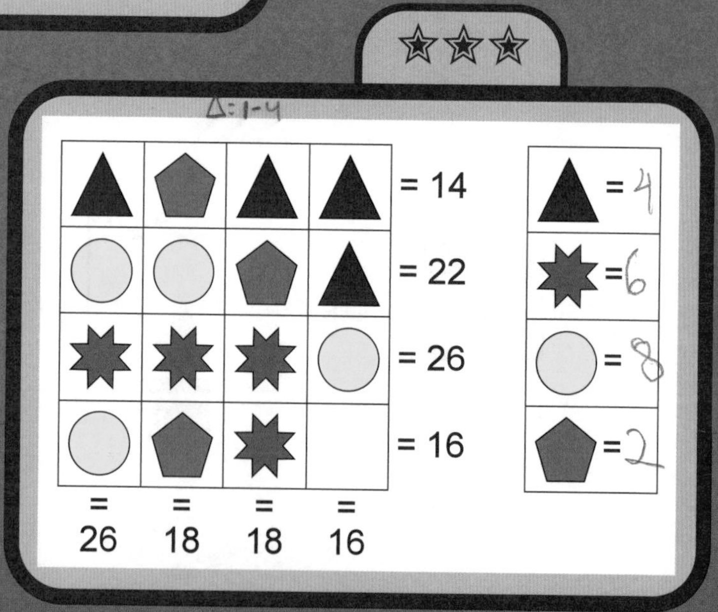

Turn to page 196 for the solutions

WHAT'S IT WORTH?

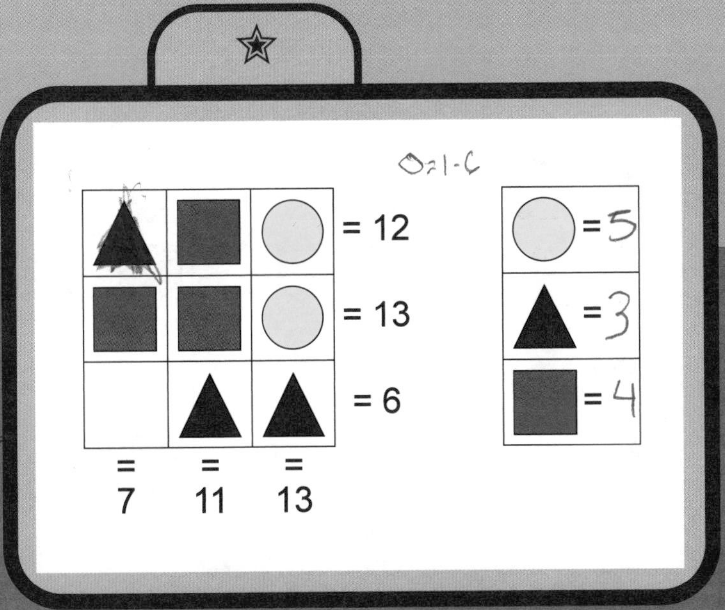

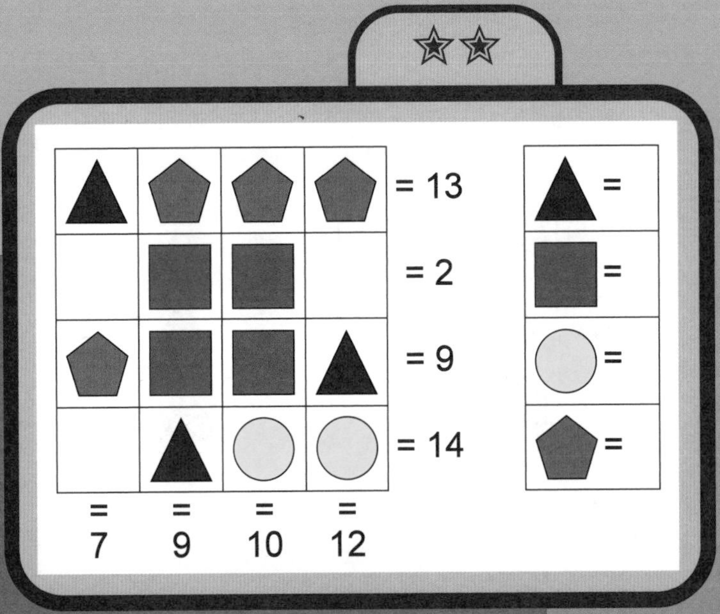

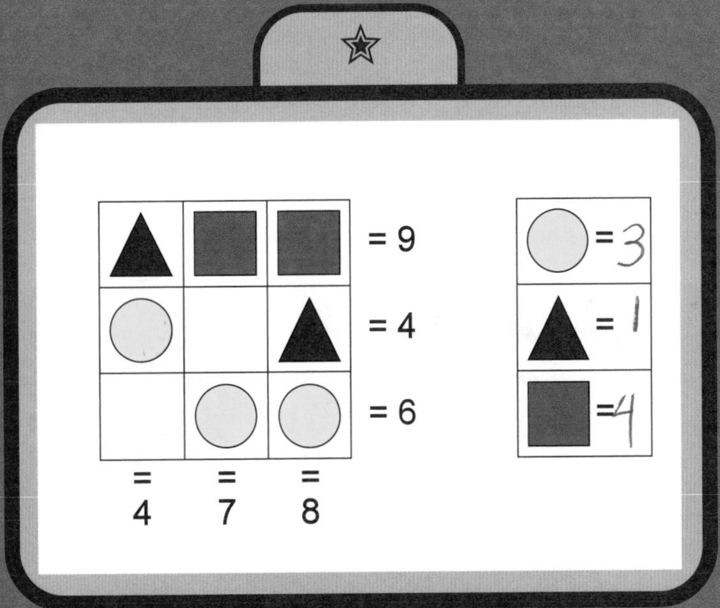

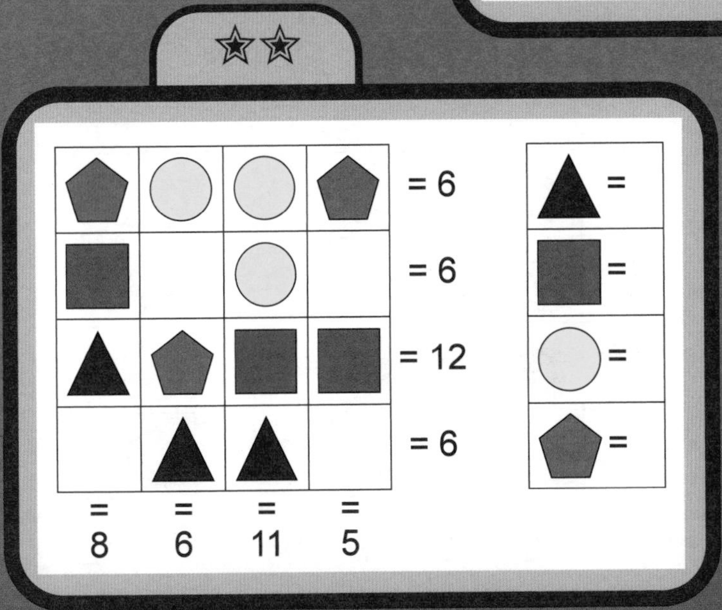

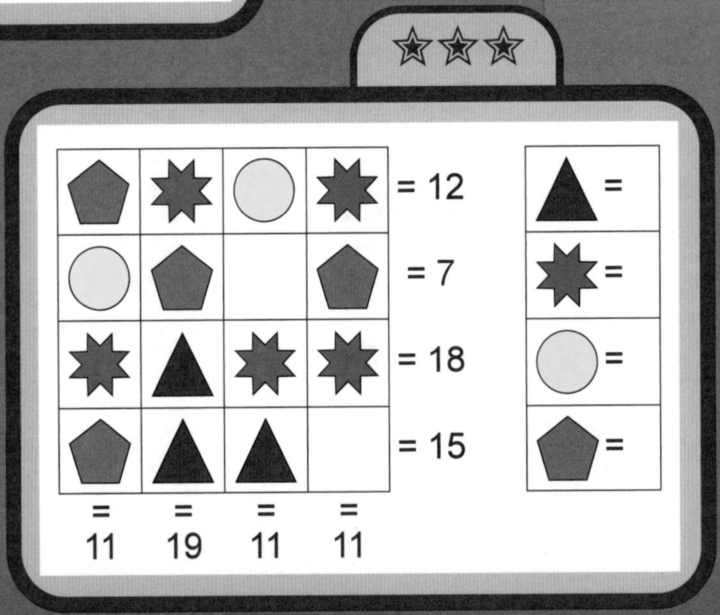

Turn to page 196 for the solutions

WHAT'S IT WORTH?

Each symbol stands for a different number. In order to reach the correct total at the end of each row and column, what is the value of the triangle, star, circle and pentagon?

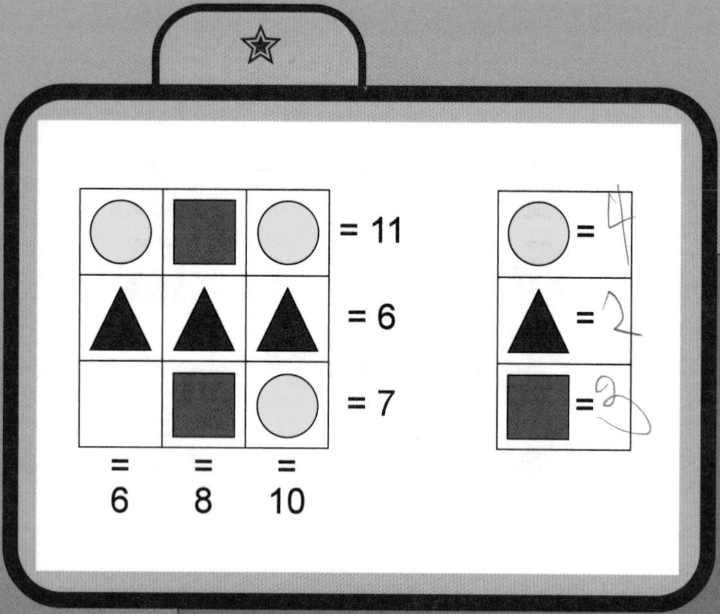

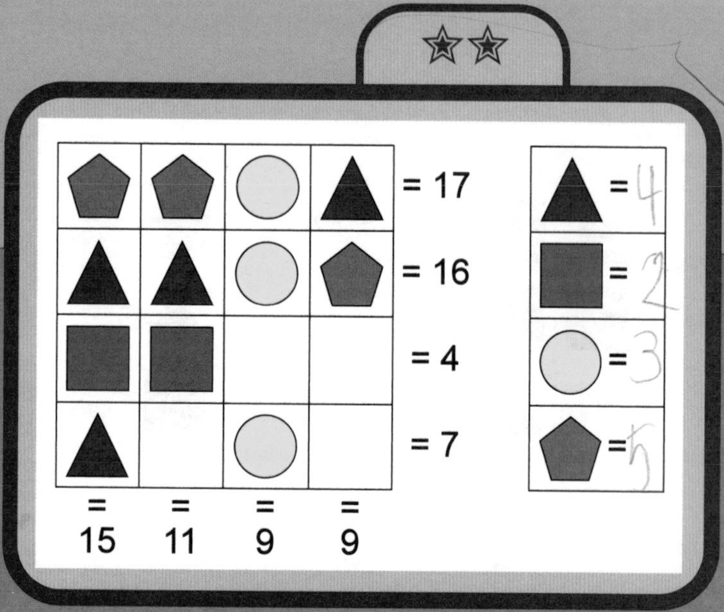

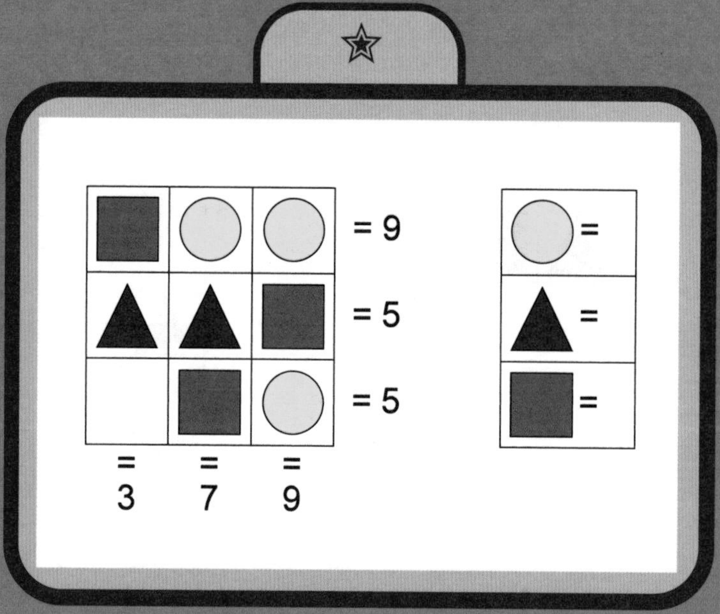

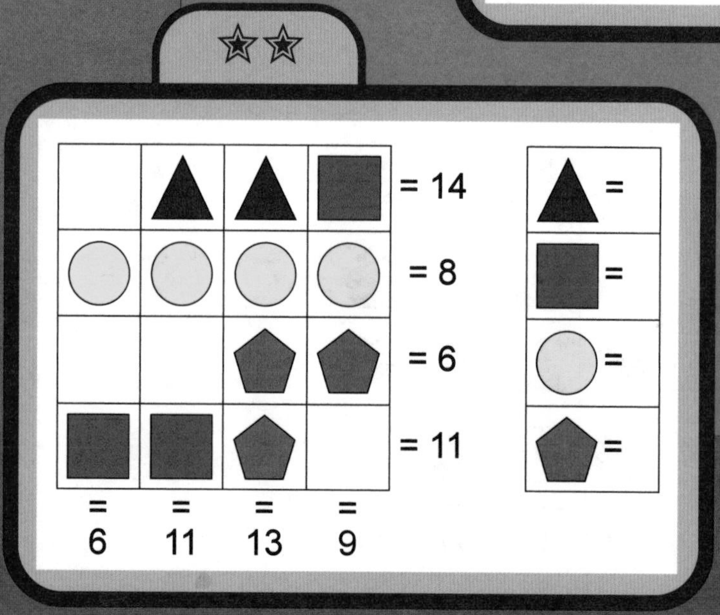

 Turn to page 196 for the solutions

WHAT'S IT WORTH?

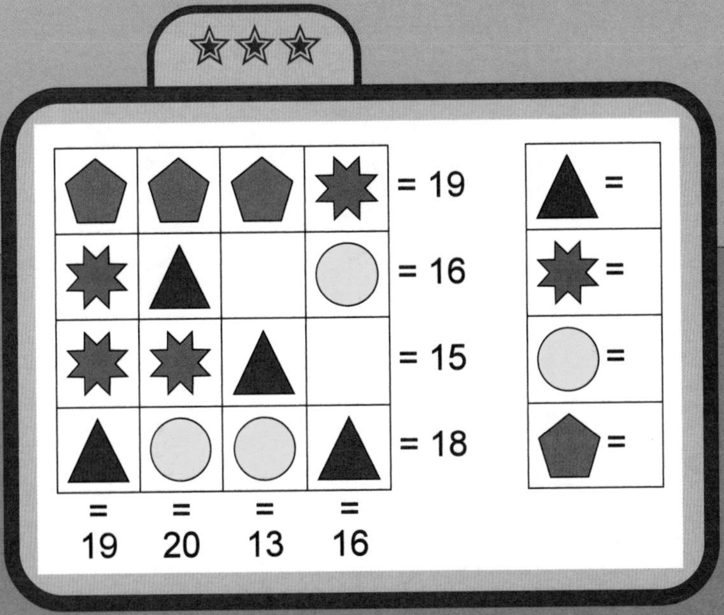

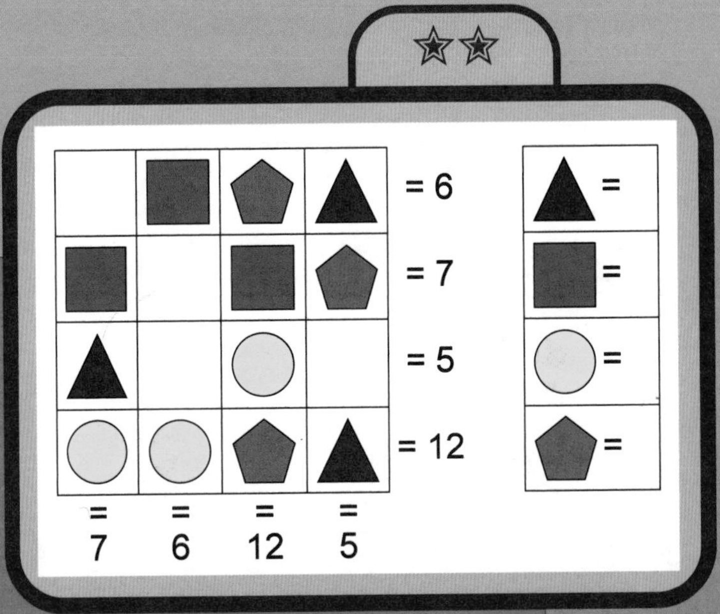

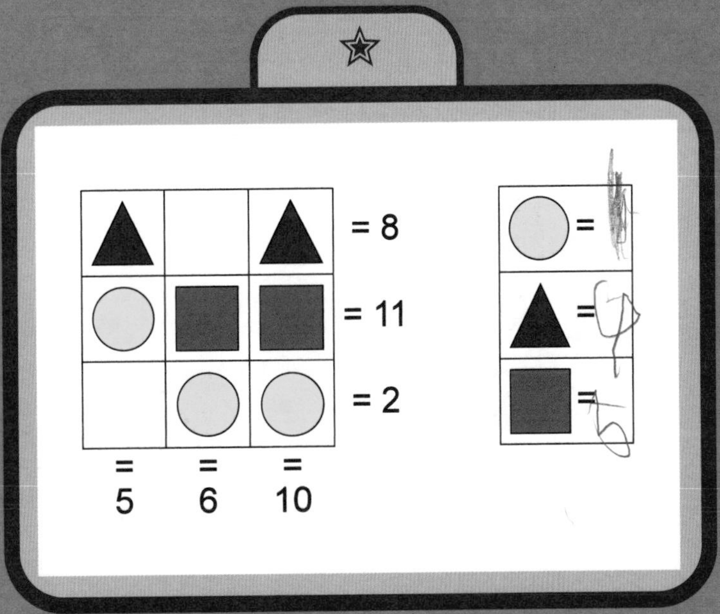

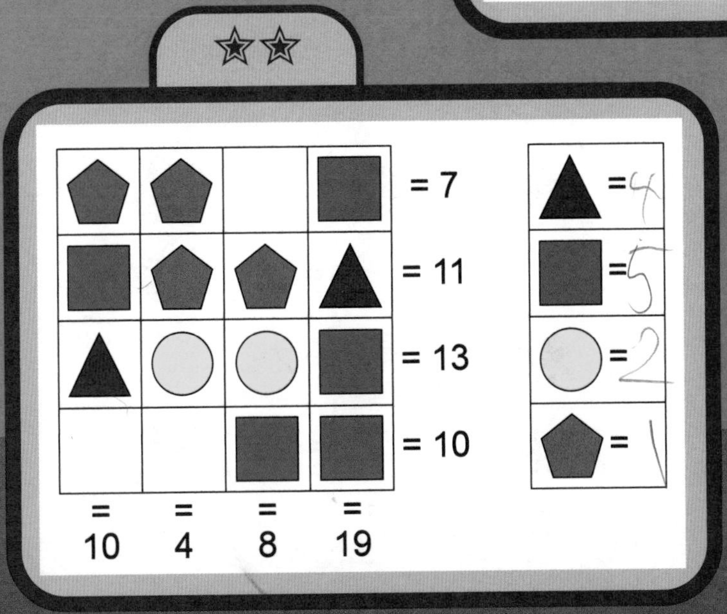

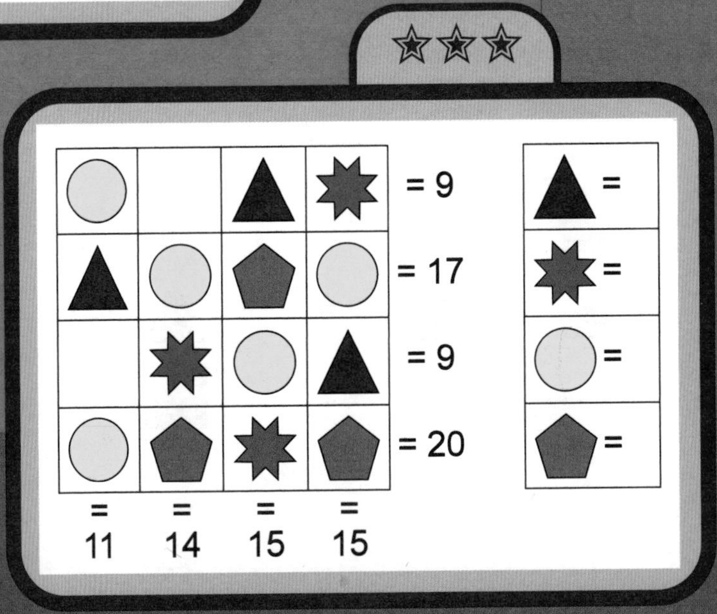

Turn to page 196 for the solutions

WHAT'S IT WORTH?

Each symbol stands for a different number. In order to reach the correct total at the end of each row and column, what is the value of the triangle, star, circle and pentagon?

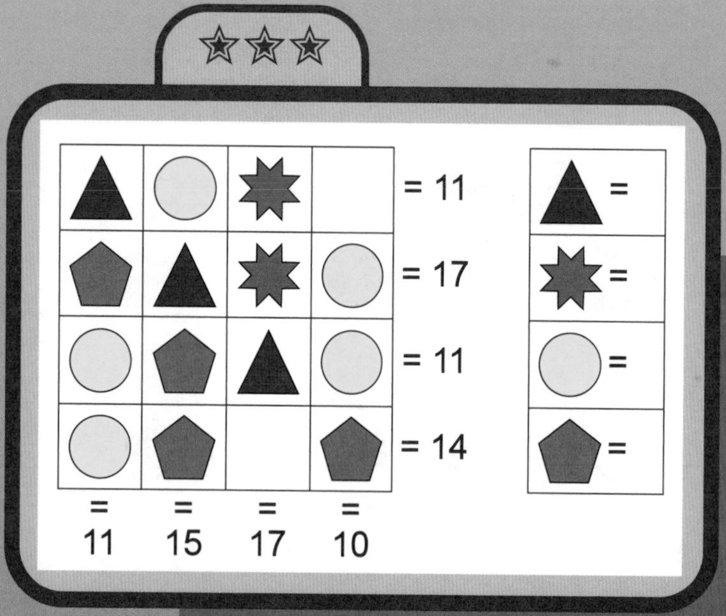

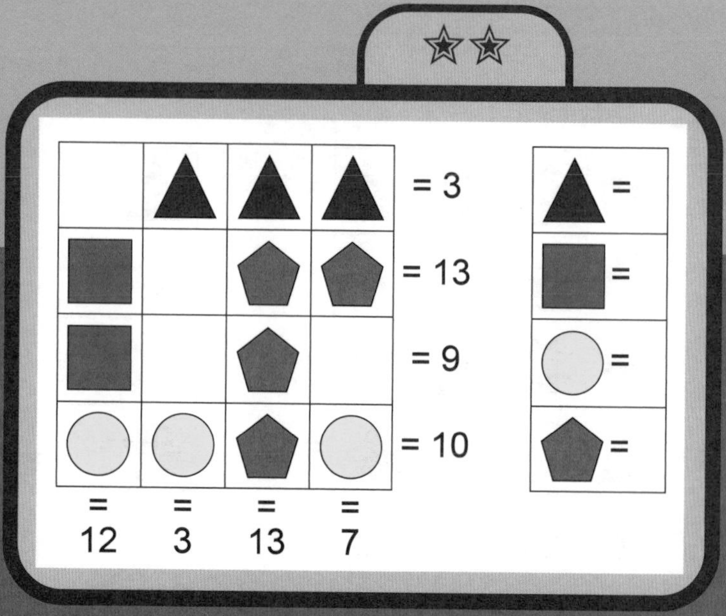

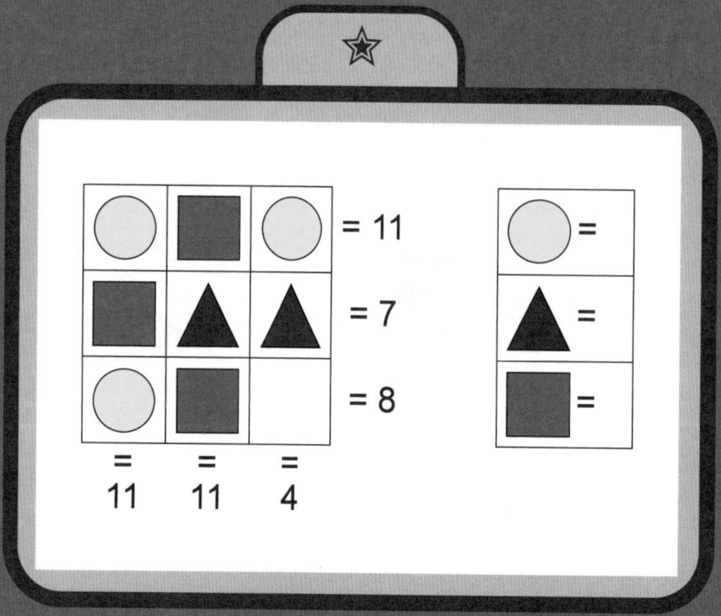

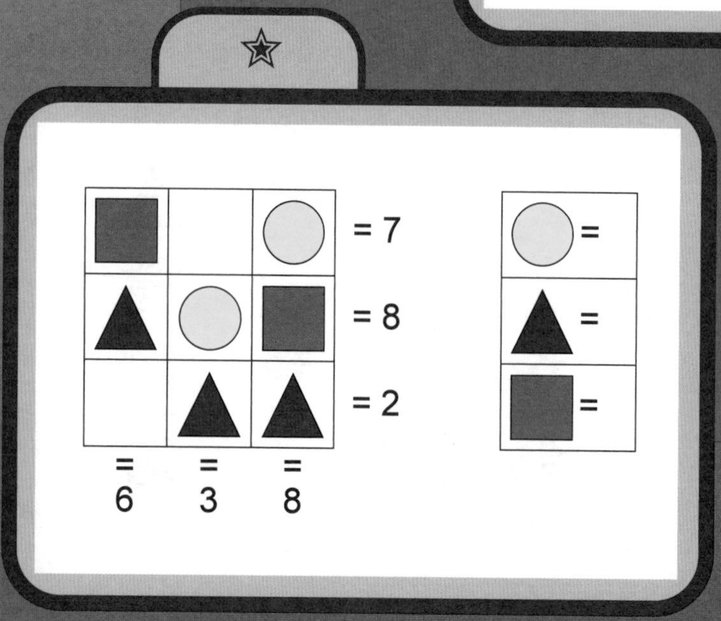

 Turn to page 196 for the solutions

WHAT'S IT WORTH?

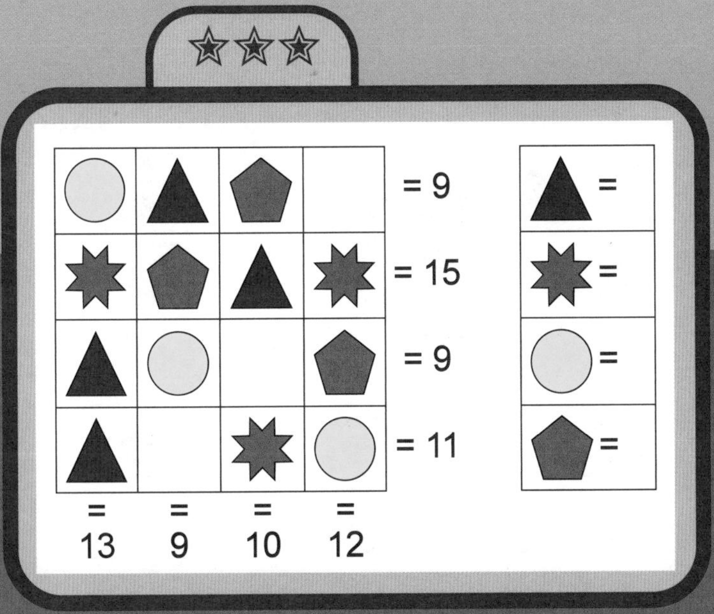

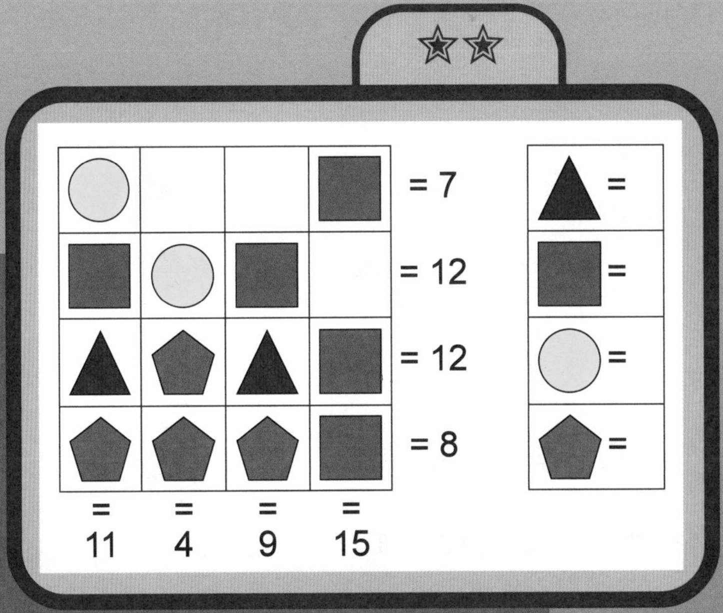

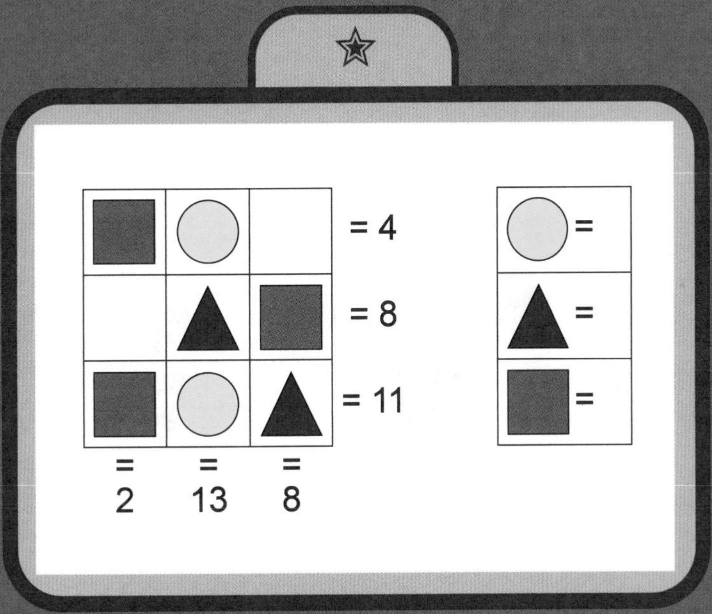

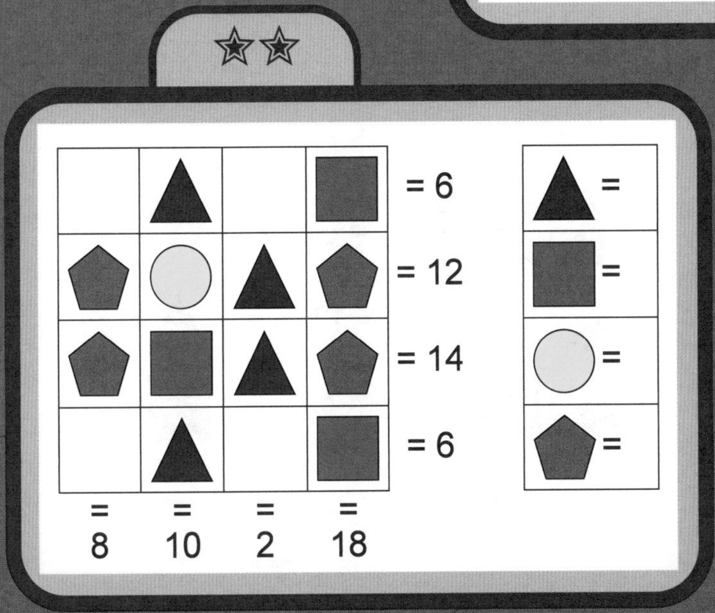

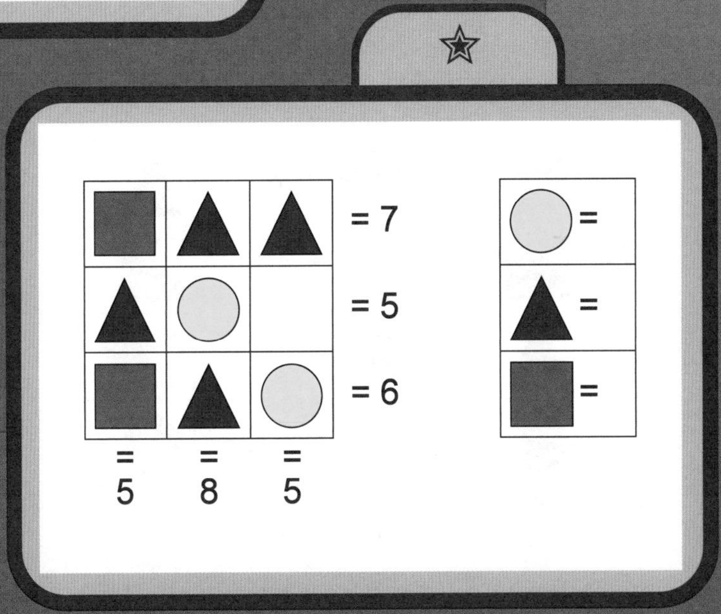

Turn to page 196 for the solutions

WHAT'S IT WORTH?

Each symbol stands for a different number. In order to reach the correct total at the end of each row and column, what is the value of the triangle, star, circle and pentagon?

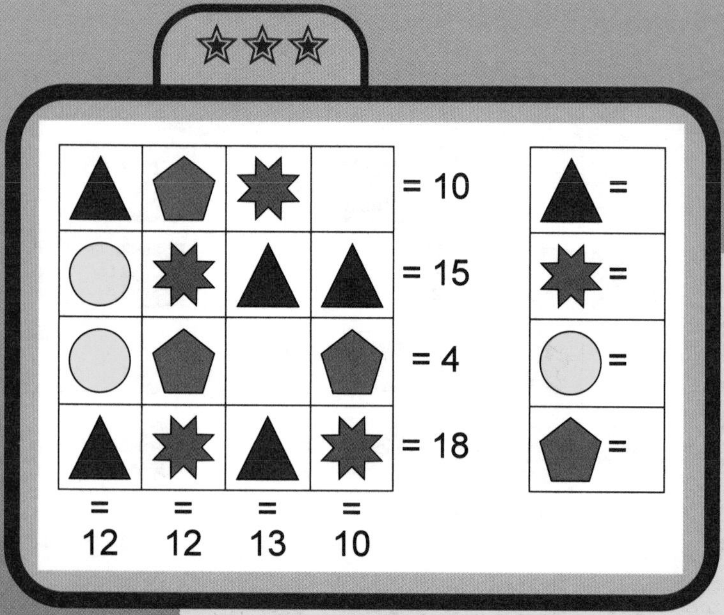

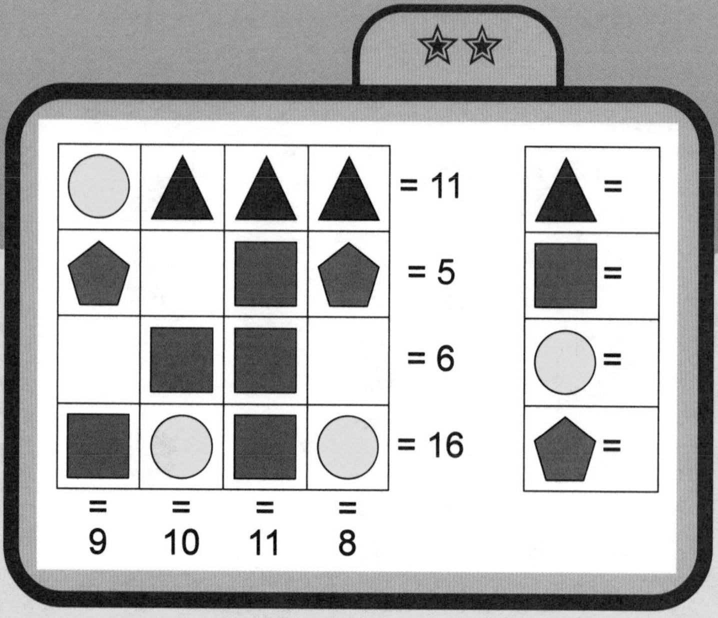

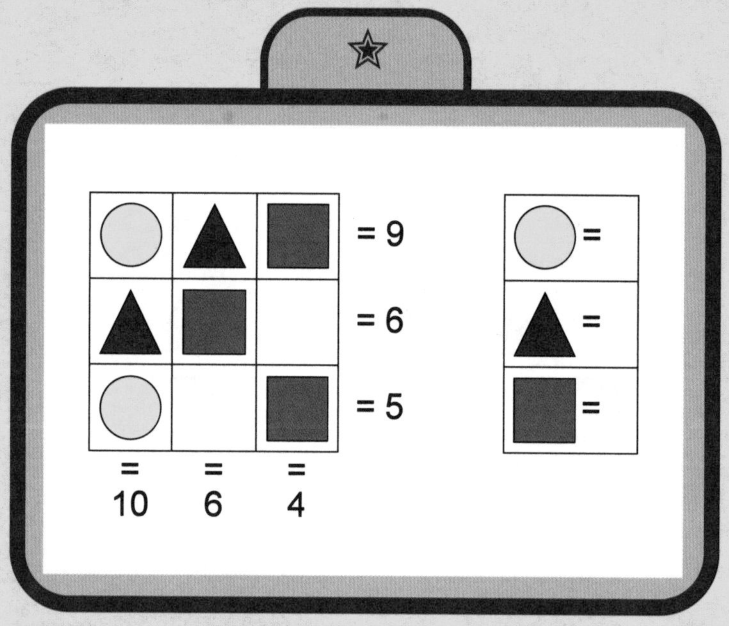

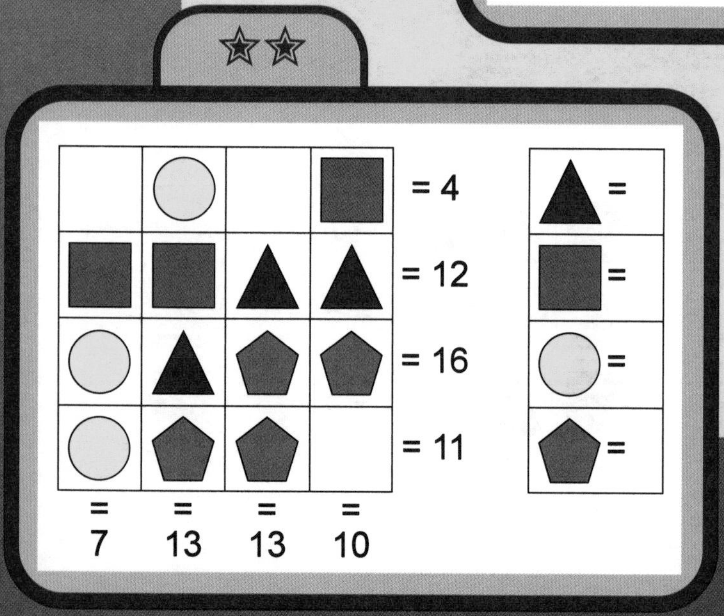

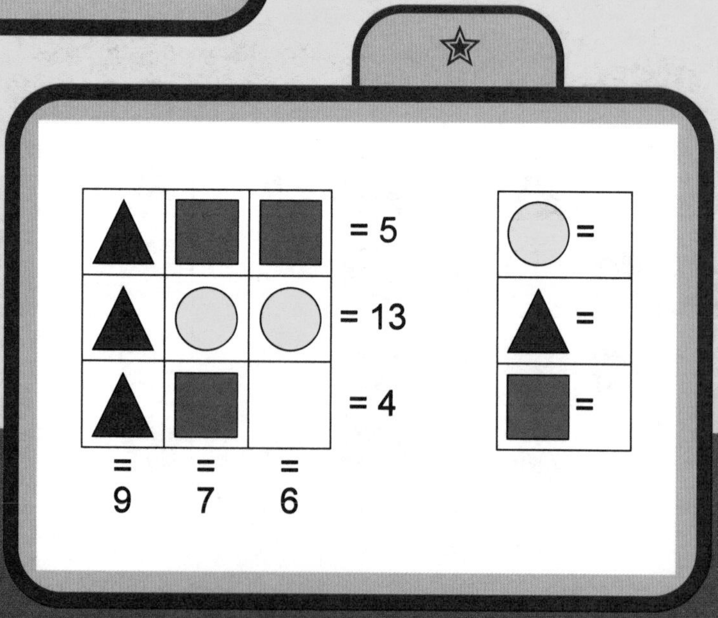

Turn to page 196 for the solutions

WHAT'S IT WORTH?

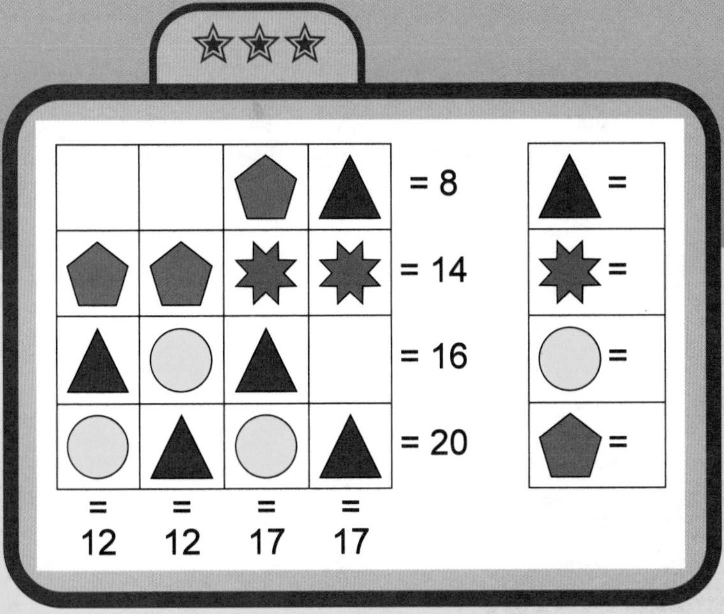

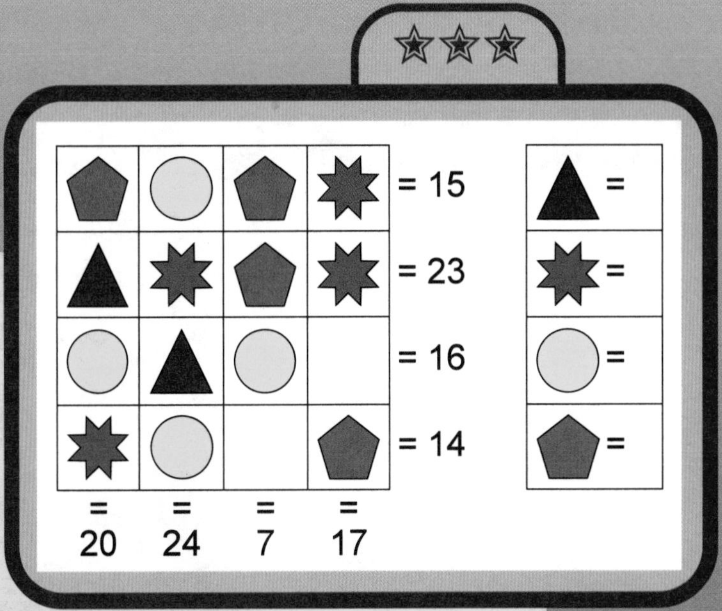

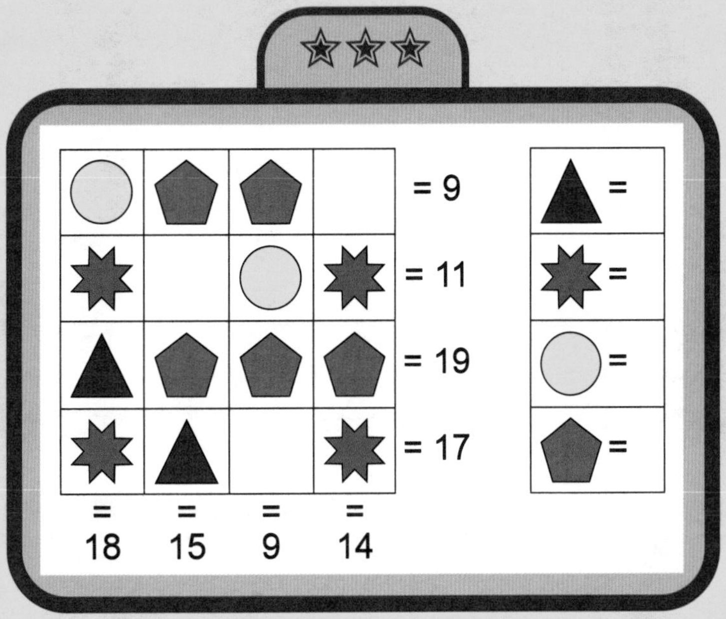

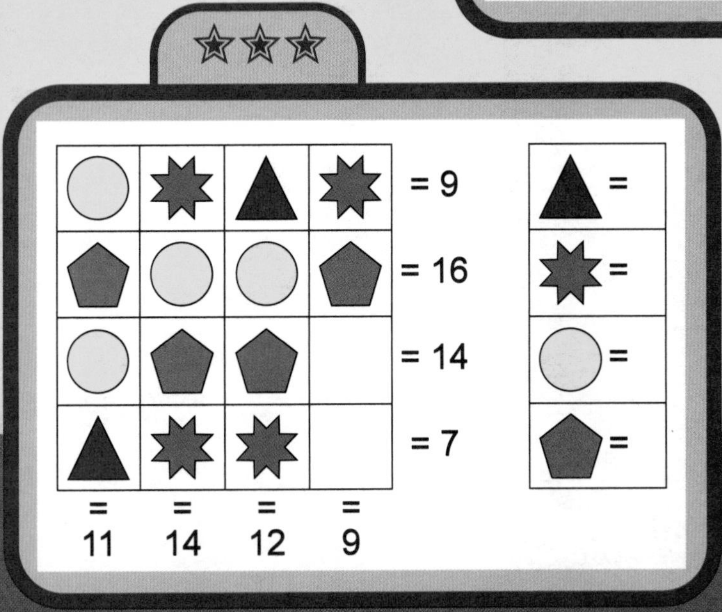

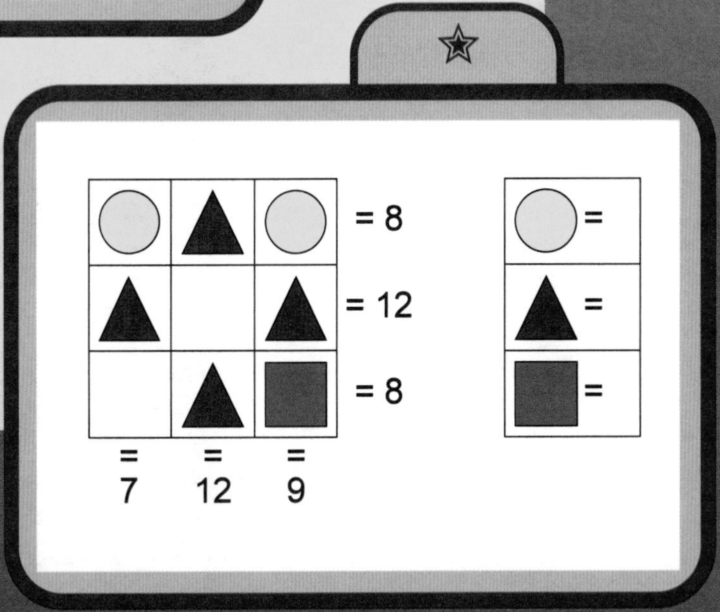

HEXAGONY

Can you place the hexagons into the grid so that where any hexagon touches another along a straight line the contents of both triangles are the same? No rotation of any hexagon is allowed!

Turn to page 196 for the solutions

HEXAGONY

Turn to page 196 for the solutions

HEXAGONY

Can you place the hexagons into the grid so that where any hexagon touches another along a straight line the contents of both triangles are the same? No rotation of any hexagon is allowed!

 Turn to page 196 for the solutions

HEXAGONY

HEXAGONY

Can you place the hexagons into the grid so that where any hexagon touches another along a straight line the contents of both triangles are the same? No rotation of any hexagon is allowed!

Turn to page 196 for the solutions

HEXAGONY

Turn to page 196 for the solutions

HEXAGONY

Can you place the hexagons into the grid so that where any hexagon touches another along a straight line the contents of both triangles are the same? No rotation of any hexagon is allowed!

Turn to page 196 for the solutions

HEXAGONY

HEXAGONY

Can you place the hexagons into the grid so that where any hexagon touches another along a straight line the contents of both triangles are the same? No rotation of any hexagon is allowed!

★★★

★★

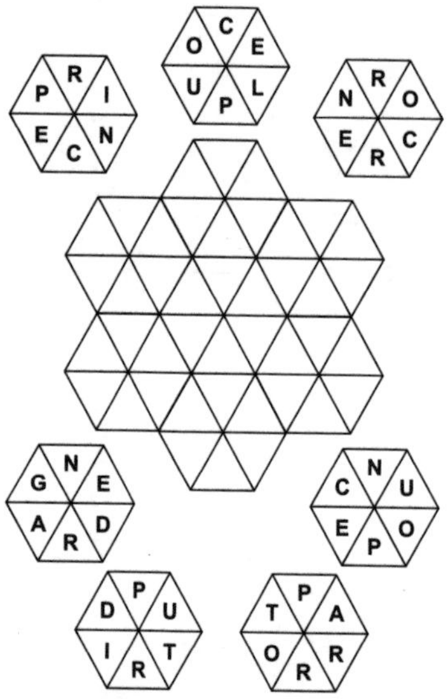

★

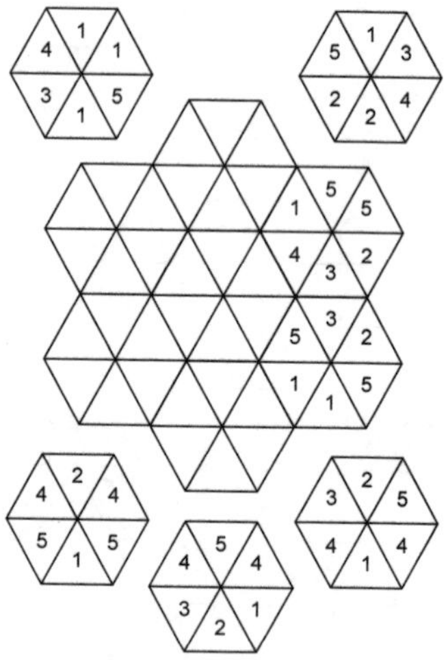

★

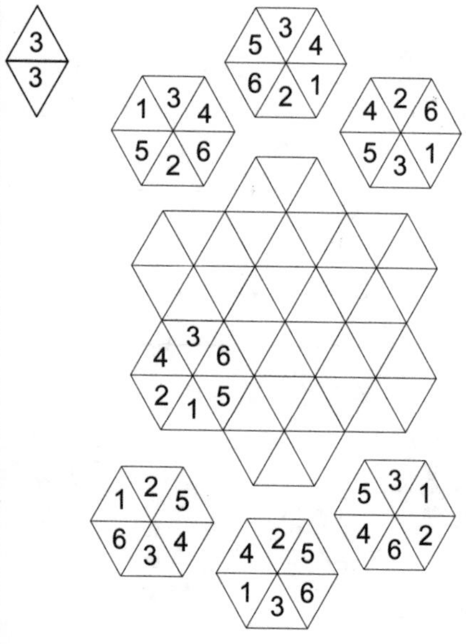

★★★

 Turn to page 196 for the solutions

HEXAGONY

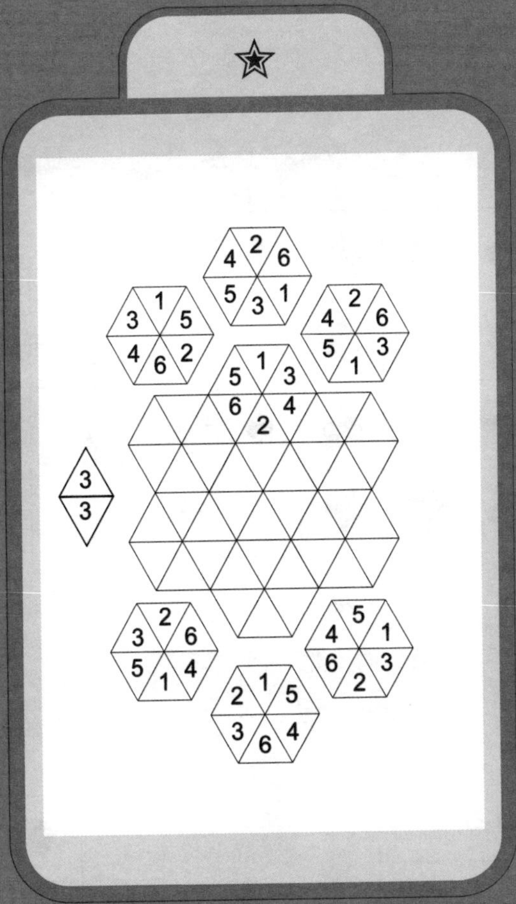

Turn to page 196 for the solutions

SUMMING UP

Each of the symbols in the puzzles below represents a different number. By using the total at the end of each row and column, work out the value of each symbol. The 'across' value of a symbol may differ from its 'down' value.

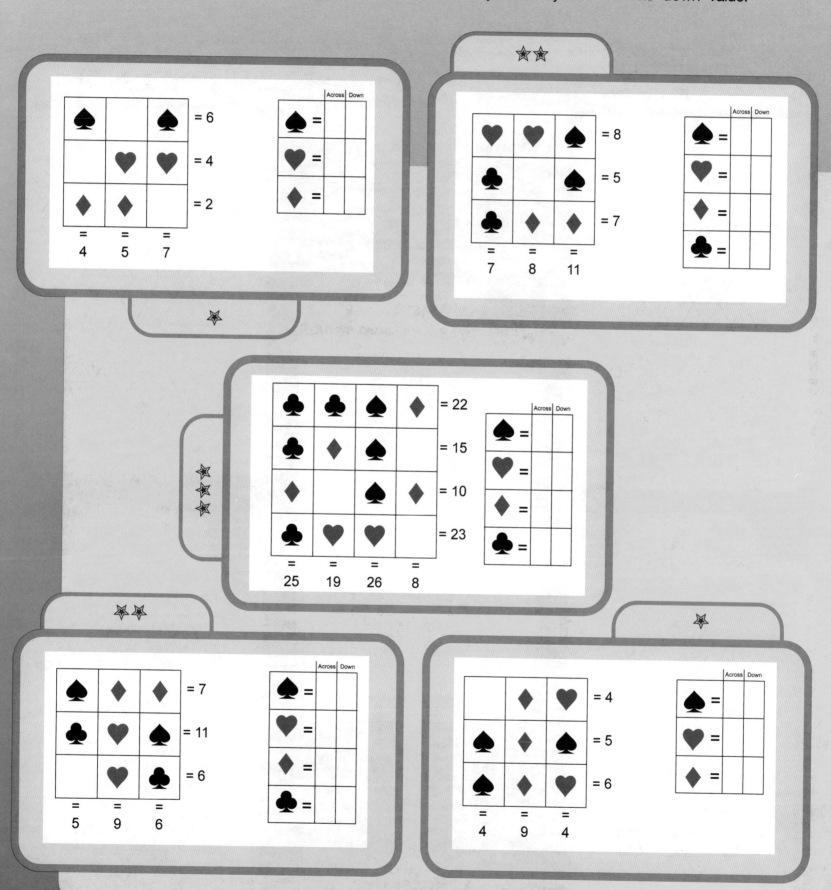

★

♠		♠	= 6
	♥	♥	= 4
♦	♦		= 2
= 4	= 5	= 7	

	Across	Down
♠ =		
♥ =		
♦ =		

★★

♥	♥	♠	= 8
♣		♠	= 5
♣	♦	♦	= 7
= 7	= 8	= 11	

	Across	Down
♠ =		
♥ =		
♦ =		
♣ =		

★★★

♣	♣	♠	♦	= 22
♣	♦	♠		= 15
♦		♠	♦	= 10
♣	♥	♥		= 23
= 25	= 19	= 26	= 8	

	Across	Down
♠ =		
♥ =		
♦ =		
♣ =		

★★

♠	♦	♦	= 7
♣	♥	♠	= 11
	♥	♣	= 6
= 5	= 9	= 6	

	Across	Down
♠ =		
♥ =		
♦ =		
♣ =		

★

	♦	♥	= 4
♠	♦	♠	= 5
♠	♦	♥	= 6
= 4	= 9	= 4	

	Across	Down
♠ =		
♥ =		
♦ =		

Turn to page 196 for the solutions

SUMMING UP

★

♦	♥	♥	= 5
♠	♥		= 3
	♥	♦	= 4
= 4	= 12	= 7	

	Across	Down
♠ =		
♥ =		
♦ =		

★★

♣	♠	♥	= 10
♦	♠	♥	= 11
♣	♦		= 7
= 6	= 8	= 6	

	Across	Down
♠ =		
♥ =		
♦ =		
♣ =		

★★★

♥	♥		♠	= 35
♣	♠		♠	= 30
♦		♣	♦	= 26
	♣	♥	♦	= 32
= 25	= 27	= 18	= 32	

	Across	Down
♠ =		
♥ =		
♦ =		
♣ =		

★

♥	♠		= 5
♦	♠	♦	= 8
♥	♥	♥	= 3
= 5	= 10	= 3	

	Across	Down
♠ =		
♥ =		
♦ =		

★★★

♠	♦		♥	= 36
	♦	♥	♣	= 39
♦	♠	♠		= 25
♦	♥	♣	♦	= 46
= 22	= 42	= 38	= 37	

	Across	Down
♠ =		
♥ =		
♦ =		
♣ =		

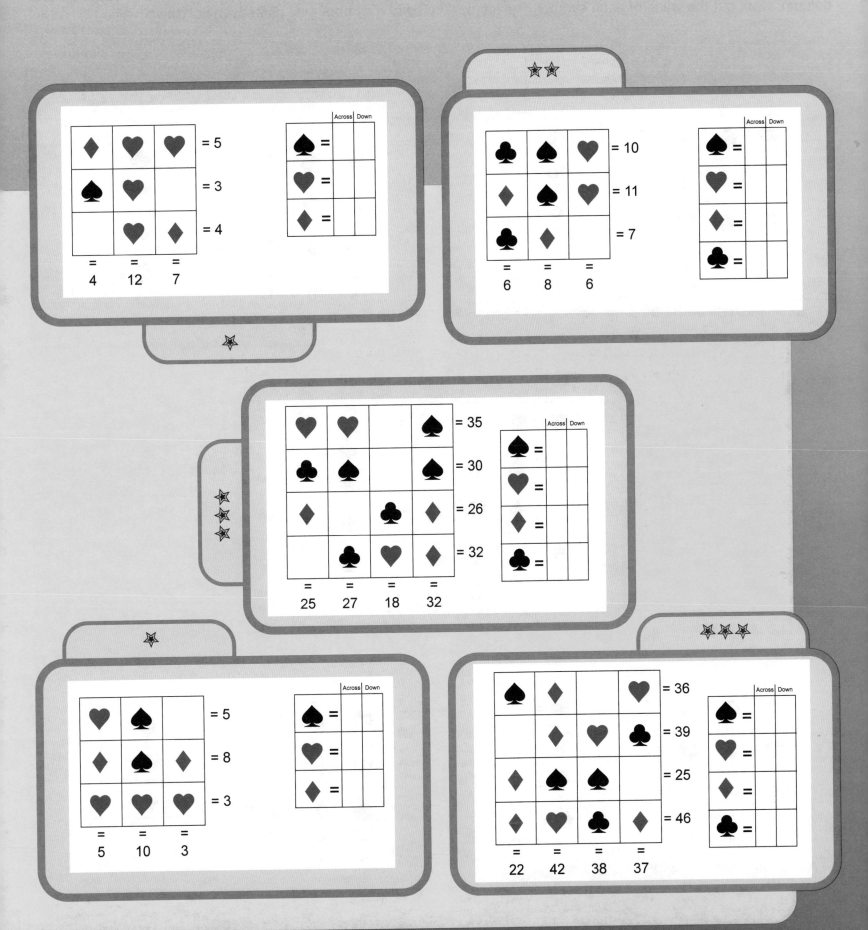

Turn to page 196 for the solutions

SUMMING UP

Each of the symbols in the puzzles below represents a different number. By using the total at the end of each row and column, work out the value of each symbol. The 'across' value of a symbol may differ from its 'down' value.

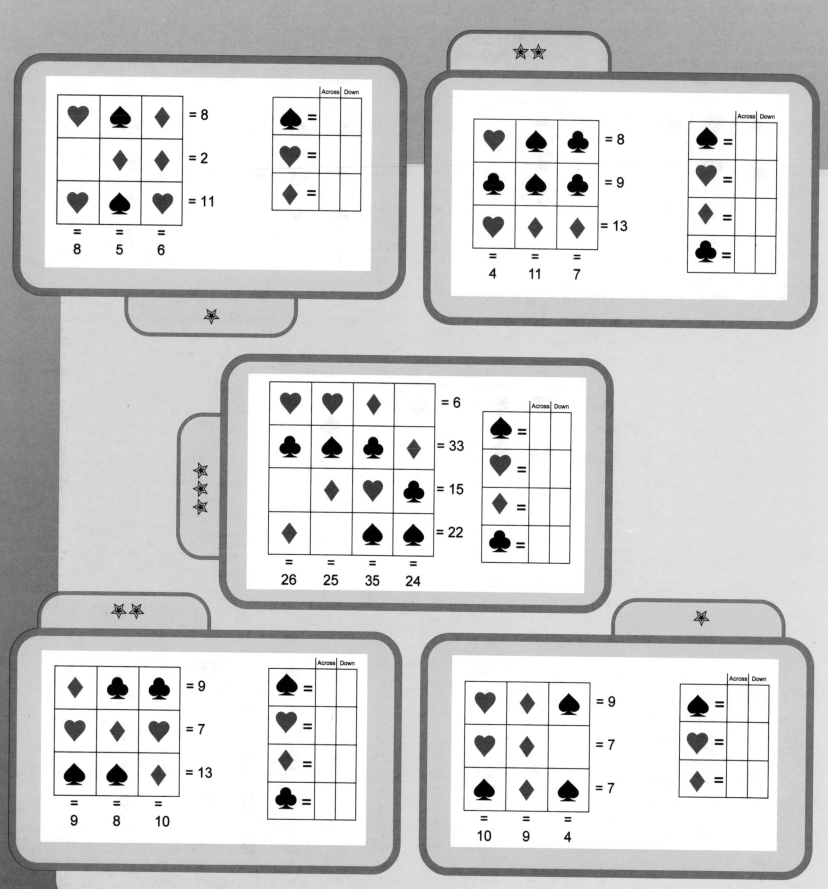

★

♥	♠	♦	= 8
	♦	♦	= 2
♥	♠	♥	= 11
= 8	= 5	= 6	

	Across	Down
♠ =		
♥ =		
♦ =		

★★

♥	♠	♣	= 8
♣	♠	♣	= 9
♥	♦	♦	= 13
= 4	= 11	= 7	

	Across	Down
♠ =		
♥ =		
♦ =		
♣ =		

★★★

♥	♥	♦		= 6
♣	♠	♣	♦	= 33
	♦	♥	♣	= 15
♦		♠	♠	= 22
= 26	= 25	= 35	= 24	

	Across	Down
♠ =		
♥ =		
♦ =		
♣ =		

★★

♦	♣	♣	= 9
♥	♦	♥	= 7
♠	♠	♦	= 13
= 9	= 8	= 10	

	Across	Down
♠ =		
♥ =		
♦ =		
♣ =		

★

♥	♦	♠	= 9
♥	♦		= 7
♠	♦	♠	= 7
= 10	= 9	= 4	

	Across	Down
♠ =		
♥ =		
♦ =		

 Turn to page 196 for the solutions

SUMMING UP

★

♠	♠	♠	= 3
	♥	♦	= 6
♦		♦	= 4
= 4	= 3	= 7	

	Across	Down
♠ =		
♥ =		
♦ =		

★★

♦	♦	♥	= 14
♣	♠	♠	= 7
♥	♦	♣	= 13
= 10	= 16	= 11	

	Across	Down
♠ =		
♥ =		
♦ =		
♣ =		

★★★

♦			♥	= 29
♠	♣	♣		= 13
♣	♦	♦	♥	= 43
♠	♣	♠	♥	= 35
= 38	= 37	= 31	= 3	

	Across	Down
♠ =		
♥ =		
♦ =		
♣ =		

★

♦		♥	= 5
♥	♥	♠	= 10
♥	♦	♠	= 9
= 8	= 5	= 5	

	Across	Down
♠ =		
♥ =		
♦ =		

★★★

♠	♠		♦	= 34
♣	♦		♥	= 29
♠	♦	♥	♣	= 42
♦	♣	♥	♥	= 40
= 25	= 28	= 22	= 39	

	Across	Down
♠ =		
♥ =		
♦ =		
♣ =		

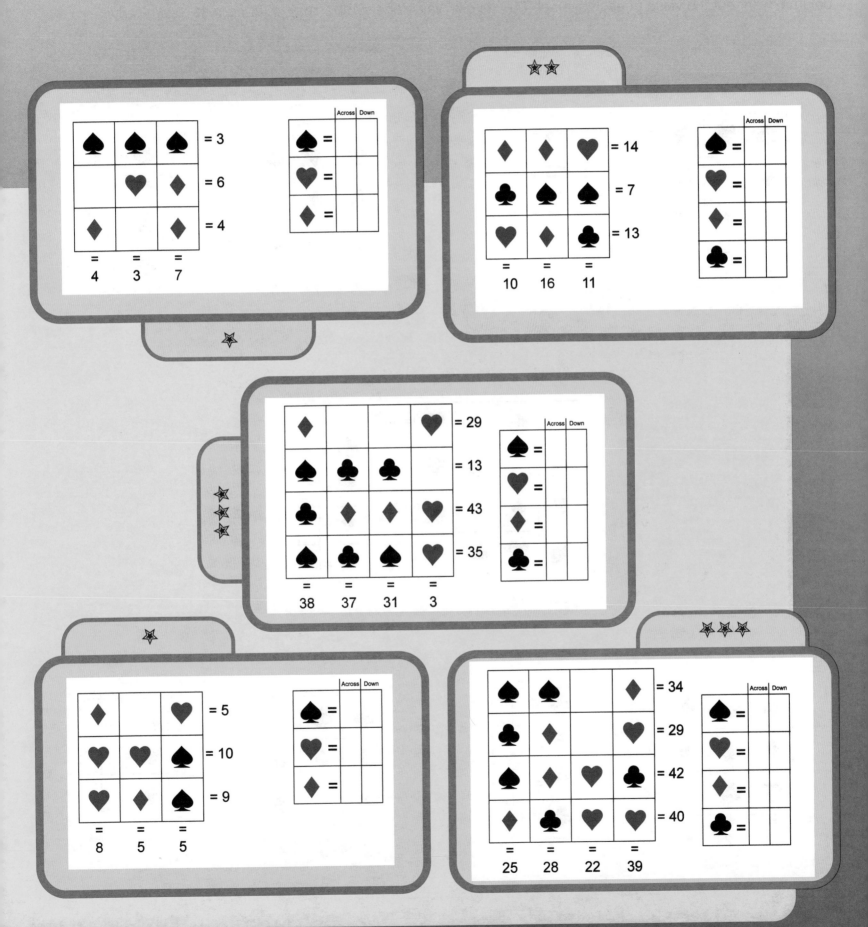

Turn to page 196 for the solutions

SUMMING UP

Each of the symbols in the puzzles below represents a different number. By using the total at the end of each row and column, work out the value of each symbol. The 'across' value of a symbol may differ from its 'down' value.

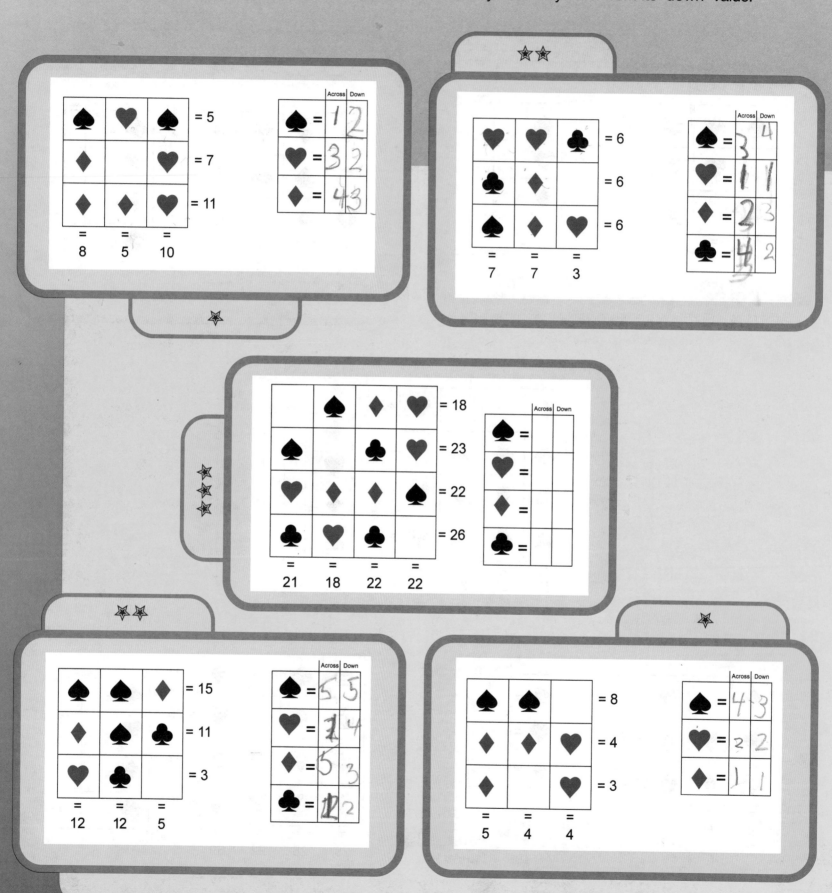

★

♠	♥	♠	= 5
♦		♥	= 7
♦	♦	♥	= 11
= 8	= 5	= 10	

	Across	Down
♠ =		
♥ =		
♦ =		

★★

♥	♥	♣	= 6
♣	♦		= 6
♠	♦	♥	= 6
= 7	= 7	= 3	

	Across	Down
♠ =		
♥ =		
♦ =		
♣ =		

★★★

	♠	♦	♥	= 18
♠		♣	♥	= 23
♥	♦	♦	♠	= 22
♣	♥	♣		= 26
= 21	= 18	= 22	= 22	

	Across	Down
♠ =		
♥ =		
♦ =		
♣ =		

★★

♠	♠	♦	= 15
♦	♠	♣	= 11
♥	♣		= 3
= 12	= 12	= 5	

	Across	Down
♠ =		
♥ =		
♦ =		
♣ =		

★

♠	♠		= 8
♦	♦	♥	= 4
♦		♥	= 3
= 5	= 4	= 4	

	Across	Down
♠ =		
♥ =		
♦ =		

Turn to page 196 for the solutions

★

♥		♦	= 6
♠	♥	♦	= 7
♠	♠	♦	= 6
= 7	= 4	= 12	

	Across	Down
♠ =		
♥ =		
♦ =		4

★★

♠	♣	♠	= 8
♥		♥	= 4
♣	♦	♦	= 12
= 6	= 9	= 9	

	Across	Down
♠ =		
♥ =		
♦ =		
♣ =		

★★★

♦	♣		♦	= 41
♣	♦	♠	♥	= 54
♣	♦	♥		= 39
	♠	♥	♠	= 39
= 49	= 54	= 31	= 33	

	Across	Down
♠ =		
♥ =		
♦ =		
♣ =		

★

♠	♦	♦	= 10
♠		♥	= 3
	♥	♥	= 2
= 8	= 4	= 5	

	Across	Down
♠ =	2	4
♥ =	1	1
♦ =	4	3

★★★

♣			♠	= 17
♥	♥	♣	♦	= 30
♦	♠	♦	♠	= 42
♥	♣			= 13
= 29	= 25	= 15	= 33	

	Across	Down
♠ =		
♥ =		
♦ =		
♣ =		

Turn to page 196 for the solutions

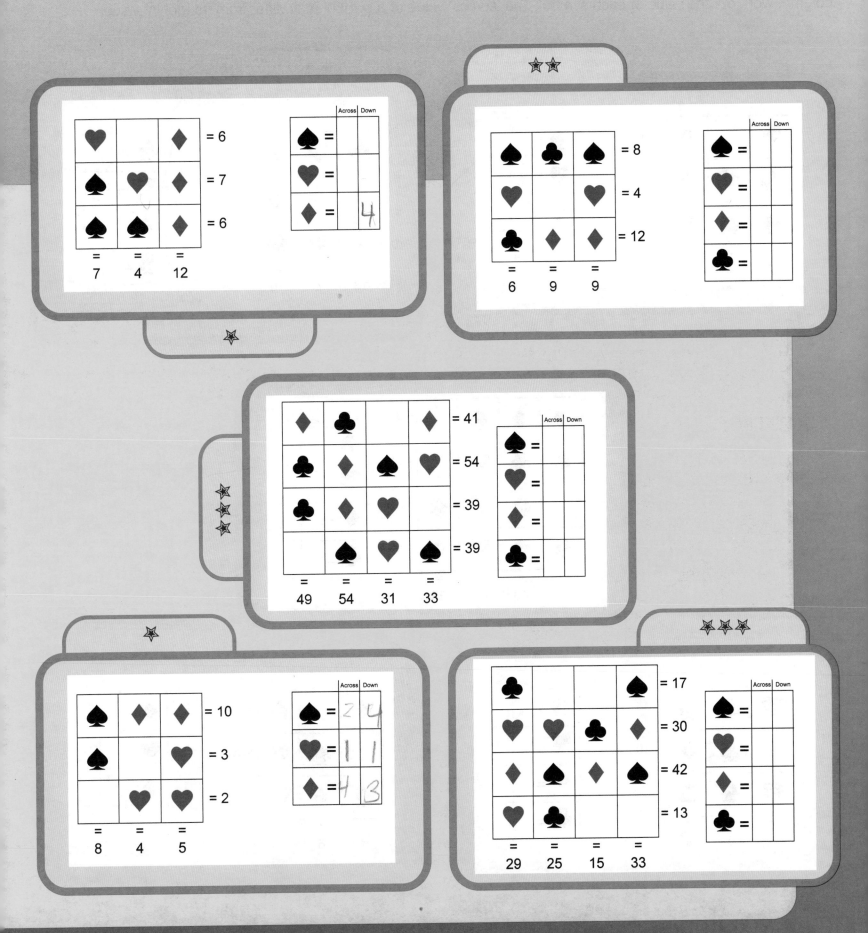

SUMMING UP

Each of the symbols in the puzzles below represents a different number. By using the total at the end of each row and column, work out the value of each symbol. The 'across' value of a symbol may differ from its 'down' value.

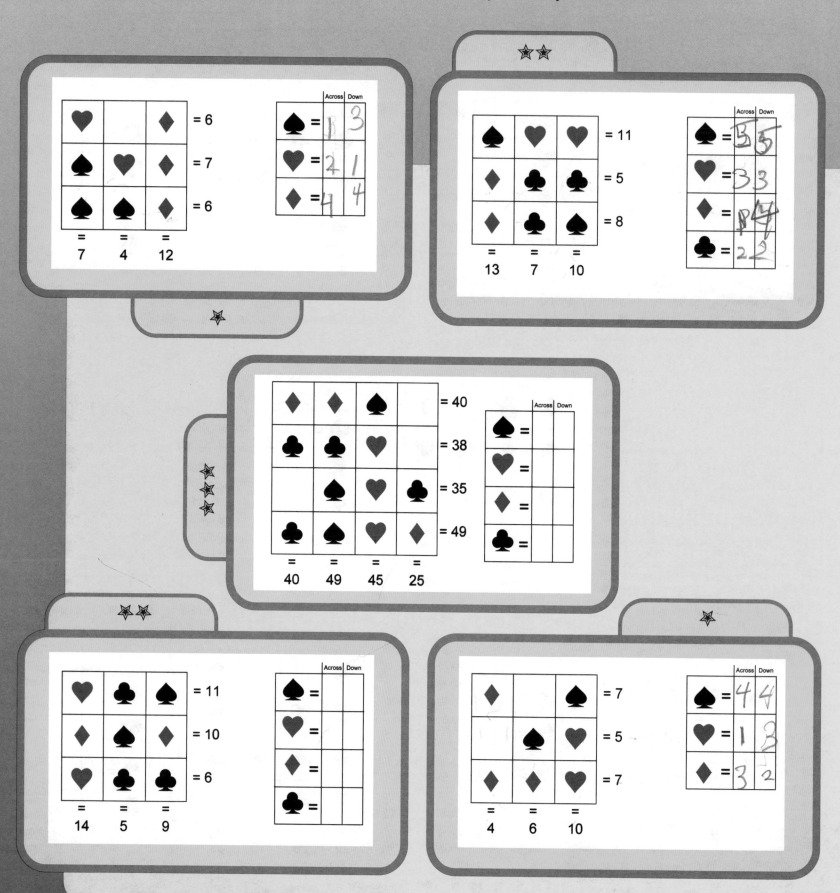

★

♥		♦	= 6
♠	♥	♦	= 7
♠	♠	♦	= 6
= 7	= 4	= 12	

	Across	Down
♠ =	1	3
♥ =	2	1
♦ =	4	4

★★

♠	♥	♥	= 11
♦	♣	♣	= 5
♦	♣	♠	= 8
= 13	= 7	= 10	

	Across	Down
♠ =	5	5
♥ =	3	3
♦ =	[illegible]	4
♣ =	2	2

★★★

♦	♦	♠		= 40
♣	♣	♥		= 38
	♠	♥	♣	= 35
♣	♠	♥	♦	= 49
= 40	= 49	= 45	= 25	

	Across	Down
♠ =		
♥ =		
♦ =		
♣ =		

★★

♥	♣	♠	= 11
♦	♠	♦	= 10
♥	♣	♣	= 6
= 14	= 5	= 9	

	Across	Down
♠ =		
♥ =		
♦ =		
♣ =		

★

♦		♠	= 7
	♠	♥	= 5
♦	♦	♥	= 7
= 4	= 6	= 10	

	Across	Down
♠ =	4	4
♥ =	1	3
♦ =	3	2

Turn to page 196 for the solutions

★

♦	♠	♦	= 7
	♠	♦	= 5
♥		♥	= 8
= 3	= 6	= 5	

	Across	Down
♠ =		
♥ =		
♦ =		

★★

♦	♥	♠	= 7
♣	♦	♥	= 9
♦	♠	♣	= 8
= 11	= 10	= 6	

	Across	Down
♠ =		
♥ =		
♦ =		
♣ =		

★★★

♠	♣	♦		= 41
♦	♥	♣	♥	= 34
♠	♣	♦	♦	= 55
♠	♦	♥	♦	= 53
= 32	= 37	= 43	= 35	

	Across	Down
♠ =		
♥ =		
♦ =		
♣ =		

★

♥	♦	♠	= 6
♦	♦	♥	= 5
♠		♥	= 4
= 7	= 4	= 6	

	Across	Down
♠ =	3	4
♥ =	[illegible]	1
♦ =	2	2

★★★

♠	♥	♥		= 5
♠		♣	♦	= 9
♦	♣		♣	= 8
♦	♥	♠		= 8
= 14	= 14	= 11	= 6	

	Across	Down
♠ =		
♥ =		
♦ =		
♣ =		

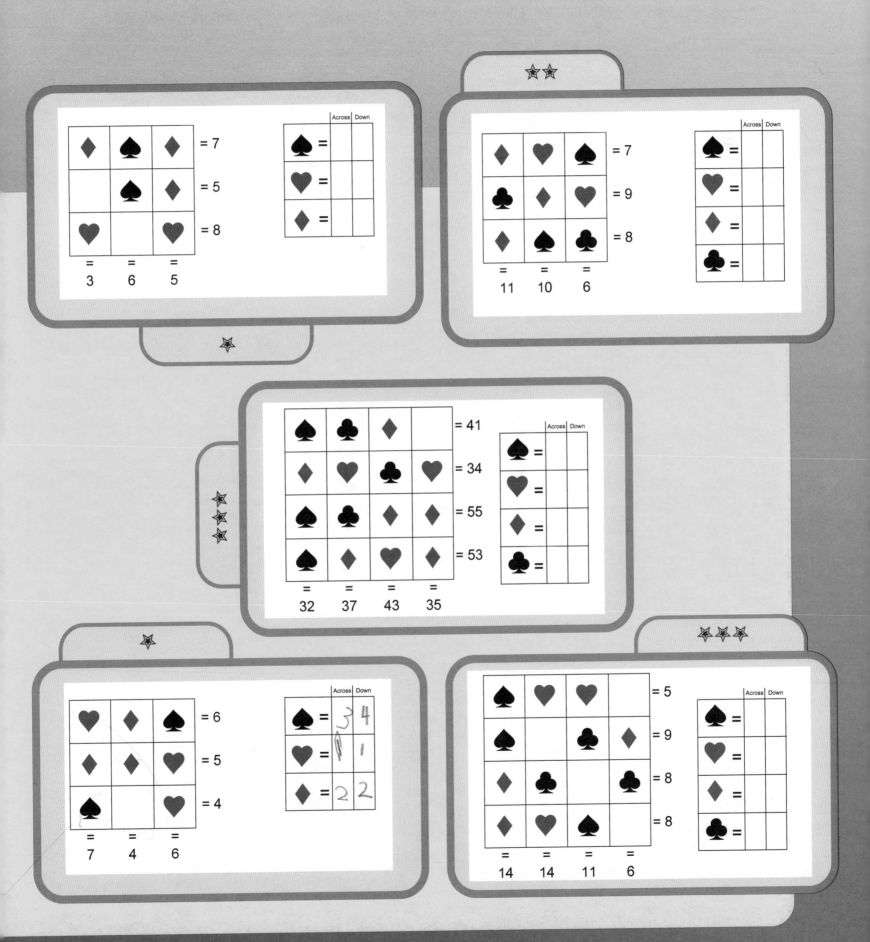

Turn to page 196 for the solutions

SUMMING UP

Each of the symbols in the puzzles below represents a different number. By using the total at the end of each row and column, work out the value of each symbol. The ‘across’ value of a symbol may differ from its ‘down’ value.

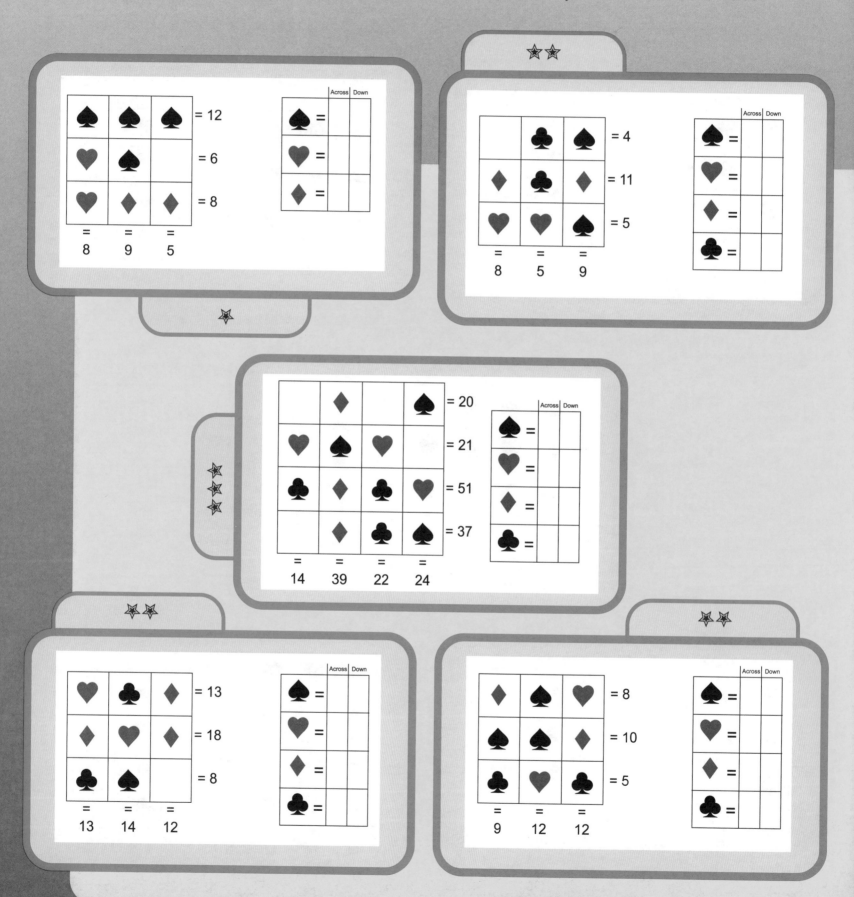

★

♠	♠	♠	= 12
♥	♠		= 6
♥	♦	♦	= 8
= 8	= 9	= 5	

	Across	Down
♠ =		
♥ =		
♦ =		

★★

	♣	♠	= 4
♦	♣	♦	= 11
♥	♥	♠	= 5
= 8	= 5	= 9	

	Across	Down
♠ =		
♥ =		
♦ =		
♣ =		

★★★

	♦		♠	= 20
♥	♠	♥		= 21
♣	♦	♣	♥	= 51
	♦	♣	♠	= 37
= 14	= 39	= 22	= 24	

	Across	Down
♠ =		
♥ =		
♦ =		
♣ =		

★★

♥	♣	♦	= 13
♦	♥	♦	= 18
♣	♠		= 8
= 13	= 14	= 12	

	Across	Down
♠ =		
♥ =		
♦ =		
♣ =		

★★

♦	♠	♥	= 8
♠	♠	♦	= 10
♣	♥	♣	= 5
= 9	= 12	= 12	

	Across	Down
♠ =		
♥ =		
♦ =		
♣ =		

Turn to page 196 for the solutions

SUMMING UP

★★

♠	♦	♥	= 7
♠	♣	♥	= 6
♣	♦	♥	= 9
= 5	= 11	= 9	

	Across	Down
♠ =		
♥ =		
♦ =		
♣ =		

★★

♦	♥	♣	= 14
♥	♠	♣	= 20
	♥	♦	= 9
= 9	= 17	= 12	

	Across	Down
♠ =		
♥ =		
♦ =		
♣ =		

★★★

♥	♣	♣		= 23
♥	♦	♥	♠	= 41
♣		♠	♦	= 35
♥	♠			= 23
= 29	= 24	= 20	= 16	

	Across	Down
♠ =		
♥ =		
♦ =		
♣ =		

★★★

♥	♦	♥	♠	= 41
	♦	♣	♦	= 41
♠	♣		♠	= 31
♣		♥		= 16
= 26	= 37	= 23	= 34	

	Across	Down
♠ =		
♥ =		
♦ =		
♣ =		

★★★

♠	♦		♥	= 32
♥	♥	♦	♣	= 68
♠	♦	♠		= 16
♣		♦	♠	= 34
= 40	= 24	= 10	= 38	

	Across	Down
♠ =		
♥ =		
♦ =		
♣ =		

Turn to page 196 for the solutions

ARROWS

This puzzle will appeal to the mathematicians among you, but anybody can solve it with the right sums! Use the numbers listed in each of the puzzles to fill in the gaps in the arrows.

1 1 1 1 2 2 2 2

The total numbers in the 3 arrows pointing at each other must add up to 5:

The total number in the arrows which are back to back must add up to 3:

1 2 3 3 3 3 3 4 5

The total numbers in the 3 arrows pointing at each other must add up to 10:

The total number in the arrows which are back to back must add up to 6:

4 5 6 6 6 7 7 7 8 9

The total numbers in the 3 arrows pointing at each other must add up to 19:

The total number in the arrows which are back to back must add up to 13:

1 1 2 2 2 3 3 4 4

The total numbers in the 3 arrows pointing at each other must add up to 11:

The total number in the arrows which are back tc back must add up to 5:

1 1 2 2 3 3 4 4 5 5

The total numbers in the 3 arrows pointing at each other must add up to 9:

The total number in the arrows which are back to back must add up to 6:

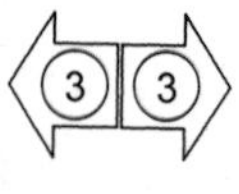

Turn to page 196 for the solutions

ARROWS

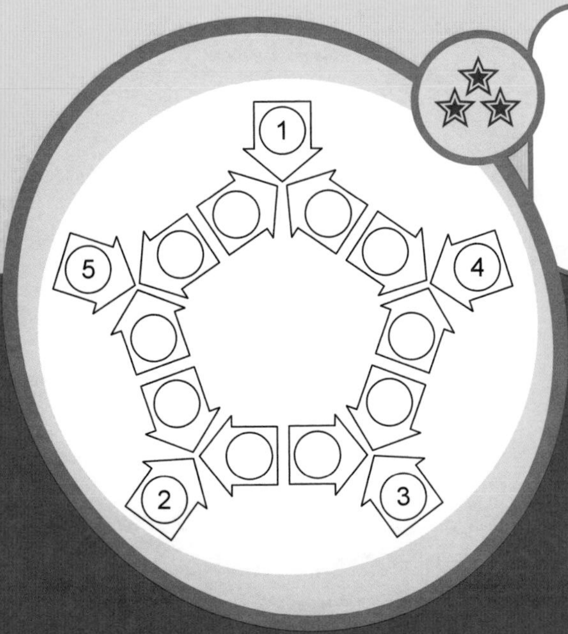

3 4 4 5 5 6 6 7 7 8

The total numbers in the 3 arrows pointing at each other must add up to 14:

The total number in the arrows which are back to back must add up to 11:

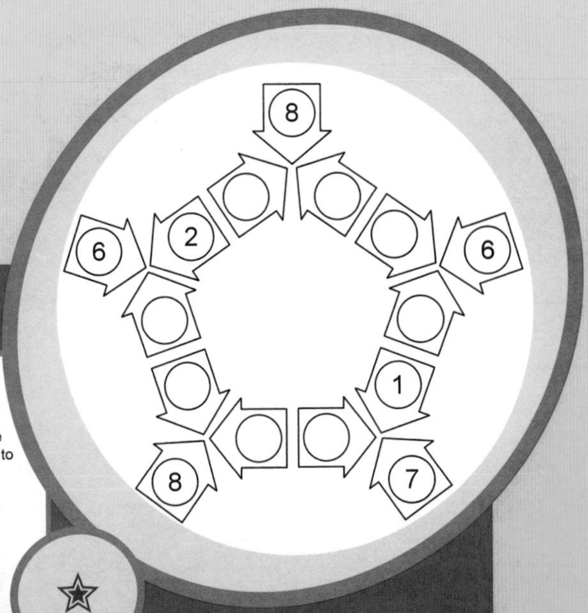

1 1 1 1 2 2 2 2

The total numbers in the 3 arrows pointing at each other must add up to 10:

The total number in the arrows which are back to back must add up to 3:

1 1 1 2 2 4 5 5 5

The total numbers in the 3 arrows pointing at each other must add up to 11:

The total number in the arrows which are back to back must add up to 6:

2 3 3 4 4 5 5 6 6 7

The total numbers in the 3 arrows pointing at each other must add up to 12:

The total number in the arrows which are back to back must add up to 9:

1 1 2 2 3 3 4 4 4

The total numbers in the 3 arrows pointing at each other must add up to 12:

The total number in the arrows which are back to back must add up to 5:

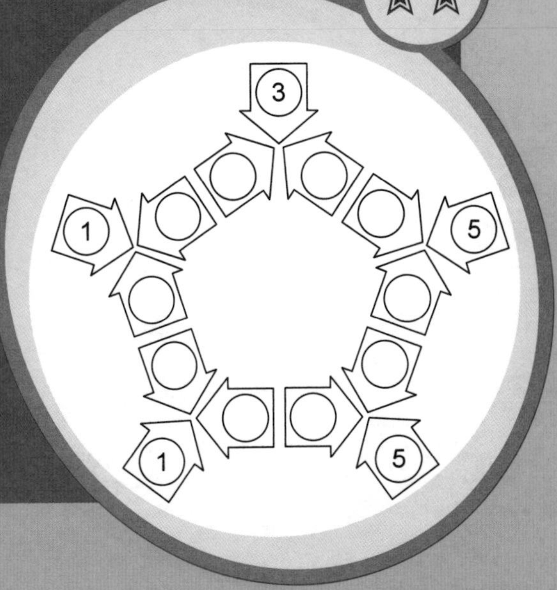

Turn to page 196 for the solutions

ARROWS

This puzzle will appeal to the mathematicians among you, but anybody can solve it with the right sums! Use the numbers listed in each of the puzzles to fill in the gaps in the arrows.

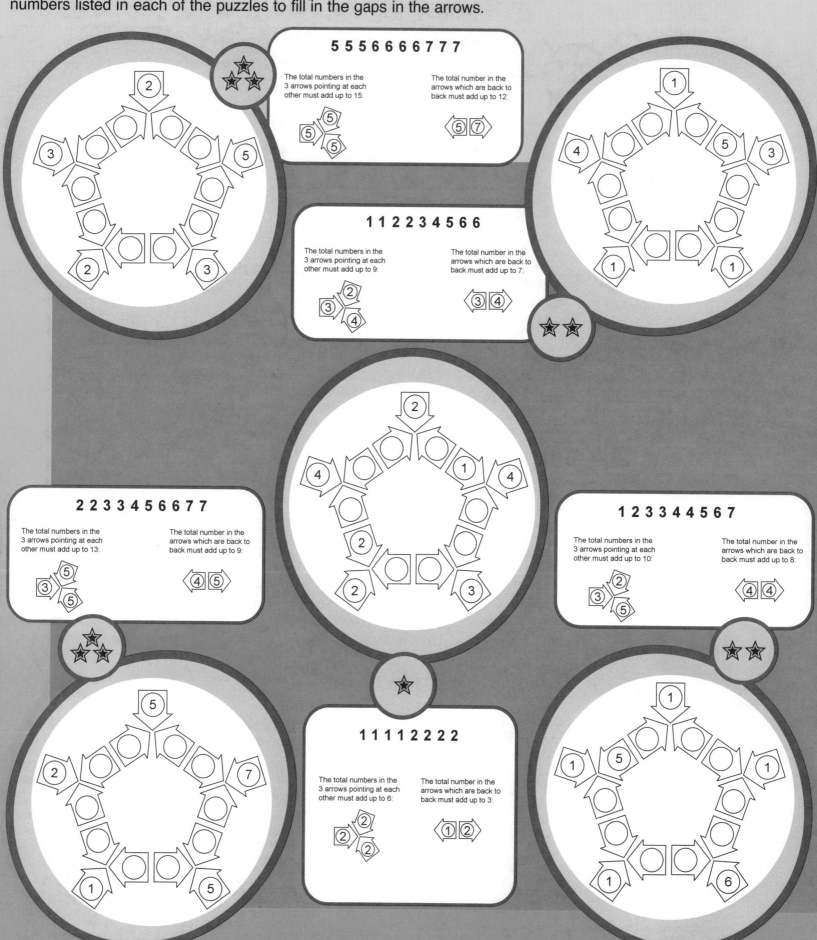

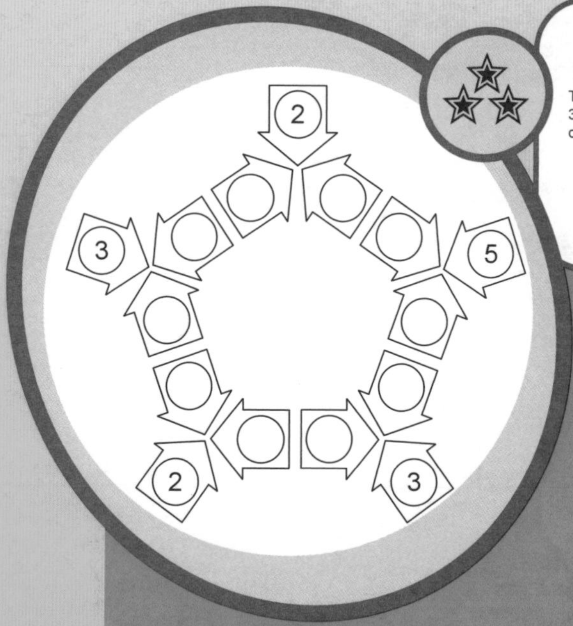

5 5 5 6 6 6 6 7 7 7

The total numbers in the 3 arrows pointing at each other must add up to 15:

The total number in the arrows which are back to back must add up to 12:

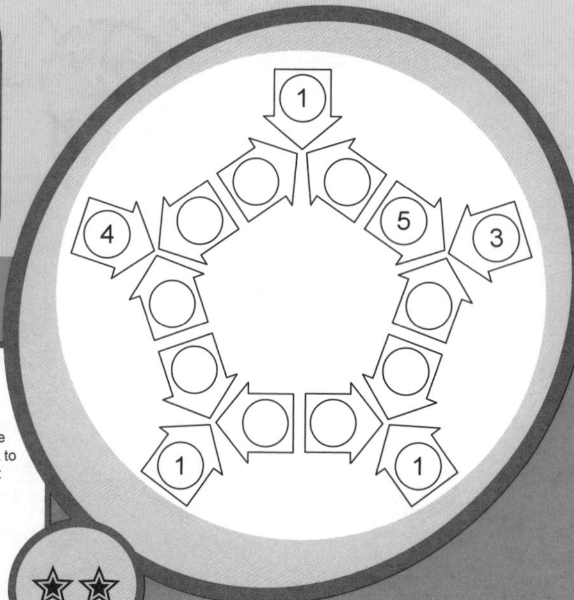

1 1 2 2 3 4 5 6 6

The total numbers in the 3 arrows pointing at each other must add up to 9:

The total number in the arrows which are back to back must add up to 7:

2 2 3 3 4 5 6 6 7 7

The total numbers in the 3 arrows pointing at each other must add up to 13:

The total number in the arrows which are back to back must add up to 9:

1 2 3 3 4 4 5 6 7

The total numbers in the 3 arrows pointing at each other must add up to 10:

The total number in the arrows which are back to back must add up to 8:

1 1 1 1 2 2 2 2

The total numbers in the 3 arrows pointing at each other must add up to 6:

The total number in the arrows which are back to back must add up to 3:

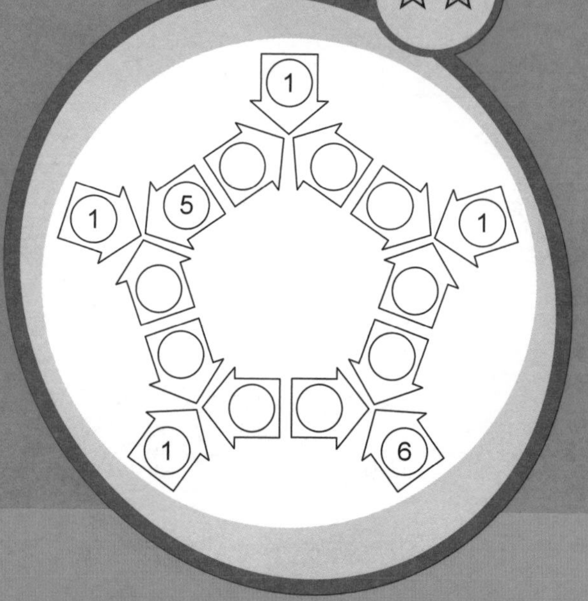

 Turn to page 196 for the solutions

☆☆

2 2 3 4 4 4 5 6 6

The total numbers in the 3 arrows pointing at each other must add up to 11:

The total number in the arrows which are back to back must add up to 8:

4 4 5 6 6 7 7 8 9 9

The total numbers in the 3 arrows pointing at each other must add up to 18:

The total number in the arrows which are back to back must add up to 13:

☆☆☆

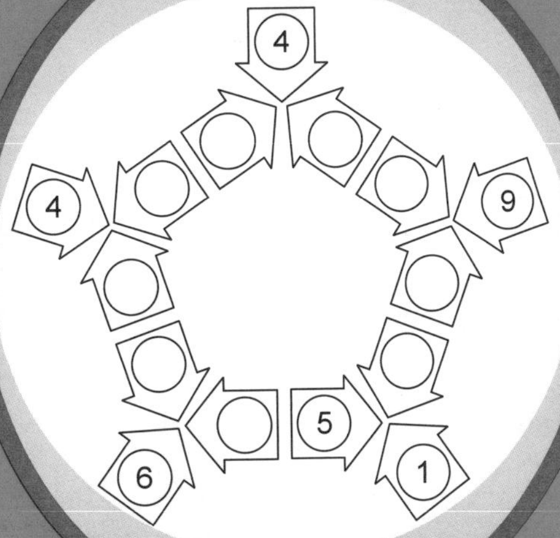

1 1 1 1 1 2 2 2

The total numbers in the 3 arrows pointing at each other must add up to 9:

The total number in the arrows which are back to back must add up to 3:

3 4 4 4 5 6 7 7 7 8

The total numbers in the 3 arrows pointing at each other must add up to 15:

The total number in the arrows which are back to back must add up to 11:

☆

☆☆

☆☆☆

1 2 2 2 3 4 5 5 6

The total numbers in the 3 arrows pointing at each other must add up to 12:

The total number in the arrows which are back to back must add up to 7:

Turn to page 196 for the solutions

ARROWS

This puzzle will appeal to the mathematicians among you, but anybody can solve it with the right sums! Use the numbers listed in each of the puzzles to fill in the gaps in the arrows.

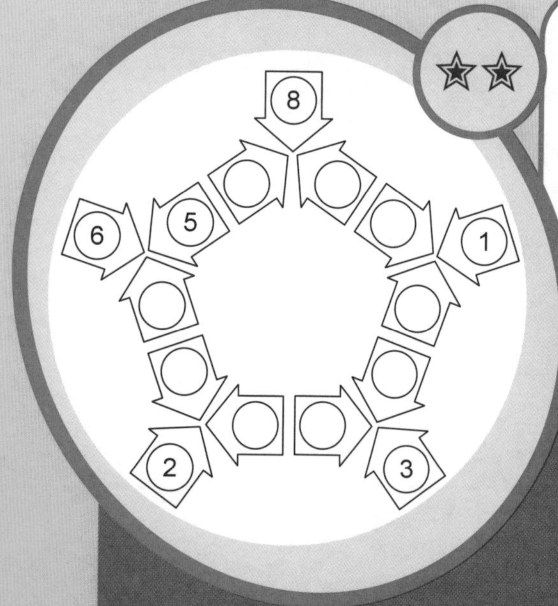

1 1 3 3 4 4 5 5 7 7

The total numbers in the 3 arrows pointing at each other must add up to 12:

The total number in the arrows which are back to back must add up to 8:

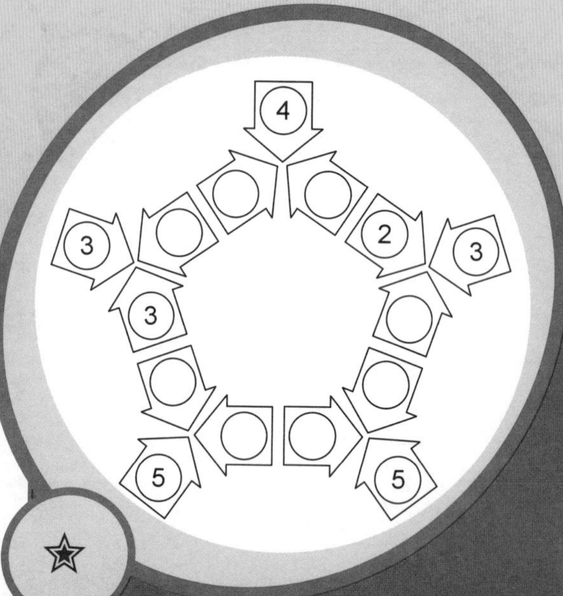

1 1 2 2 2 2 2 3

The total numbers in the 3 arrows pointing at each other must add up to 8:

The total number in the arrows which are back to back must add up to 4:

2 2 3 3 4 7 8 8 9 9

The total numbers in the 3 arrows pointing at each other must add up to 16:

The total number in the arrows which are back to back must add up to 11:

1 2 2 3 3 4 5 5 6

The total numbers in the 3 arrows pointing at each other must add up to 13:

The total number in the arrows which are back to back must add up to 7:

3 4 5 5 6 6 7 7 8 9

The total numbers in the 3 arrows pointing at each other must add up to 16:

The total number in the arrows which are back to back must add up to 12:

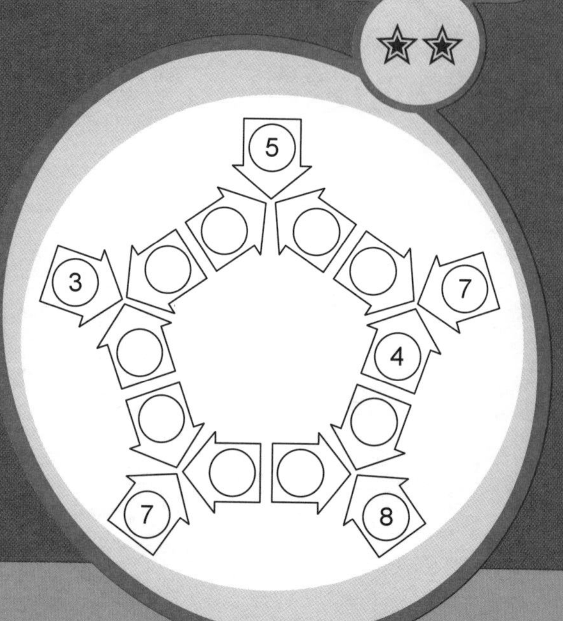

Turn to page 196 for the solutions

2 3 4 4 4 5 5 5 6 7

The total numbers in the 3 arrows pointing at each other must add up to 14:

The total number in the arrows which are back to back must add up to 9:

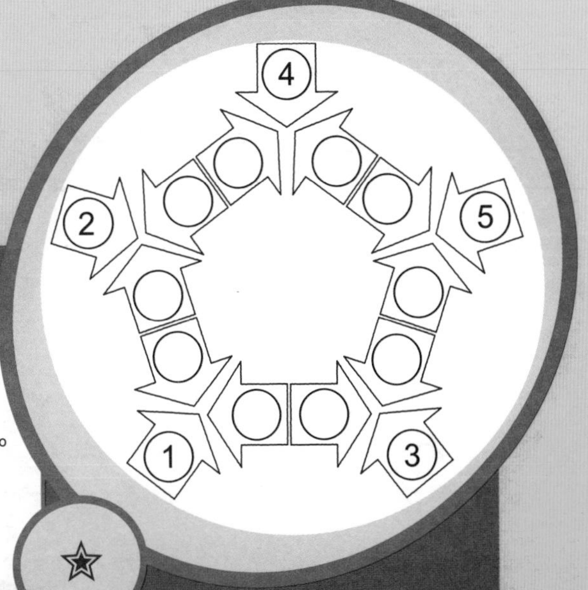

1 1 2 3 3 3 3 4 5 5

The total numbers in the 3 arrows pointing at each other must add up to 9:

The total number in the arrows which are back to back must add up to 6:

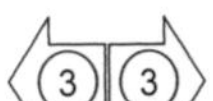

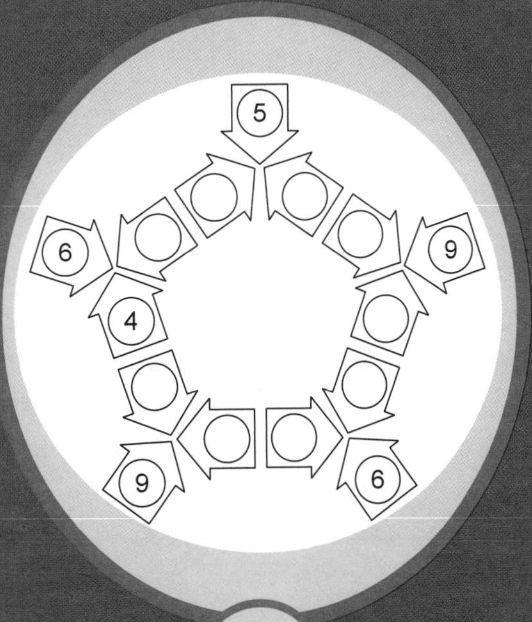

1 1 1 2 2 2 3 3

The total numbers in the 3 arrows pointing at each other must add up to 9:

The total number in the arrows which are back to back must add up to 4:

2 2 3 3 4 7 8 8 9 9

The total numbers in the 3 arrows pointing at each other must add up to 17:

The total number in the arrows which are back to back must add up to 11:

1 2 3 3 3 4 4 5 6

The total numbers in the 3 arrows pointing at each other must add up to 14:

The total number in the arrows which are back to back must add up to 7:

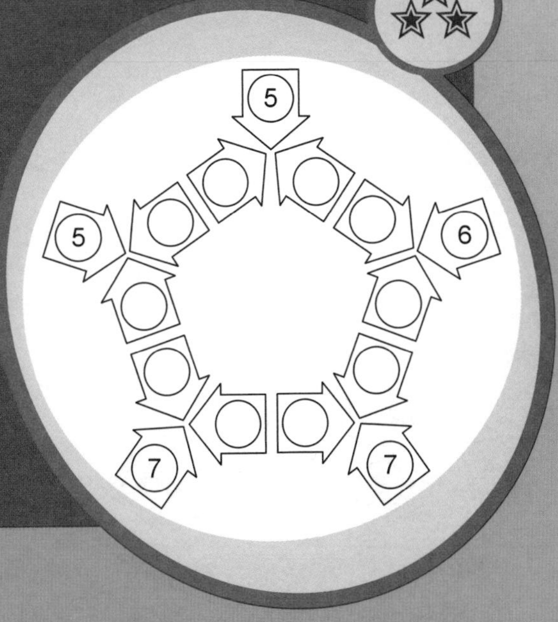

Turn to page 196 for the solutions

ARROWS

This puzzle will appeal to the mathematicians among you, but anybody can solve it with the right sums! Use the numbers listed in each of the puzzles to fill in the gaps in the arrows.

1 1 2 2 3 3 4 4 5 5

The total numbers in the 3 arrows pointing at each other must add up to 9:

The total number in the arrows which are back to back must add up to 6:

1 2 3 4 4 4 5 6 7

The total numbers in the 3 arrows pointing at each other must add up to 13:

The total number in the arrows which are back to back must add up to 8:

1 1 1 2 2 3 3 3

The total numbers in the 3 arrows pointing at each other must add up to 10:

The total number in the arrows which are back to back must add up to 4:

1 2 3 3 4 4 5 5 6

The total numbers in the 3 arrows pointing at each other must add up to 10:

The total number in the arrows which are back to back must add up to 7:

2 3 4 4 5 5 6 6 7 8

The total numbers in the 3 arrows pointing at each other must add up to 17:

The total number in the arrows which are back to back must add up to 10:

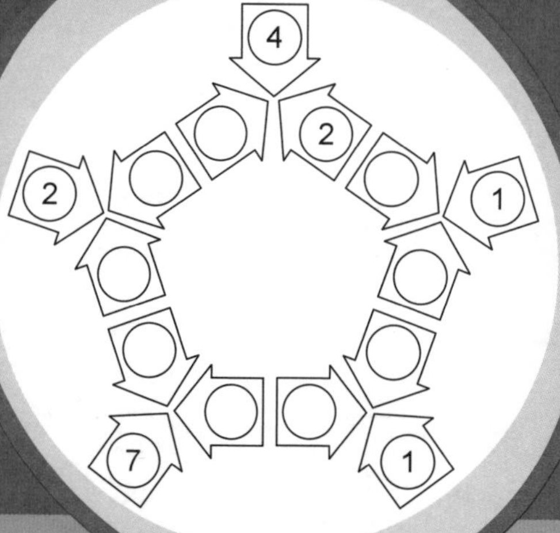

Turn to page 196 for the solutions

ARROWS

3 4 4 5 5 5 5 6 6 7

The total numbers in the 3 arrows pointing at each other must add up to 12:

The total number in the arrows which are back to back must add up to 10:

1 1 1 2 3 3 4 4

The total numbers in the 3 arrows pointing at each other must add up to 9:

The total number in the arrows which are back to back must add up to 5:

1 2 3 3 3 4 4 5 6

The total numbers in the 3 arrows pointing at each other must add up to 11:

The total number in the arrows which are back to back must add up to 7:

2 3 4 5 5 6 6 7 8 9

The total numbers in the 3 arrows pointing at each other must add up to 18:

The total number in the arrows which are back to back must add up to 11:

1 2 2 3 3 4 4 5 5 6

The total numbers in the 3 arrows pointing at each other must add up to 11:

The total number in the arrows which are back to back must add up to 7:

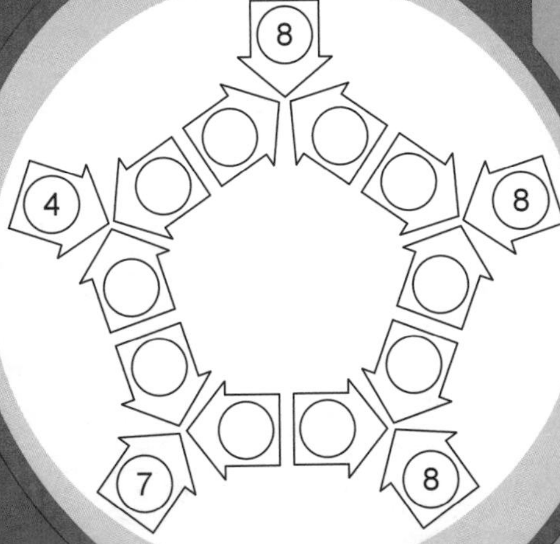

Turn to page 196 for the solutions

ARROWS

This puzzle will appeal to the mathematicians among you, but anybody can solve it with the right sums! Use the numbers listed in each of the puzzles to fill in the gaps in the arrows.

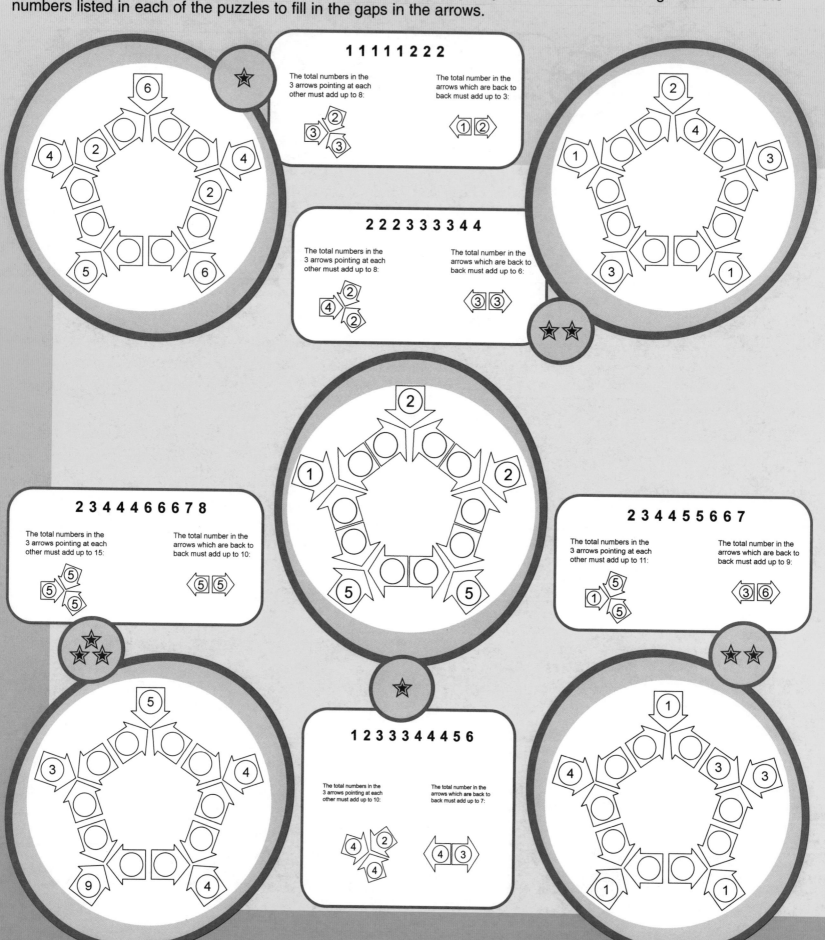

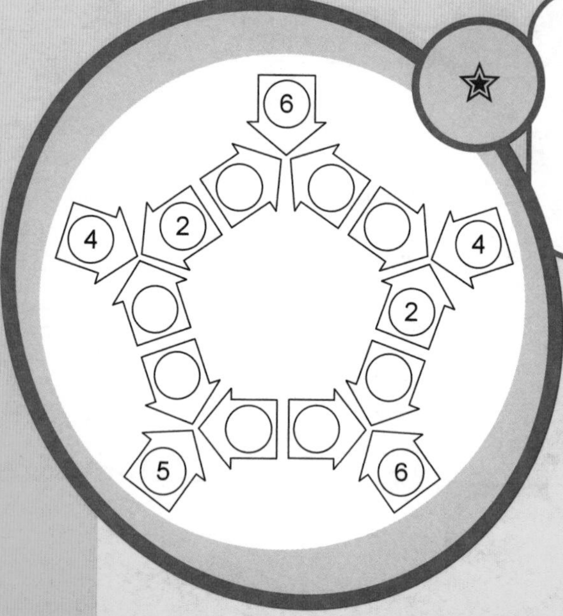

1 1 1 1 1 2 2 2

The total numbers in the 3 arrows pointing at each other must add up to 8:

The total number in the arrows which are back to back must add up to 3:

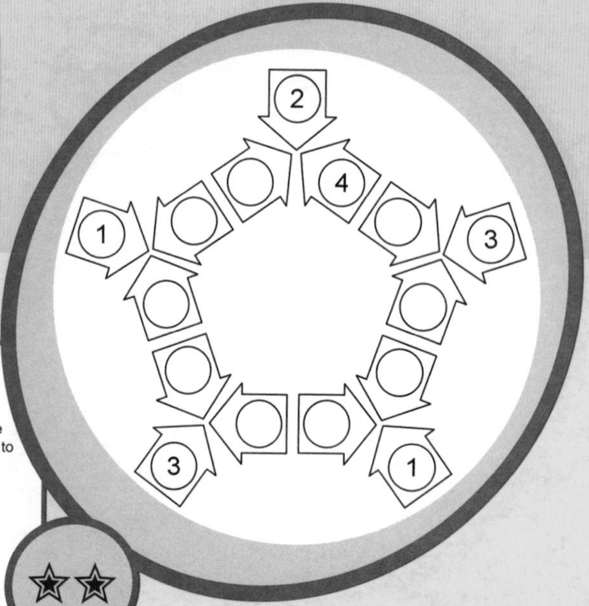

2 2 2 3 3 3 3 4 4

The total numbers in the 3 arrows pointing at each other must add up to 8:

The total number in the arrows which are back to back must add up to 6:

2 3 4 4 4 6 6 6 7 8

The total numbers in the 3 arrows pointing at each other must add up to 15:

The total number in the arrows which are back to back must add up to 10:

2 3 4 4 5 5 6 6 7

The total numbers in the 3 arrows pointing at each other must add up to 11:

The total number in the arrows which are back to back must add up to 9:

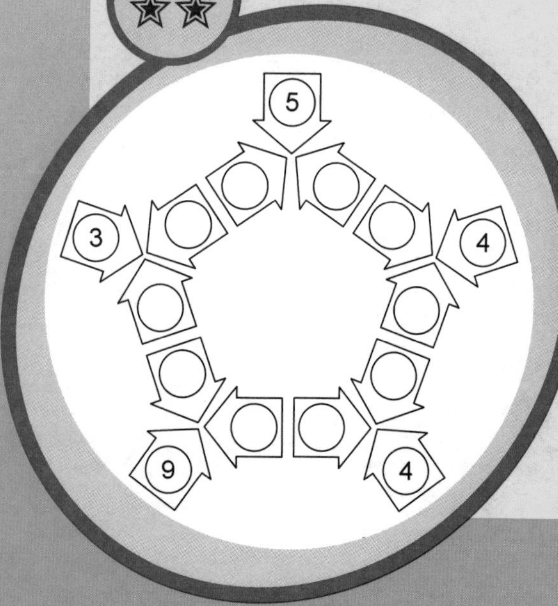

1 2 3 3 3 4 4 4 5 6

The total numbers in the 3 arrows pointing at each other must add up to 10:

The total number in the arrows which are back to back must add up to 7:

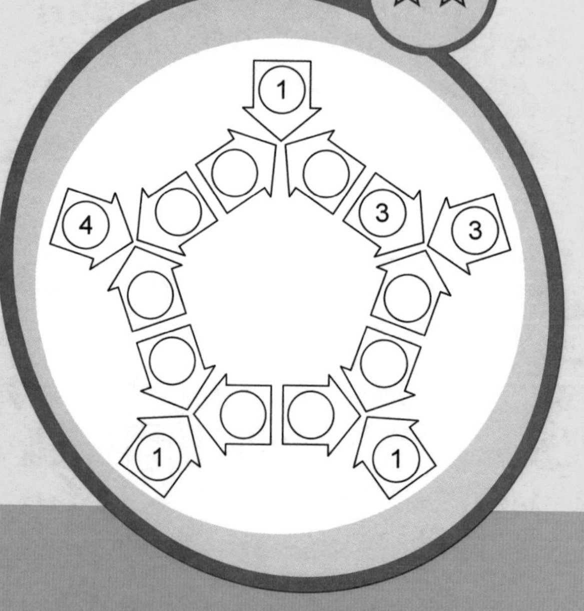

Turn to page 196 for the solutions

ARROWS

1 3 4 4 5 5 6 6 7 9

The total numbers in the 3 arrows pointing at each other must add up to 16:

The total number in the arrows which are back to back must add up to 10:

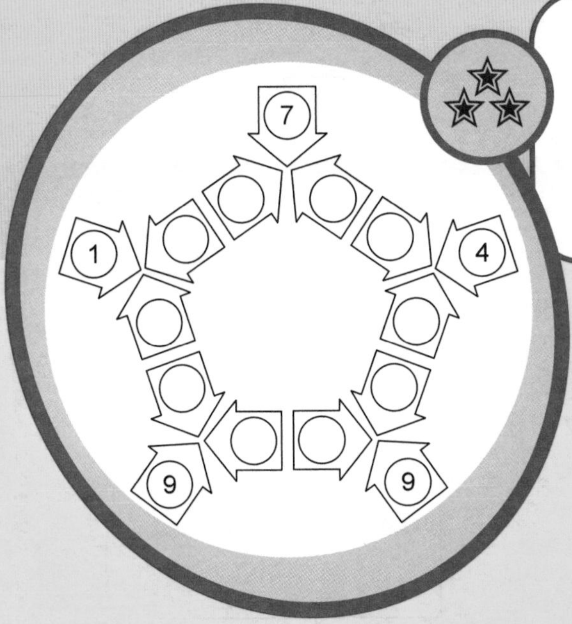

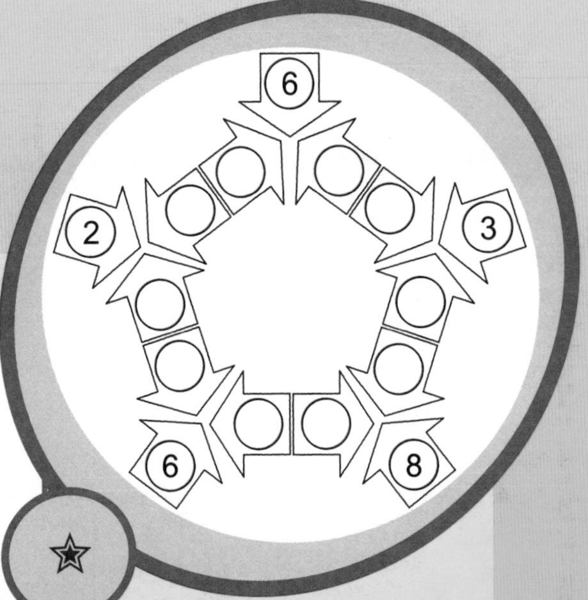

1 2 3 3 4 4 5 5 6 7

The total numbers in the 3 arrows pointing at each other must add up to 13:

The total number in the arrows which are back to back must add up to 8:

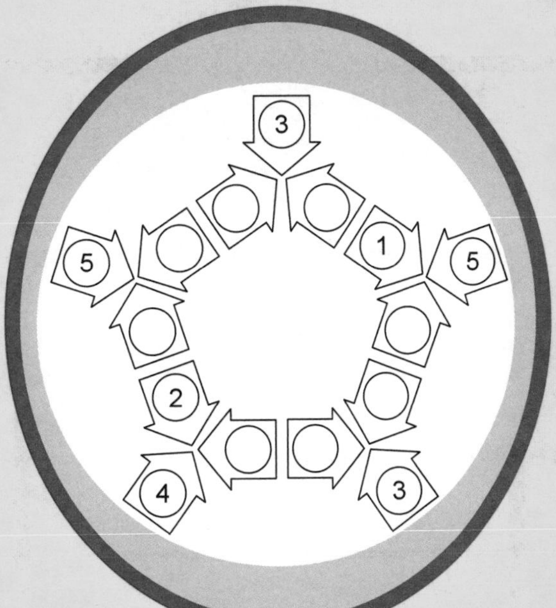

2 2 3 3 4 4 5 5 6

The total numbers in the 3 arrows pointing at each other must add up to 14:

The total number in the arrows which are back to back must add up to 8:

4 5 5 6 6 6 6 7 7 8

The total numbers in the 3 arrows pointing at each other must add up to 14:

The total number in the arrows which are back to back must add up to 12:

1 1 1 1 2 2 2 2

The total numbers in the 3 arrows pointing at each other must add up to 7:

The total number in the arrows which are back to back must add up to 3:

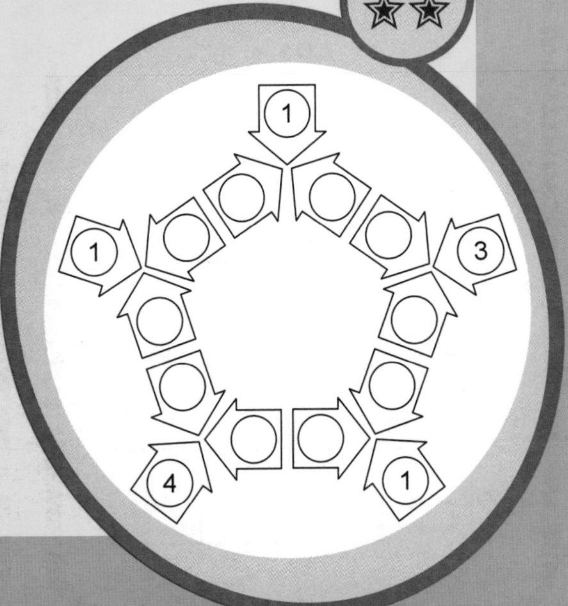

Turn to page 196 for the solutions

LETTER SUM SQUARES

The grid should be filled with the numbers running down the side of each grid, so that each number appears just once in every row and column. The clues refer to the digit totals in the squares, eg A 1 2 3 = 6 means that the numbers in squares A1, A2 and A3 add up to 6.

★

1 AB1 = 5
2 C23 = 5
3 BC3 = 4
4 A12 = 4

	A	B	C
1	2	3	
2		3	
3			

★★

1 AB1 = 3
2 A124 = 6
3 CD3 = 3
4 B34 = 7
5 ABC2 = 6
6 C23 = 3
7 A34 = 6

	A	B	C	D
1				
2	3			
3				
4				

★★

1 A34 = 4
2 BD4 = 3
3 D14 = 3
4 BD2 = 7
5 C12 = 3
6 AD1 = 5

	A	B	C	D
1			2	
2				
3				
4				

★

1 B12 = 4
2 BC3 = 3
3 C23 = 3
4 A13 = 5

	A	B	C
1			
2		3	
3			

★★★

1 C345 = 12
2 BD3 = 9
3 E134 = 6
4 A35 = 3
5 CE3 = 4
6 ABDE1 = 14
7 AB3 = 6
8 BC2 = 3
9 B12 = 6
10 AD2 = 8

	A	B	C	D	E
1					
2			2		
3					
4					
5					

 Turn to page 196 for the solutions

LETTER SUM SQUARES

★★★

1 D123 = 6
2 ADE3 = 12
3 BE5 = 3
4 C34 = 3
5 BC1 = 9
6 E14 = 4
7 B24 = 8
8 ABC1 = 11

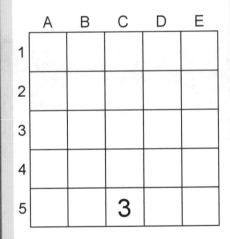

	A	B	C	D	E
1					
2					
3					
4					
5			3		

★

1 C12 = 3
2 AB2 = 5
3 AC3 = 4
4 B23 = 5

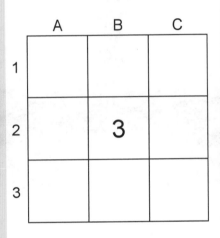

	A	B	C
1			
2		3	
3			

★★

1 AB2 = 4
2 C12 = 3
3 D12 = 7
4 BD3 = 3
5 A24 = 4
6 B23 = 3

	A	B	C	D
1				
2				
3			3	
4				

★★★

1 E123 = 6
2 AE4 = 9
3 C25 = 9
4 ADE1 = 10
5 A235 = 6
6 BD3 = 9
7 D24 = 4
8 CD3 = 8

	A	B	C	D	E
1					
2					
3					
4		2			
5					

★

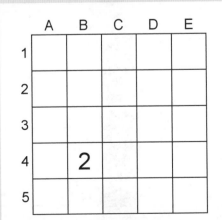

1 BC2 = 3
2 A12 = 5
3 AB1 = 3
4 BC3 = 5

	A	B	C
1			
2		2	
3			

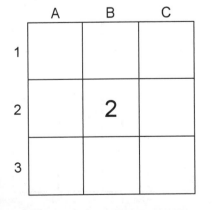

Turn to page 196 for the solutions

LETTER SUM SQUARES

The grid should be filled with the numbers running down the side of each grid, so that each number appears just once in every row and column. The clues refer to the digit totals in the squares, eg A 1 2 3 = 6 means that the numbers in squares A1, A2 and A3 add up to 6.

★

1 B23 = 3
2 C12 = 3
3 BC3 = 5
4 A23 = 4

	A	B	C
1			
2		1	
3			

★★

1 C12 = 6
2 AC3 = 7
3 AC4 = 3
4 D23 = 3
5 B14 = 7
6 BD1 = 7
7 D13 = 6

	A	B	C	D
1				
2			4	
3				
4				

★★

1 B23 = 7
2 CD2 = 3
3 D24 = 3
4 A24 = 7
5 BC3 = 6
6 ACD3 = 6

	A	B	C	D
1				
2				
3		4		
4				

★

1 AC1 = 3
2 BC2 = 3
3 AB3 = 3
4 A23 = 5

	A	B	C
1			
2		2	
3			

★★★

1 C235 = 6
2 E35 = 9
3 B145 = 6
4 AC1 = 9
5 ABD2 = 12
6 D135 = 6
7 BC2 = 7
8 C13 = 6
9 BE1 = 4

	A	B	C	D	E
1					
2					
3	2				
4					
5					

Turn to page 196 for the solutions

LETTER SUM SQUARES

★★★

1 B24 = 3
2 ABD5 = 6
3 E15 = 9
4 C25 = 9
5 A135 = 6
6 CD3 = 8
7 D12 = 4
8 BC4 = 3

	A	B	C	D	E
1		5			
2					
3					
4					
5					

★

1 B13 = 3
2 BC2 = 4
3 A12 = 3
4 C13 = 5

	A	B	C
1			
2		3	
3			

★★

1 AB3 = 6
2 D34 = 7
3 BC3 = 3
4 ABC4 = 6
5 C234 = 6
6 A12 = 5

	A	B	C	D
1				
2	2			
3				
4				

★★★

1 BCD1 = 6
2 E13 = 9
3 AC4 = 7
4 C123 = 6
5 D35 = 9
6 AB2 = 9
7 CD5 = 9
8 D15 = 8
9 A23 = 5

	A	B	C	D	E
1			1		
2					
3					
4					
5					

★

1 C23 = 3
2 AC2 = 3
3 B23 = 5
4 AB1 = 3

	A	B	C
1			
2		3	
3			

Turn to page 196 for the solutions

LETTER SUM SQUARES

The grid should be filled with the numbers running down the side of each grid, so that each number appears just once in every row and column. The clues refer to the digit totals in the squares, eg A 1 2 3 = 6 means that the numbers in squares A1, A2 and A3 add up to 6.

★

1 B23 = 4
2 BC1 = 3
3 AC3 = 3
4 C23 = 5

	A	B	C
1			
2		1	
3			

★★

1 ABD2 = 6
2 C14 = 5
3 BC4 = 3
4 D34 = 7
5 AD2 = 3
6 B23 = 7

	A	B	C	D
1				
2				
3				
4			2	

★★

1 BC2 = 3
2 C34 = 4
3 BD3 = 7
4 ABD1 = 6
5 BC4 = 7
6 BCD4 = 9

	A	B	C	D
1				
2			2	
3				
4				

★

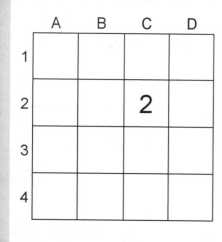

1 AB3 = 5
2 C12 = 5
3 BC3 = 4
4 A23 = 3

	A	B	C
1			
2		2	
3			

★★★

1 AE2 = 6
2 BC3 = 9
3 C125 = 6
4 E24 = 8
5 AC2 = 3
6 D34 = 3
7 B24 = 4
8 DE1 = 6

	A	B	C	D	E
1	2				
2					
3					
4					
5					

Turn to page 196 for the solutions

LETTER SUM SQUARES

★★★

1. C134 = 6
2. AD4 = 9
3. B45 = 3
4. E15 = 9
5. D125 = 6
6. ABC2 = 12
7. CD1 = 5
8. A23 = 6

	A	B	C	D	E
1					
2					1
3					
4					
5					

★

1. AC1 = 3
2. B23 = 3
3. AB3 = 5
4. A23 = 5

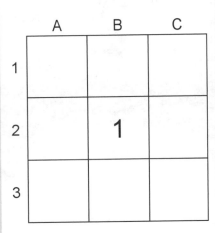

	A	B	C
1			
2		1	
3			

★★

1. C12 = 3
2. D23 = 7
3. AC2 = 3
4. BD4 = 3
5. B34 = 3
6. BC2 = 5

	A	B	C	D
1				
2				
3		1		
4				

★★★

1. C23 = 9
2. AD1 = 9
3. E135 = 6
4. D25 = 4
5. B345 = 12
6. CDE2 = 12
7. A23 = 3
8. AC5 = 6

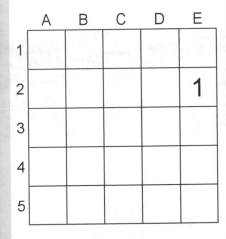

	A	B	C	D	E
1					
2		2			
3					
4					
5					

★

1. C13 = 3
2. AC2 = 4
3. B12 = 5
4. AB1 = 5

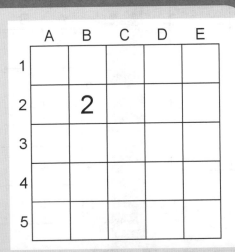

	A	B	C
1			
2		2	
3			

Turn to page 196 for the solutions

LETTER SUM SQUARES

The grid should be filled with the numbers running down the side of each grid, so that each number appears just once in every row and column. The clues refer to the digit totals in the squares, eg A 1 2 3 = 6 means that the numbers in squares A1, A2 and A3 add up to 6.

★

1 BC2 = 3
2 C23 = 3
3 AC2 = 5
4 C12 = 5

	A	B	C
1			
2		1	
3			

★★

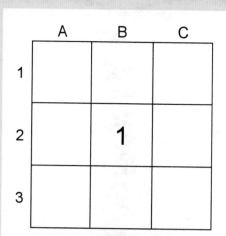

1 BC2 = 5
2 B34 = 3
3 BD4 = 3
4 A34 = 7
5 B123 = 9
6 D12 = 7
7 AB3 = 6

	A	B	C	D
1				
2			1	
3				
4				

★★

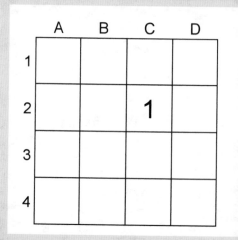

1 CD3 = 3
2 C12 = 7
3 A14 = 6
4 ACD3 = 6
5 B24 = 5
6 D34 = 3
7 C23 = 6

	A	B	C	D
1				
2				
3				
4			1	

★

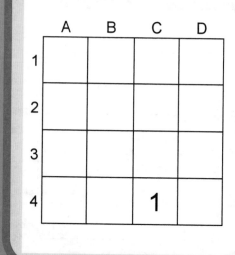

1 C13 = 3
2 B12 = 3
3 AB1 = 5
4 AB3 = 4

	A	B	C
1			
2		1	
3			

★★★

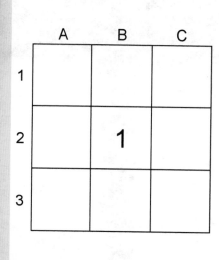

1 BCD3 = 6
2 E23 = 9
3 A124 = 6
4 DE5 = 3
5 C12 = 5
6 B1234 = 11
7 D24 = 9
8 E35 = 6

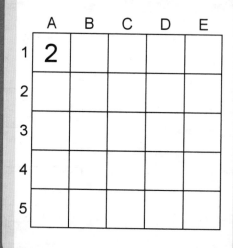

	A	B	C	D	E
1	2				
2					
3					
4					
5					

 Turn to page 196 for the solutions

LETTER SUM SQUARES

★★★

1 ABC1 = 8
2 C34 = 5
3 DE5 = 4
4 E23 = 5
5 B24 = 3
6 D13 = 3
7 C25 = 9
8 A145 = 9

	A	B	C	D	E
1					
2					
3					
4		1			
5					

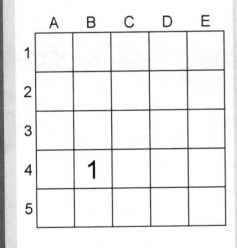

★

1 B23 = 5
2 AB2 = 5
3 AB3 = 3
4 C12 = 3

	A	B	C
1			
2		3	
3			

★★

1 CD1 = 3
2 D34 = 7
3 ABD3 = 7
4 B23 = 3
5 A13 = 6
6 CD4 = 5

	A	B	C	D
1				
2		2		
3				
4				

★★★

1 DE5 = 9
2 B124 = 12
3 C23 = 3
4 A145 = 6
5 E12 = 3
6 C14 = 9
7 AC1 = 8
8 BD3 = 6

	A	B	C	D	E
1					
2					
3					
4				2	
5					

★

1 AB2 = 5
2 C23 = 3
3 A12 = 3
4 BC2 = 4

	A	B	C
1			
2		3	
3			

Turn to page 196 for the solutions

LETTER SUM SQUARES

The grid should be filled with the numbers running down the side of each grid, so that each number appears just once in every row and column. The clues refer to the digit totals in the squares, eg A 1 2 3 = 6 means that the numbers in squares A1, A2 and A3 add up to 6.

★★★

1 DE1 = 7
2 E45 = 3
3 ACD3 = 6
4 B24 = 4
5 AE5 = 3
6 C15 = 9
7 D23 = 3
8 B35 = 9
9 B12 = 3

	A	B	C	D	E
1		2			
2					
3					
4					
5					

★★

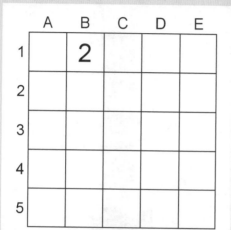

1 ACD2 = 9
2 B24 = 3
3 AC3 = 4
4 C34 = 7
5 BC2 = 3
6 CD4 = 5

	A	B	C	D
1				
2		1		
3				
4				

★★

1 C23 = 3
2 AB3 = 7
3 ABD4 = 6
4 BD1 = 3
5 B23 = 7
6 BC3 = 6

	A	B	C	D
1				
2				
3				
4				3

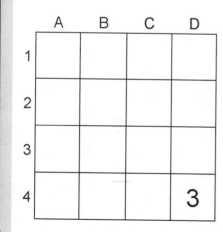

★★★

1 B135 = 6
2 CDE5 = 8
3 A24 = 3
4 E35 = 4
5 D124 = 6
6 ADE3 = 12
7 BC3 = 3
8 C14 = 9
9 CD1 = 6

	A	B	C	D	E
1		1			
2					
3					
4					
5					

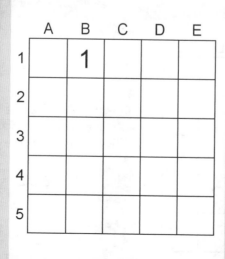

★★★

1 A12 = 9
2 E123 = 6
3 BCD3 = 12
4 B45 = 6
5 CD1 = 5
6 AB3 = 6
7 CE5 = 9
8 D25 = 3

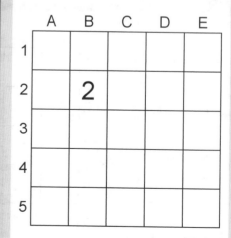

	A	B	C	D	E
1					
2		2			
3					
4					
5					

 Turn to page 196 for the solutions

LETTER SUM SQUARES

★★★

1 B234 = 6
2 BCD3 = 6
3 E23 = 9
4 AE2 = 8
5 C123 = 7
6 D34 = 3
7 C23 = 3
8 DE2 = 9
9 AB2 = 5

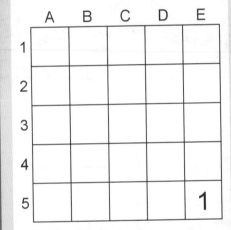

	A	B	C	D	E
1					
2					
3					
4					
5					1

★★

1 A 2 3 4 = 6
2 A B 1 = 5
3 C D E 4 = 15
4 B C 3 = 7
5 C 2 3 4 = 15
6 A B 2 = 9

	A	B	C	D	E	F
1						
2						
3						
4						
5						
6						

★★

1 AB2 = 3
2 B34 = 5
3 AD4 = 7
4 D13 = 3
5 ABC3 = 9
6 C23 = 6

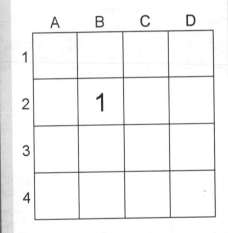

	A	B	C	D
1				
2		1		
3				
4				

★★

1 C23 = 3
2 AD4 = 3
3 BCD4 = 9
4 B23 = 3
5 CD1 = 5
6 BC3 = 3

	A	B	C	D
1				
2				
3				
4		4		

★★

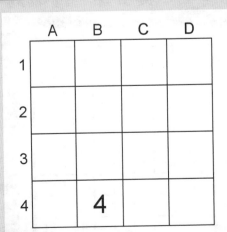

1 F 1 2 3 = 13
2 A 4 5 = 6
3 A B C 4 = 8
4 B C 2 = 6
5 C D E 1 = 8

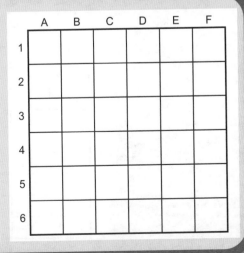

	A	B	C	D	E	F
1						
2						
3						
4						
5						
6						

Turn to page 196 for the solutions

SUDOKU

Fill in the spaces in each puzzles so that every row, column and box contains the numbers 1-9.

★★

	8		6		1		7	
		1				3		
	2	7		5		1	6	
			3		7			
		6				4		
			5		6			
	3	8		7		6	9	
		4				2		
	5		4		2		8	

★★

6		3	4		2	7		8
2				7				4
			8	6	1			
		7				3		
4								2
		9				5		
			7	9	5			
5				1				3
7		1	2		3	8		9

★★★

5					4			
4		2			8	5		
	6			3				7
			5				1	4
		9				2		
3	2				6			
2				9			5	
		3	8			9		6
			7					1

★

	9				3	2		
2			8			6		4
8		5		2	6	7	1	
	8			6		1		
6	2			7	1	5		8
	5		2					
3			9	5			4	1
		9		4	8	3		6
	4		6	3	2		5	

★

	4	6	1			7		9
	5		3		9	8		
7	9		4	6		5		
1		8		2		3		5
				3	6		2	
5	3	2	8			4		6
9		4	7				5	
6			2		3			
	8		6	9			4	

★★

	2						1	9
	6		2				3	5
8			7	1				
6					2			
5		4				2		3
			9					4
				2	1			7
1	5				9		4	
7	4						2	

★★★

7		5						
2				6				
8	6				4			
	2	6			5	8		
	9		8		1		5	
		4	7			3	2	
			1				8	3
				3				7
						9		5

 Turn to page 196 for the solutions

★★

		9	5	1	4	7		
	7	4	3		6	1	9	
7		2	4		3	8		1
4								9
5		8	7		9	4		6
	8	5	6		7	9	2	
		7	1	4	5	6		

★

6		9			8			7
		4		3	1			
	5	8	7		6		2	
4	3		8		5	7	1	9
			1		4			2
1	8	7		2	3		6	5
5			6		7			1
	4	6				2	5	
8		1		5	2		7	3

★★★

1	4			6				
					7		1	6
		2			5	4	8	
6						7	4	
	5	7						2
	2	8	9			1		
5	9		3					
				4			2	5

★

6		4					8	
	8					6		1
		3		1	8		2	
		8	9					5
4	7		2	5	1		9	3
5			7	8				4
3		1			9	7	5	6
8	6						4	
	2	5		7				

★★

	3	1	6		2	8	9	
		9				6		
			8	1	9			
	8	5	9		1	7	4	
	4						1	
	1	7	3		5	9	8	
			7	3	4			
		3				2		
	9	4	1		6	3	7	

★

7	5	6		3	8			9
			7		5		1	
2			9	6	4			
6		1	4	7		3		8
9	4			8		1	7	
				5	1			4
	6		5	1		7	9	
	9	7	2	4			3	
5	3				7	4	6	

★★★

		9	1					
			8			7		5
	2	5		4			8	
		3	5			6		9
6								7
9		1			4	8		
	6			5		2	9	
3		4			6			
					9	3		

Turn to page 196 for the solutions

SUDOKU

Fill in the spaces in each puzzles so that every row, column and box contains the numbers 1-9.

★

1		4	6	3		7		
6			7		9		8	1
	5			8		3		4
8	1	5		7		4	3	
	4	6			3		7	8
	9	7		6	4	1		2
5		8				2	1	3
9		3	1		8		4	7
	6				7		9	

★★

	6	4						
5			4					8
	2	7		5				
4	3		8					
	5			6			1	
					9		6	3
				1		6	5	
9					7			1
						4	2	

★★★

1					6			
8	6			7			3	
					3	1		2
3		6	7					1
		9				3		
5					2	6		4
9		7	5					
	5			2			8	7
			4					6

★

3	5	6		1				9
		2	7	5	8			4
	8				3	1	2	
7	6		4	3	1	2		8
	3	8			6	7		1
				9			6	3
5		1		7	9		8	2
6	2	9					1	7
8	7				2	9		

★★★

		6			3			
	5			9			6	
3	4				8	2		
2	1				6			
		5				7		
			4				1	8
		9	7				8	6
	7			5			9	
			9			4		

★★

	3		9		1		5	
1								7
6	7						8	3
		1	6	4	2	7		
		4	3	5	8	9		
5	6						7	9
4								8
	9		2		7		1	

★★★

			8					
			5	9		3		
		6						
	7						1	6
	5			2			9	
8	3						4	
						5		
		4		7	6			
					1			

Turn to page 196 for the solutions

★★

	9						1	
		4	9		1	2		
6				5				4
9	7		6		3		2	5
			2		5			
2	1		8		9		3	6
8				3				2
		7	1		6	8		
	5						7	

★

4	1	7			5	2	6	9
			4		6			
5	6	8			9		7	4
8		4		2	1			6
	5		3		7		9	
2	7		6		4			1
		1		6	2		4	7
7	9	2						5
6				9	8	1		

★★★

		7			3			
	8			5			7	
3	4				1	9		
			4				2	1
		8				6		
9	2				7			
		5	6				1	7
	6			8			5	
			5			4		

★

	5		4	3	6	8		7
	1		8	7	2			3
7				5	1		4	
8			3		5	6		2
3	4		6	2	8			5
6			1	9				8
2	3			1		5		4
	9	7	2	6	4	3		
1		4	5		3			9

★★

			5		9			
8		6				2		3
3	5						9	1
		5	7		4	8		
			9		1			
		2	3		6	7		
6	8						4	2
4		1				5		8
			8		2			

★★

	5	6	2		4	1	9	
			9	5	1			
	1						2	
	7	5	6		3	9	1	
		8				5		
	3	9	1		5	8	7	
	6						4	
			7	6	8			
	8	1	5		2	7	6	

★★★

7				6	9			
		6				5		
2			7		3	1	9	
6	9				2			
		1				2		
			1				3	8
	7	5	6		8			4
		9				8		
			9	4				1

Turn to page 196 for the solutions

SUDOKU

Fill in the spaces in each puzzles so that every row, column and box contains the numbers 1-9.

★★★

	5					7		
			8					
			6	9	1			
2	7							
	9			4			3	
							8	6
			3	7	5			
					2			
		8					1	

★★

		7			8	4	6	
	6				9			2
1	3					8		
					2		9	
5								6
	4		5					
		3					7	1
8			3				2	
	9	4	2			3		

★★★

7			8	3				
			1					
								6
		9				7	1	
		3		5		8		
	6	4				2		
8								
					4			
				2	6			9

★

3	8	4				1		
7		9		8	5			2
				4	7	6		9
	3			1	6	5		7
	1		4	7			2	8
4				5	8	3		6
8			5	3	1			4
2		1	8				9	
6		3		2	9			1

★

2	7	4	6	1	9	3		5
		6	2	8	5			4
	1		3	7	4			
4	5				3		1	8
9		8	1	4				3
				5		4		7
		9	7	2			3	
				9	8		5	2
6	8	2	5	3	1	7		

★★

4	5		8					
		2		5				
1	7		4		9			
5	8		2		4		7	3
		7				2		
9	2		3		6		1	5
			9		5		2	8
				6		9		
					8		6	7

★★★

	2		1				3	5
			7			6		4
3		4		6				
		6					7	3
1	7					2		
				3		1		2
9		1			8			
2	5				9		4	

 Turn to page 196 for the solutions

★★

				3		2	4	
8					6			
		3	4	8			5	
7			8					
	4			5			3	
					9			1
	1			9	2	6		
			7					9
	2	5		4				

★

7	5	8	9					1
	1				6	2	4	5
2	6		3	5	1	7		9
5			2	1		4	9	
	4			9		8	5	6
		3	4		5			
8			5	3	9	6		
6		5	1			9		
4	9	1	6	8	2	5		7

★★★

		8						
					9			
				1	4	3		
5							8	6
4				7				1
3	9							2
		2	8	5				
			6					
						4		

★

7	8	9	2		5	1	6	3
6				8	9			5
5		4		3	6			9
4	5		3		2			8
3		8		7		5		6
	7			6	8	9	3	
9		5	8	1		6	4	
1		2				8	9	7
8	6		9		4	3		1

★★

		9	6					
								7
			7	1			2	8
		5			9	7	4	
8				7				1
	2	7	4			3		
2	7			8	6			
3								
					5	4		

★

5			4	3	1	8	9	2
	8		9	5		7	6	4
4				8				3
	9	3	8	6	5	2		
8				4	3	9		6
6		2		9			3	8
				7			2	9
	5	6	3	1	9	4	8	7
9		4		2		3		5

★★★

	8			3				7
		7			6			
	2	1					9	
4				1				5
			6		5			
9				7				2
	3					2	1	
			5			6		
7				9			8	

Turn to page 196 for the solutions

SUDOKU

Fill in the spaces in each puzzles so that every row, column and box contains the numbers 1-9.

★★★

				5		7	9	
	5	9			4			
7		3			6			2
4		7					5	
	2					6		4
9			8			2		3
			1			8	6	
	6	2		7				

★

		9	2		7			
			6		3		4	
	4	6		1	9	2		8
2	1				4			5
	9	4	1	6	5	7	3	2
6	3	5		7				4
4		1	9			3		
7	2	8	4	3		5	9	1
		3		2		4		

★

2		3	5	8	1	4	7	9
	4	5	9					1
	9			4	6		8	
5	3	2	8	6	7			
9	7	8	1	5			6	2
6				2			5	
7	5		4		2			6
3		9	6	1			4	7
	2		7	3			9	

★★

3			9		5			8
	5	9				6	7	
8								2
		2		4		1		
6			2		7			4
		8		6		7		
7								1
	2	4				3	5	
1			5		3			9

★★★

						7	4	
			3				9	8
				9			1	
6		5			4	8		
7			8		3			4
		2	1			9		6
	6			5				
5	8				2			
	1	4						

★

	9	3	6	2	1	4	7	8
	7	4	5	3	9	6		
1		2					3	
3	5				2			6
	2	6		8		1	5	
7	8		1	6			2	
9	1		2			7		
		5	7	9	4		8	
2	4	7	3	1	8			9

★★

			3	4				9
9	7	1		6				2
					1			8
	9					8		
5	6						4	1
		3					9	
6			5					
2				8		5	7	3
3				2	9			

★★★

		4			6			
	1	2					3	
	8			5				4
3				4				1
			6		9			
7				2				9
4				3			8	
	5					1	2	
			9			6		

 Turn to page 196 for the solutions

NUMBER CROSS

With the aid of the starter already given, can you fit all of the listed numbers into the grid?

☆

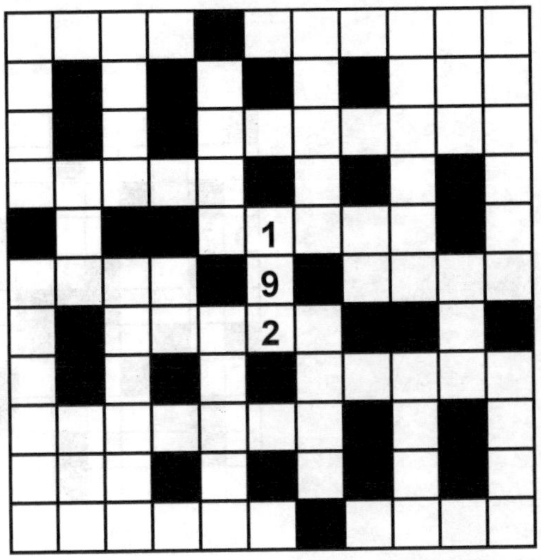

2 digits
13
20

3 digits
163
~~192~~
327
428
468
921
966

4 digits
1926
3195
3891
4000
4332
5199
7016
7222
7256
8229

5 digits
11611
12756
12775
21999
22411
60128

6 digits
189850
217694
367379
469231
483275
648211

7 digits
2435742
8870863

☆☆

2 digits
25
61
82
92

3 digits
138
265
484
~~400~~
563
600
615
711
933
935

4 digits
1298
1311
1551
2056
2246
2559
3506
3620
3754
5283
6497
6591
6761
6853
7216
7367
7519
7675
8312
9280
9586
9959

5 digits
50709
90804

6 digits
176522
193705
528908
589026
734767
735243
743286
771036
846219
853211
892060
908060
942713
947563

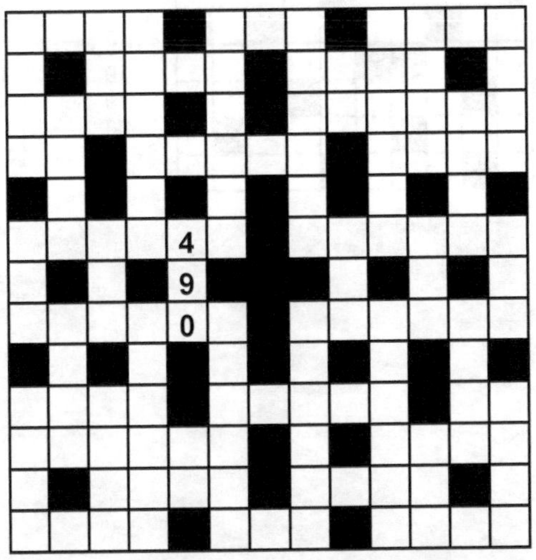

Turn to page 196 for the solutions

NUMBER CROSS

Can you fit all of the listed numbers into the grid? We have given you a head start in some.

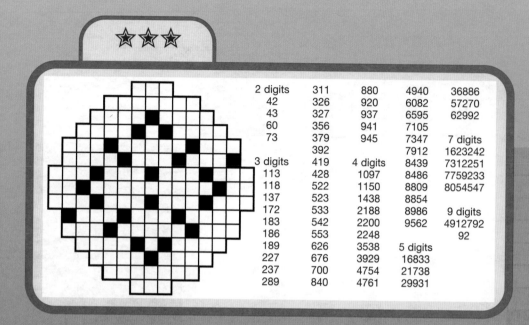

★★★

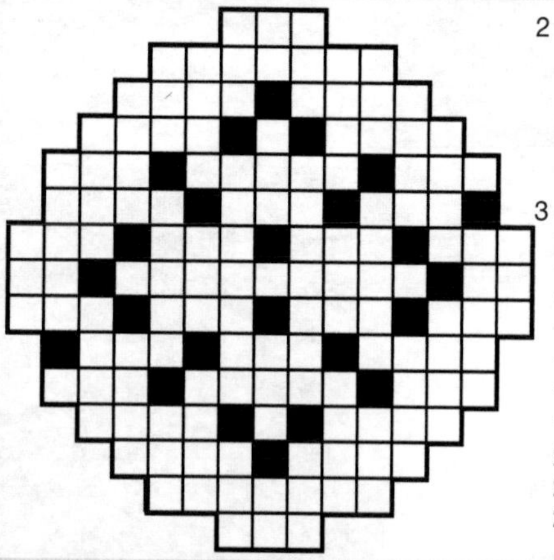

2 digits: 42, 43, 60, 73

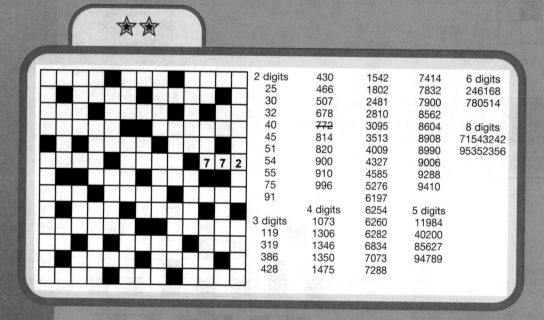

3 digits: 113, 118, 137, 172, 183, 186, 189, 227, 237, 289, 311, 326, 327, 356, 379, 392, 419, 428, 522, 523, 533, 542, 553, 626, 676, 700, 840, 880, 920, 937, 941, 945

4 digits: 1097, 1150, 1438, 2188, 2200, 2248, 3538, 3929, 4754, 4761, 4940, 6082, 6595, 7105, 7347, 7912, 8439, 8486, 8809, 8854, 8986, 9562

5 digits: 16833, 21738, 29931, 36886, 57270, 62992

7 digits: 1623242, 7312251, 7759233, 8054547

9 digits: 491279292

★

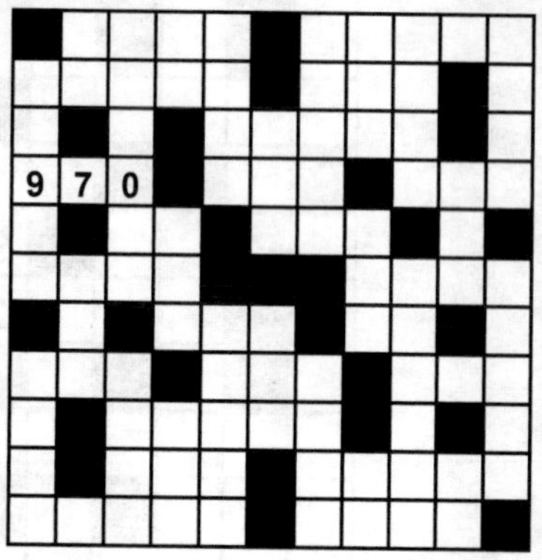

2 digits: 17, 29, 37, 62, 78, 96

3 digits: 104, 228, 250, 269, 320, 379, 428, 469, 635, 751, 755, 757, 764, 862, 863, 909, ~~970~~, 982

4 digits: 1078, 1857, 2679, 4378, 5833, 6688, 6811, 7256, 8114, 9256

5 digits: 22956, 32320, 33562, 37932, 48560, 59470, 61957, 62970, 74303, 76876

6 digits: 196548, 897035

★★

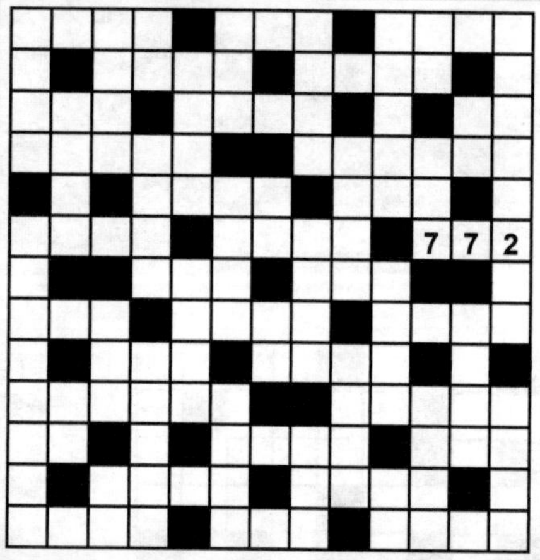

2 digits: 25, 30, 32, 40, 45, 51, 54, 55, 75, 91

3 digits: 119, 319, 386, 428, 430, 466, 507, 678, ~~772~~, 814, 820, 900, 910, 996

4 digits: 1073, 1306, 1346, 1350, 1475, 1542, 1802, 2481, 2810, 3095, 3513, 4009, 4327, 4585, 5276, 6197, 6254, 6260, 6282, 6834, 7073, 7288, 7414, 7832, 7900, 8562, 8604, 8908, 8990, 9006, 9288, 9410

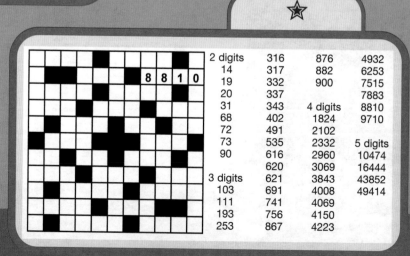

5 digits: 11984, 40200, 85627, 94789

6 digits: 246168, 780514

8 digits: 71543242, 95352356

★

2 digits: 14, 19, 20, 31, 68, 72, 73, 90

3 digits: 103, 111, 193, 253, 316, 317, 332, 337, 343, 402, 491, 535, 616, 620, 621, 691, 741, 756, 867, 876, 882, 900

4 digits: 1824, 2102, 2332, 2960, 3069, 3843, 4008, 4069, 4150, 4223, 4932, 6253, 7515, 7883, 8810, 9710

5 digits: 10474, 16444, 43852, 49414

 Turn to page 196 for the solutions

NUMBER CROSS

★★

2 digits
31
33
39
53
59
65
67
83
90
91

3 digits
130
147
167
175
226
465
514
517
607
611
690
~~804~~
808
931

4 digits
1060
1131
1156
1522
1770
2002
2572
2850
3200
3690
4974
5023
5109
5589
5619
5716
5779
5996
6654
7017
7400
7604
7650
7745
8509
8655
8766
8831
9003
9105
9600
9700

5 digits
27453
74909
79581
92514

6 digits
634905
945636

8 digits
23456981
28962764

★

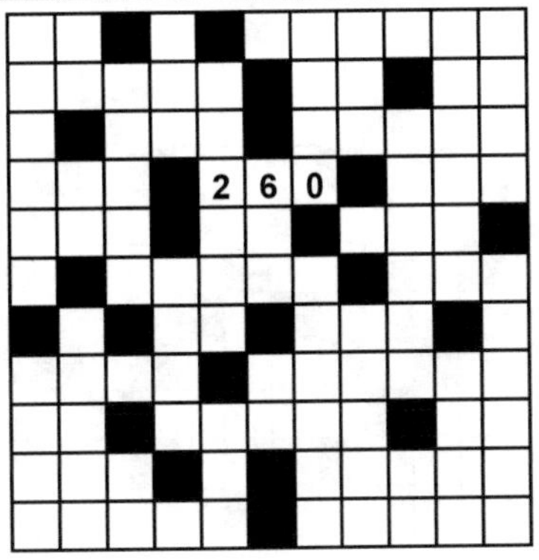

2 digits
22
23
28
34
36
66
73
78
82
83
87
90

3 digits
147
150
200
~~260~~
321
430
592
600
602
622
657
724
801

4 digits
1490
1600
2280
5985
7265
7808

5 digits
15526
16101
22800
28109
49307
52429
55664
56322
84309
88856

6 digits
190607
302210
364802
527881
610624
820348
830070
922850

★★★

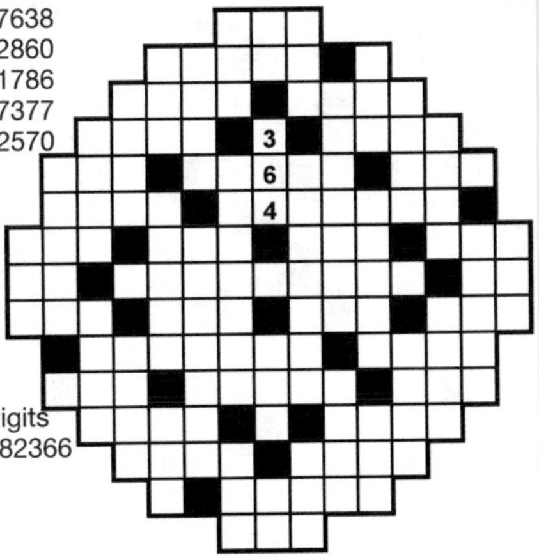

2 digits
10
32
41
96

3 digits
190
205
217
264
337
339
~~364~~
412
457
480
499
565
569
596
607
625
632
644
669
709
736
764
872
886
960
985

4 digits
2806
3064
3542
3649
3673
3980
4044
4534
4544
4574
4604
5267
5979
6460
6670
7473
7757
8666
9000
9959

5 digits
12868
14020
31364
39668
46529
50703
54626
67656

7 digits
2301547
2767638
5252860
5491786
7427377
7752570

9 digits
853282366

★

2 digits
25
42
43
48
55
66
73
75

3 digits
137
160
165
181
240
242
250
331
410
452
524
~~569~~
631
744
906
970

4 digits
1412
1595
1755
1816
2722
2966
5655
6085
6507
6707
7562
7690

5 digits
10419
10795
16216
16394
26284
30522
31455
35344
38625
54458
54851
60500
61567
62410
62900
65500

Turn to page 196 for the solutions

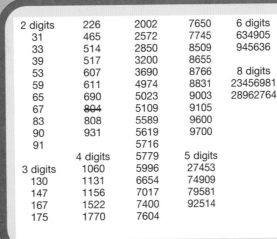

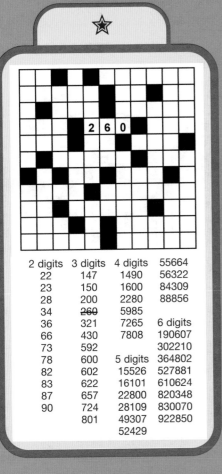

NUMBER CROSS

Can you fit all of the listed numbers into the grid? We have given you a head start in some.

★★

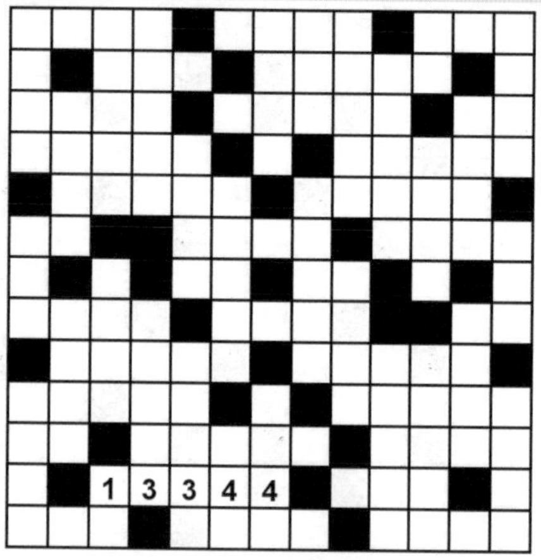

2 digits
18, 23, 38, 49, 50, 63, 65, 91

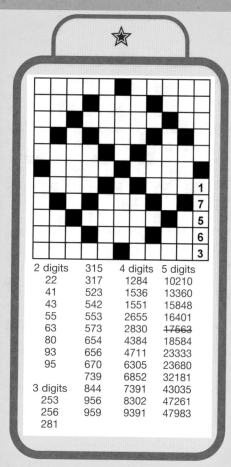

3 digits
218, 334, 445, 550, 605, 937, 960, 998

4 digits
1044, 1082, 1339, 1629, 3045, 3226, 4015, 4133, 4313, 4563, 5107, 5771, 6285, 6722, 7135, 7825, 8443, 8465, 8487, 8558, 8721, 8884, 9630, 9870

5 digits
12351, 13188, ~~13344~~, 13863, 13991, 16937, 26791, 26904, 29861, 31640, 33143, 38151, 41824, 45138, 50342, 53465, 53933, 55691, 58138, 59878, 61101, 61400

★

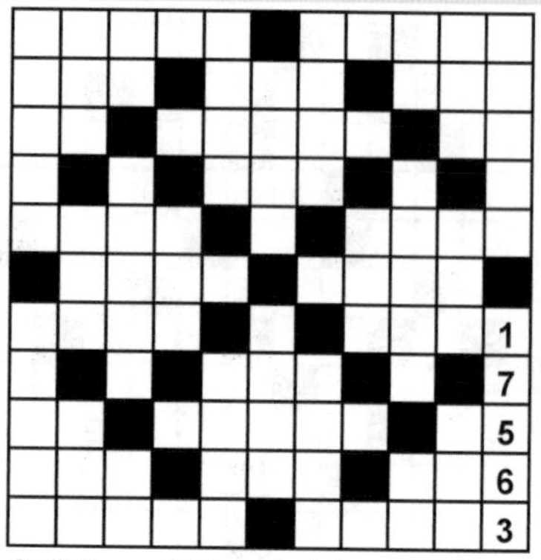

2 digits
22, 41, 43, 55, 63, 80, 93, 95

3 digits
253, 256, 281, 315, 317, 523, 542, 553, 573, 654, 656, 670, 739, 844, 956, 959

4 digits
1284, 1536, 1551, 2655, 2830, 4384, 4711, 6305, 6852, 7391, 8302, 9391

5 digits
10210, 13360, 15848, 16401, ~~17563~~, 18584, 23333, 23680, 32181, 43035, 47261, 47983

★★★

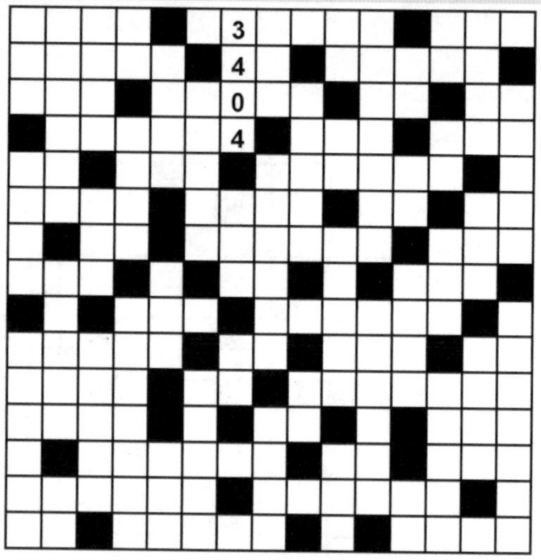

2 digits
18, 20, 26, 35, 41, 43, 48, 50, 52, 53, 55, 58, 68, 70, 71, 73, 74, 78, 80, 81, 83, 86, 87, 89, 97

3 digits
115, 192, 194, 201, 230, 236, 268, 301, 419, 429, 446, 535, 557, 651, 671, 746, 809, 840, 848, 851, 890

4 digits
1238, 1460, 2728, ~~3404~~, 3675, 4090, 4200, 7076, 7580, 7691, 7776, 8076, 8106, 8472, 9070

5 digits
11434, 15691, 15800, 26967, 29186, 31006, 32726, 39948, 42002, 54000, 57949, 59346, 78970

6 digits
156000, 233050, 255505, 325005, 528613, 554694, 632444, 695757, 705696, 786543, 792061, 989300

7 digits
1164942, 1950166, 4591057, 5486303

★★

3 digits
128, 152, 177, 244, 324, 576, 585, 589, 591, 626, 652, 724, 733, 755, 771, 852

4 digits
1737, 2214, 2402, 2515, 3267, 3351, 3894, 4797, 5166, 6382, 7895, ~~8665~~

5 digits
19271, 34639, 37739, 40293, 47727, 49155, 58403, 87874

6 digits
511033, 678907, 732255, 803177, 895515, 984562

7 digits
5123437, 6802633, 7563005, 8465356

8 digits
70850252, 78866526

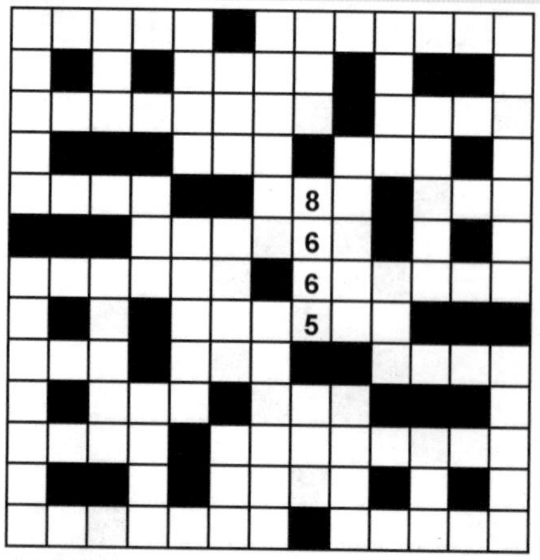

 Turn to page 196 for the solutions

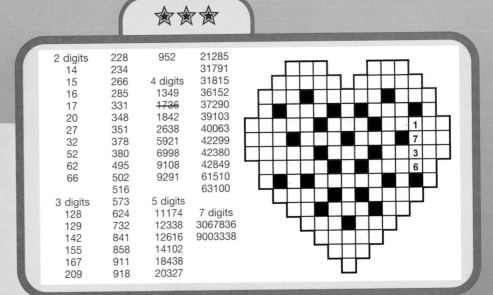

NUMBER CROSS

★★★

2 digits
14
15
16
17
20
27
32
52
62
66

3 digits
128
129
142
155
167
209
228
234
266
285
331
348
351
378
380
495
502
516
573
624
732
841
858
911
918
952

4 digits
1349
~~1736~~
1842
2638
5921
6998
9108
9291

5 digits
11174
12338
12616
14102
18438
20327
21285
31791
31815
36152
37290
39103
40063
42299
42380
42849
61510
63100

7 digits
3067836
9003338

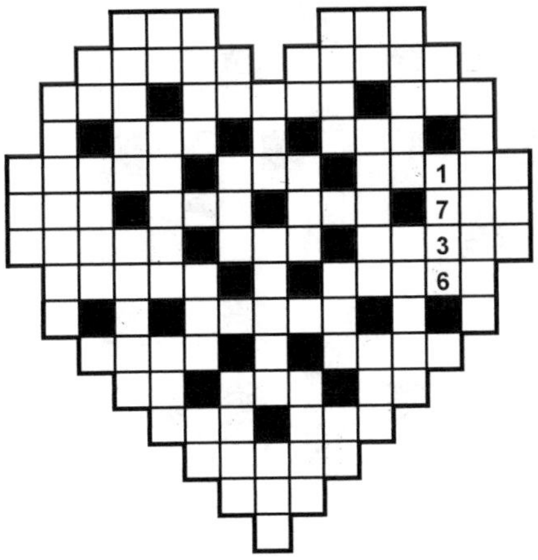

★

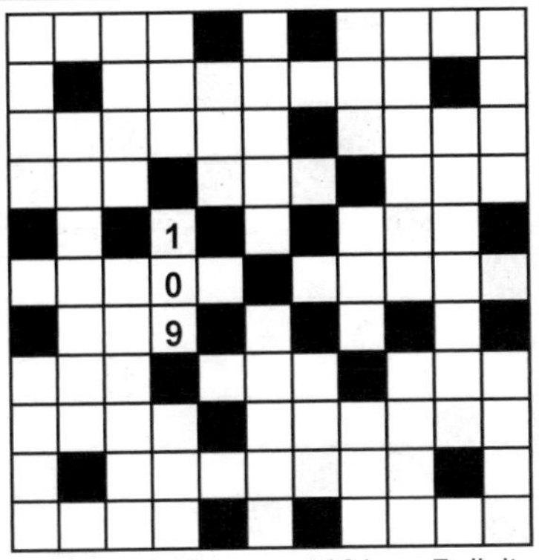

3 digits
~~109~~
192
203
413
458
462
481
483
489
494
655
776
863
884
931
945

4 digits
1775
2171
2284
2436
2529
3217
4341
5457
6202
6967
7132
9201

5 digits
21104
38383
51909
58775

6 digits
234661
758109
847193
983420

7 digits
1348743
2907863
4871403
5520070

★★

3 digits
163
204
306
311
372
417
429
430
431
437
492
~~574~~
780
930

4 digits
1463
2363
2563
3389
5125
5456
6119
6254
6986
7307
7774
8163
8422
9295

5 digits
20206
33712
46666
57465
59730
70101
72469
82327
90441
94535

6 digits
236234
266342
495739
535840
785916
844639

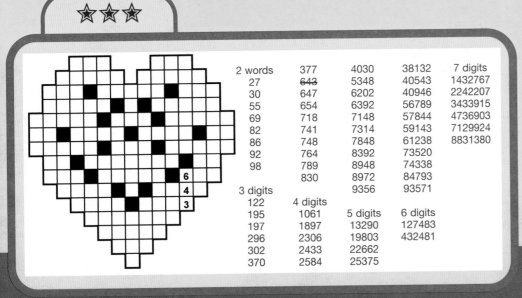

7 digits
2468013
2894100
3342499
4247772

8 digits
11189067
78916595

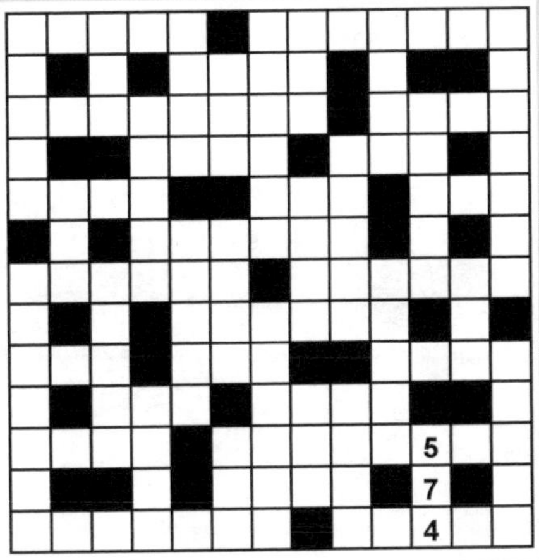

★★★

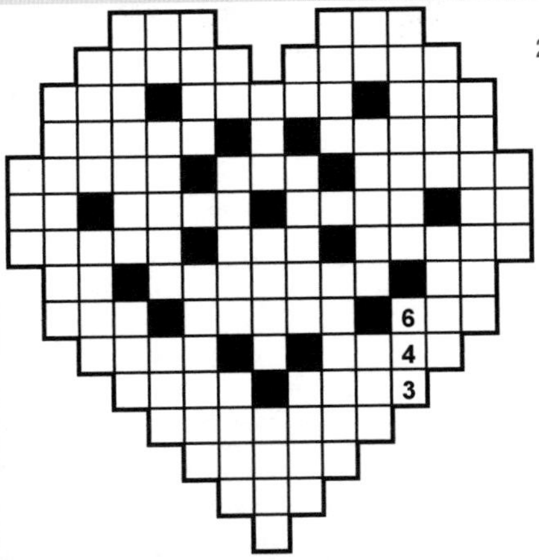

2 words
27
30
55
69
82
86
92
98

3 digits
122
195
197
296
302
370
377
~~643~~
647
654
718
741
748
764
789
830

4 digits
1061
1897
2306
2433
2584
4030
5348
6202
6392
7148
7314
7848
8392
8948
8972
9356

5 digits
13290
19803
22662
25375
38132
40543
40946
56789
57844
59143
61238
73520
74338
84793
93571

6 digits
127483
432481

7 digits
1432767
2242207
3433915
4736903
7129924
8831380

Turn to page 196 for the solutions

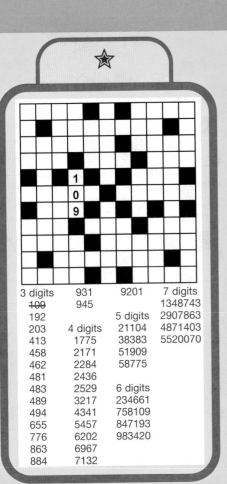

NUMBER CROSS

Can you fit all of the listed numbers into the grid? We have given you a head start in some.

★

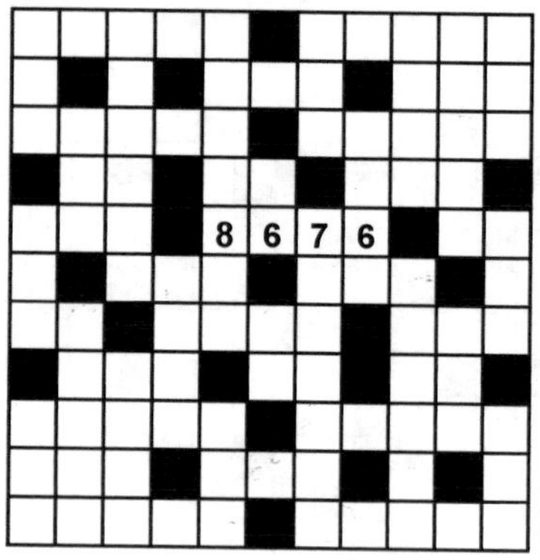

2 digits: 21, 22, 31, 49, 51, 63, 75, 96

3 digits: 111, 113, 124, 136, 203, 212, 220, 257, 266, 283, 337, 344, 351, 391, 521, 582, 633, 728, 826, 895

4 digits: 2372, 5130, 7264, 7464, ~~8676~~, 8788

5 digits: 11382, 17562, 23536, 27333, 31335, 37312, 48265, 57131, 61203, 62100

6 digits: 432351, 532165

7 digits: 2354824, 7341356

★★

2 digits: 12, 14, 15, 27, 35, 42, 62, 80

3 digits: ~~172~~, 336, 411, 460, 584, 695, 808, 895, 990

4 digits: 1164, 1229, 1597, 1931, 2158, 2588, 2646, 2661, 2769, 2905, 4336, 4730, 5214, 5272, 5441, 5810, 5927, 6073, 6942, 8622, 9084, 9286, 9646, 9722

5 digits: 11194, 11815, 15784, 18622, 24179, 25868, 28704, 28788, 40458, 44265, 46904, 57211, 60710, 85384, 97827

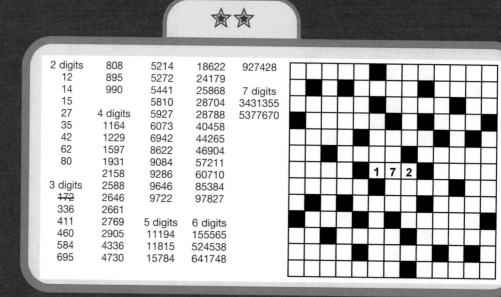

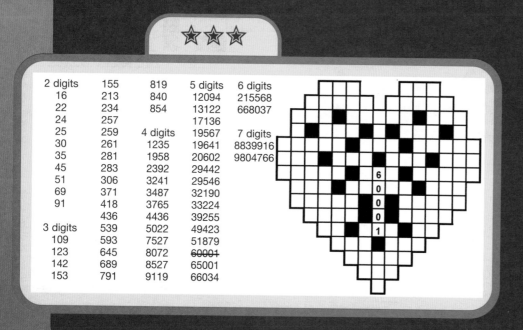

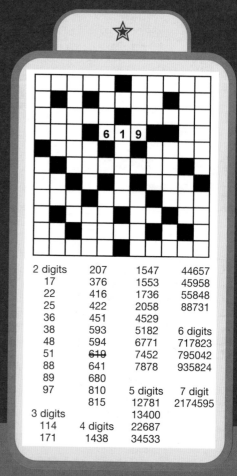

6 digits: 155565, 524538, 641748, 927428

7 digits: 3431355, 5377670

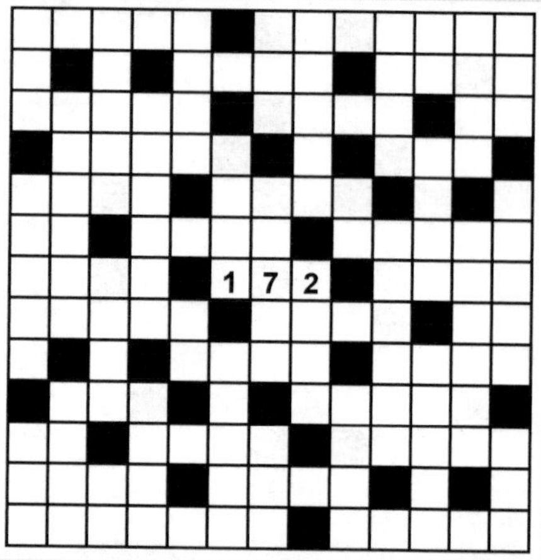

★★★

2 digits: 16, 22, 24, 25, 30, 35, 45, 51, 69, 91

3 digits: 109, 123, 142, 153, 155, 213, 234, 257, 259, 261, 281, 283, 306, 371, 418, 436, 539, 593, 645, 689, 791, 819, 840, 854

4 digits: 1235, 1958, 2392, 3241, 3487, 3765, 4436, 5022, 7527, 8072, 8527, 9119

5 digits: 12094, 13122, 17136, 19567, 19641, 20602, 29442, 29546, 32190, 33224, 39255, 49423, 51879, ~~60001~~, 65001, 66034

6 digits: 215568, 668037

7 digits: 8839916, 9804766

★

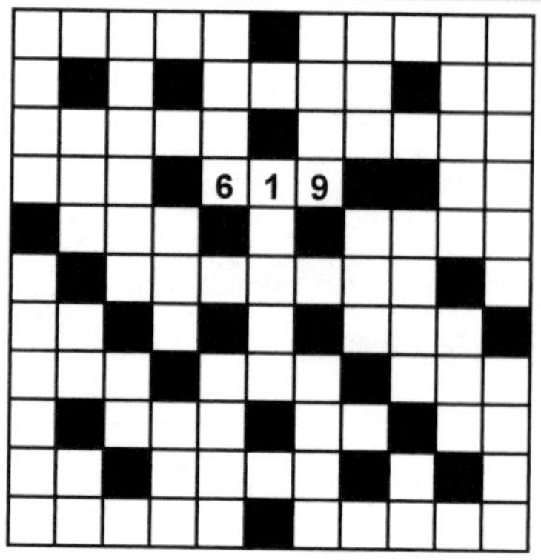

2 digits: 17, 22, 25, 36, 38, 48, 51, 88, 89, 97

3 digits: 114, 171, 207, 376, 416, 422, 451, 593, 594, ~~619~~, 641, 680, 810, 815

4 digits: 1438, 1547, 1553, 1736, 2058, 4529, 5182, 6771, 7452, 7878

5 digits: 12781, 13400, 22687, 34533, 44657, 45958, 55848, 88731

6 digits: 717823, 795042, 935824

7 digit: 2174595

 Turn to page 196 for the solutions

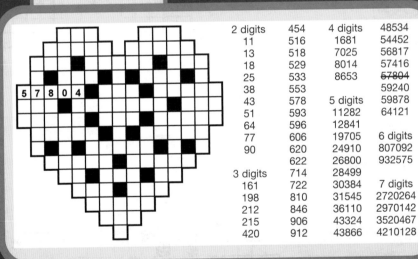

NUMBER CROSS

★★★

2 digits
10
12
23
39
47
50
53
62
63
68
72
73
74
78
89
99

3 digits
116
134
141
193
222
228
248
293
303
343
377
381
461
576
597
801
834
861
891
895
929
~~930~~
991

4 digits
1468
1899
1932
2118
2241
2744
2840
3229
3260
3272
3416
3479
3932
4628
4934
4994
5492
5937
6202
6463
6607
6661
6820
7147
7148
9250
9827
9859

5 digits
10250
16267
17936
22387
25317
25736
29498
29889
32170
37022
42207
54093
55851
83134

6 digits
164952
462579
734083
812003
848962
899034

7 digits
5162430
7806104
8912753

★★★

2 digits
11
13
18
25
38
43
51
64
77
90

3 digits
161
198
212
215
420
454
516
518
529
533
553
578
593
596
606
620
622
714
722
810
846
906
912

4 digits
1681
7025
8014
8653

5 digits
11282
12841
19705
24910
26800
28499
30384
31545
36110
43324
43866
48534
54452
56817
57416
~~57804~~
59240
59878
64121

6 digits
807092
932575

7 digits
2720264
2970142
3520467
4210128

★★

2 digits
21
28
31
37
46
71
76
94

3 digits
234
265
323
359
447
554
587
601
829
951

4 digits
1439
1470
1775
2173
3475
3698
6833
6844
7190
8432

5 digits
10376
20013
23134
30211
35095
35207
43139
43217
53820
56498
70281
76298
83214
~~85432~~
90824
91617
93247
95178

6 digits
401076
470986

★★

2 digits
10
16
17
41
50
89
92
94

3 digits
127
128
198
328
338
366
586
670
830
935

4 digits
2196
3876
4236
5842
6576
6578
6635
7279
8268
9264

5 digits
10026
17077
18015
18657
22676
28782
37033
40012
46127
47826
48956
49559
50428
62430
~~64236~~
64277
65052
65487

6 digits
719324
800003

Turn to page 196 for the solutions

NUMBER CROSS

Can you fit all of the listed numbers into the grid? We have given you a head start in some.

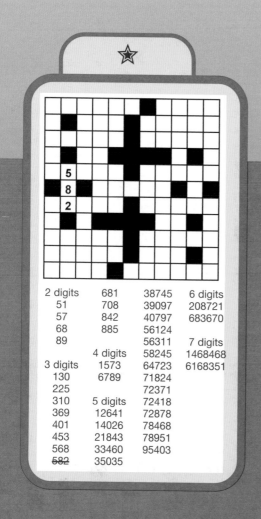

★

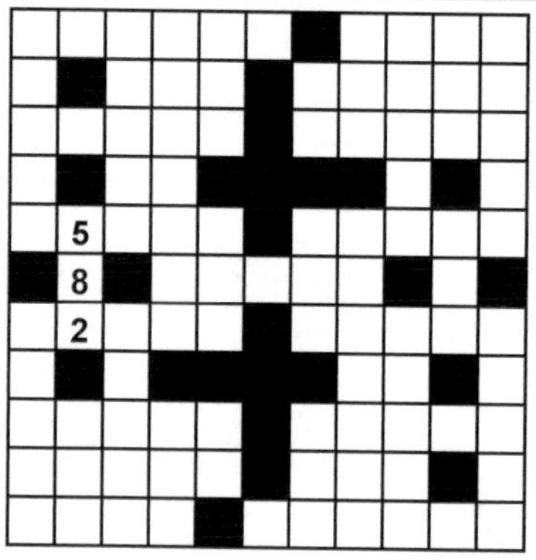

2 digits
51
57
68
89

3 digits
130
225
310
369
401
453
568
~~582~~
681
708
842
885

4 digits
1573
6789

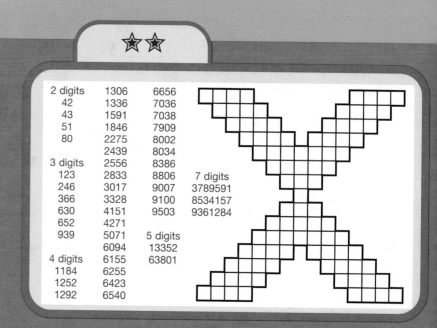

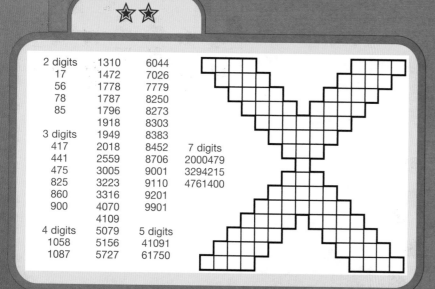

5 digits
12641
14026
21843
33460
35035
38745
39097
40797
56124
56311
58245
64723
71824
72371
72418
72878
78468
78951
95403

6 digits
208721
683670

7 digits
1468468
6168351

★★

2 digits
42
43
51
80

3 digits
123
246
366
630
652
939

4 digits
1184
1252
1292
1306
1336
1591
1846
2275
2439
2556
2833
3017
3328
4151
4271
5071
6094
6155
6255
6423
6540
6656
7036
7038
7909
8002
8034
8386
8806
9007
9100
9503

5 digits
13352
63801

7 digits
3789591
8534157
9361284

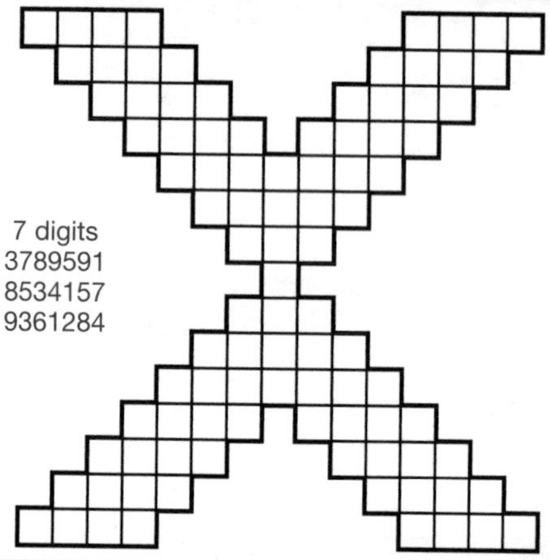

★

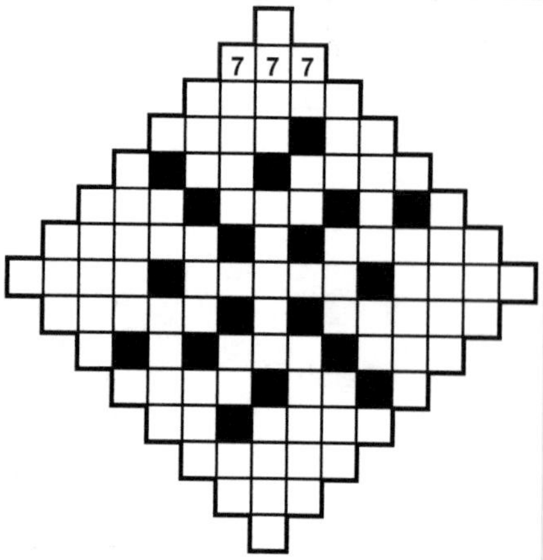

2 digits
14
18
32
50
52
53
69
70
79
82

3 digits
152
178
206
244
421
475
476
513
620
732
~~777~~
891
910
970

4 digits
1783
2568
2733
3025
5077
5243
6479
6905
7324
9700

5 digits
10141
11496
15227
15663
20546
24311
26032
27280
33995
38134
41310
48809
57390
78399

★★

2 digits
17
56
78
85

3 digits
417
441
475
825
860
900

4 digits
1058
1087
1310
1472
1778
1787
1796
1918
1949
2018
2559
3005
3223
3316
4070
4109
5079
5156
5727
6044
7026
7779
8250
8273
8303
8383
8452
8706
9001
9110
9201
9901

5 digits
41091
61750

7 digits
2000479
3294215
4761400

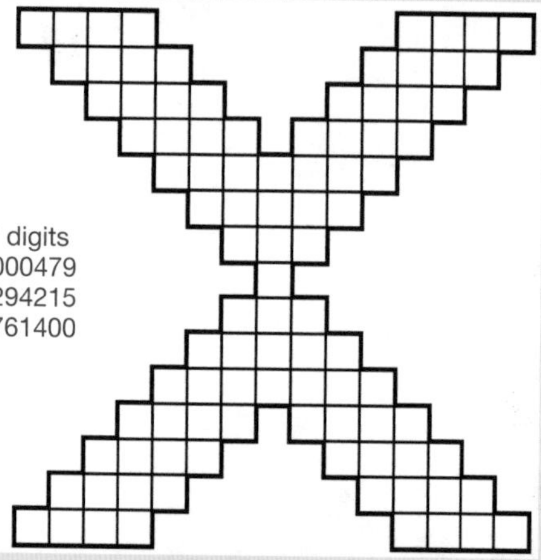

 Turn to page 196 for the solutions

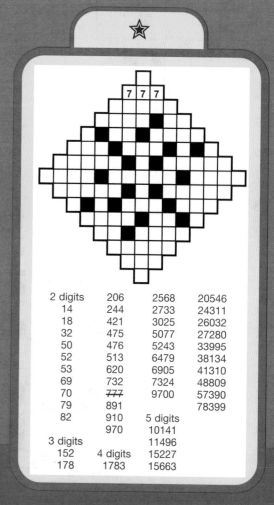

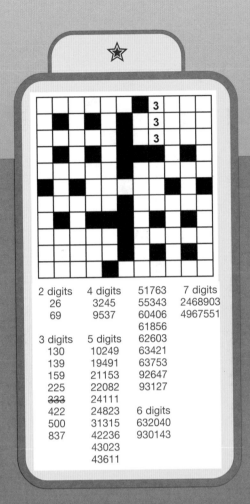

NUMBER CROSS

★★

2 digits
17
27
42
86

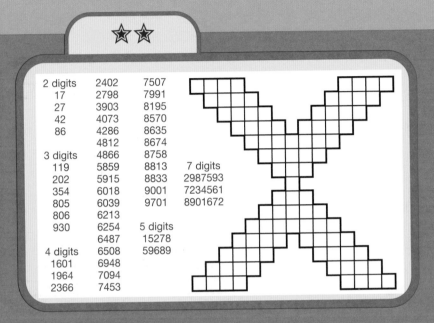

3 digits
119
202
354
805
806
930

4 digits
1601
1964
2366
2402
2798
3903
4073
4286
4812
4866
5859
5915
6018
6039
6213
6254
6487
6508
6948
7094
7453
7507
7991
8195
8570
8635
8674
8758
8813
8833
9001
9701

5 digits
15278
59689

7 digits
2987593
7234561
8901672

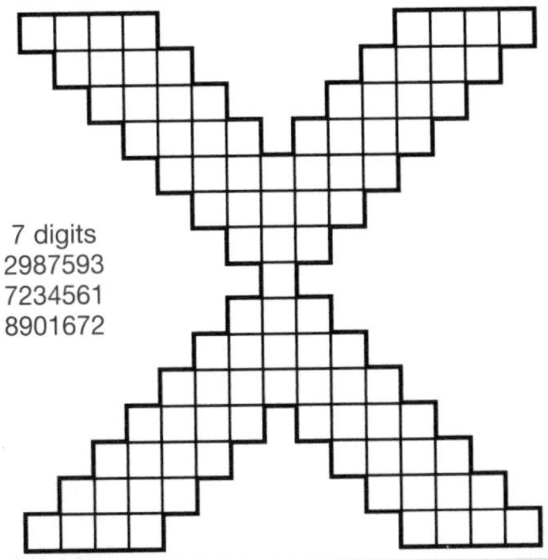

★

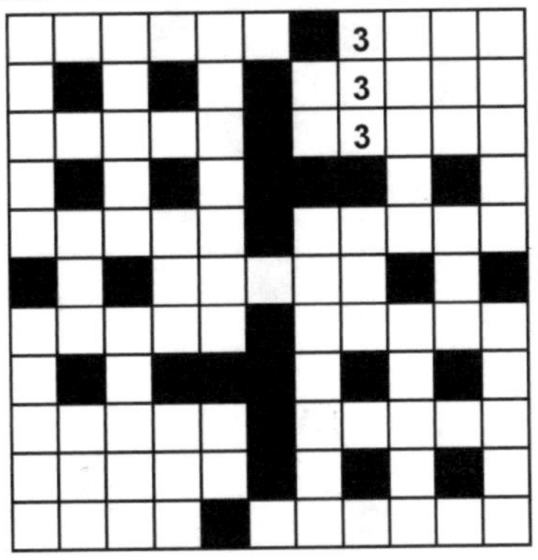

2 digits
26
69

3 digits
130
139
159
225
~~333~~
422
500
837

4 digits
3245
9537

5 digits
10249
19491
21153
22082
24111
24823
31315
42236
43023
43611
51763
55343
60406
61856
62603
63421
63753
92647
93127

6 digits
632040
930143

7 digits
2468903
4967551

★

2 digits
48
50

3 digits
161
~~205~~
323
569
788
794
868
929

4 digits
2853
5479

5 digits
15098
17335
27150
28420
44461
44763
45114
45370
46493
56373
72345
76527
78092
81122
82054
88790
89745
92311
93541

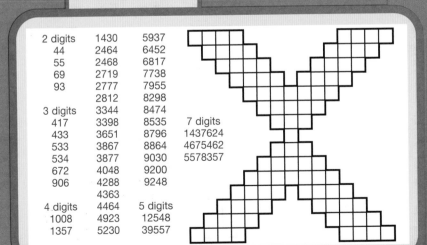

6 digits
297891
734952

7 digits
5233270
9540819

★★

2 digits
44
55
69
93

3 digits
417
433
533
534
672
906

4 digits
1008
1357
1430
2464
2468
2719
2777
2812
3344
3398
3651
3867
3877
4048
4288
4363
4464
4923
5230
5937
6452
6817
7738
7955
8298
8474
8535
8796
8864
9030
9200
9248

5 digits
12548
39557

7 digits
1437624
4675462
5578357

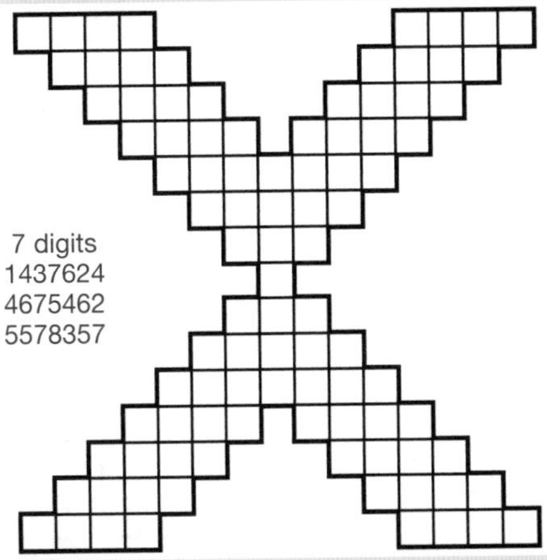

Turn to page 196 for the solutions

NUMBER CROSS

Can you fit all of the listed numbers into the grid? We have given you a head start in some.

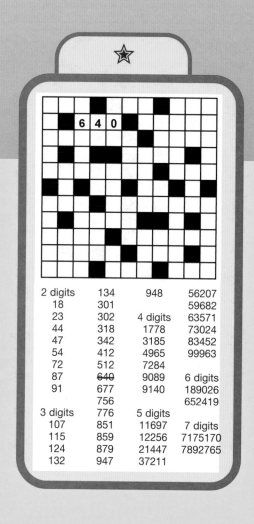

★

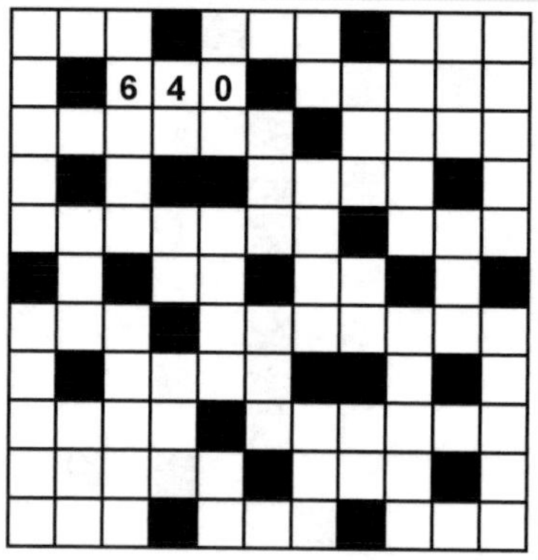

2 digits
18
23
44
47
54
72
87
91

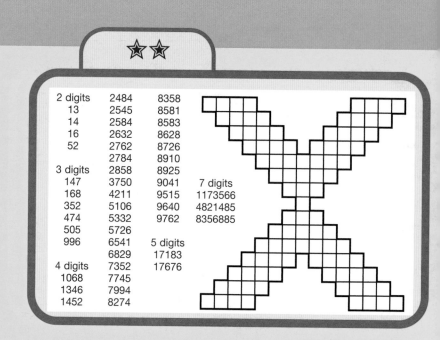

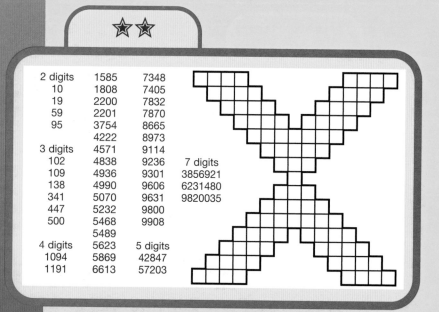

3 digits
107
115
124
132
134
301
302
318
342
412
512
~~640~~
677
756
776
851
859
879
947
948

4 digits
1778
3185
4965
7284
9089
9140

5 digits
11697
12256
21447
37211
56207
59682
63571
73024
83452
99963

6 digits
189026
652419

7 digits
7175170
7892765

★★

2 digits
13
14
16
52

3 digits
147
168
352
474
505
996

4 digits
1068
1346
1452
2484
2545
2584
2632
2762
2784
2858
3750
4211
5106
5332
5726
6541
6829
7352
7745
7994
8274
8358
8581
8583
8628
8726
8910
8925
9041
9515
9640
9762

5 digits
17183
17676

7 digits
1173566
4821485
8356885

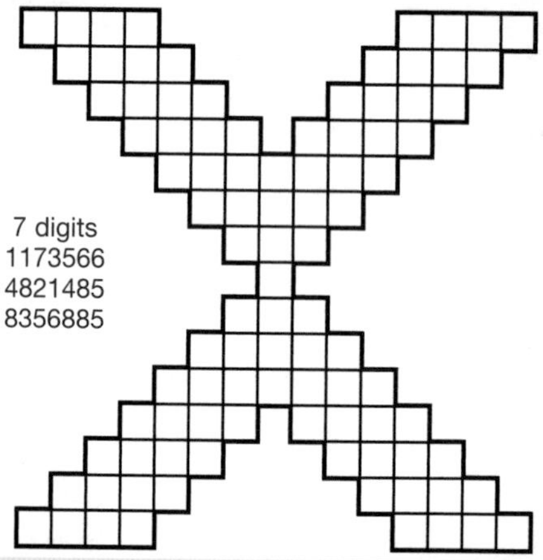

★

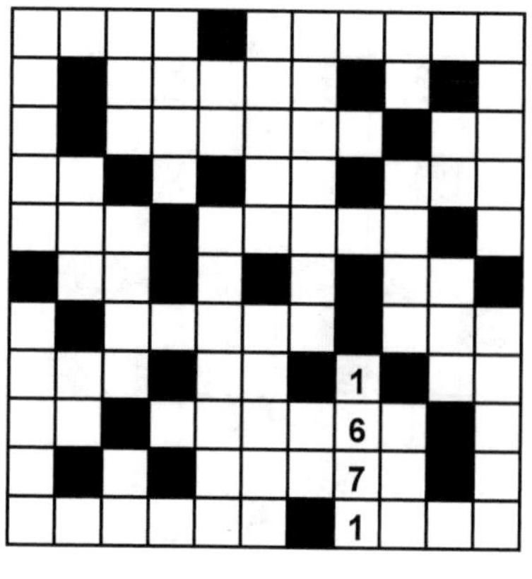

2 digits
11
18
20
26
32
38
42
44
45
48
52
62
88
90

3 digits
187
212
234
414
488
535
581
810

4 digits
1032
1164
~~1671~~
4797
5261
5744

5 digits
32630
35197
46712
48473
51155
53871
60235
63792
72981
87236

6 digits
146368
678194
785910
890714

7 digits
7123451
7610995

★★

2 digits
10
19
59
95

3 digits
102
109
138
341
447
500

4 digits
1094
1191
1585
1808
2200
2201
3754
4222
4571
4838
4936
4990
5070
5232
5468
5489
5623
5869
6613
7348
7405
7832
7870
8665
8973
9114
9236
9301
9606
9631
9800
9908

5 digits
42847
57203

7 digits
3856921
6231480
9820035

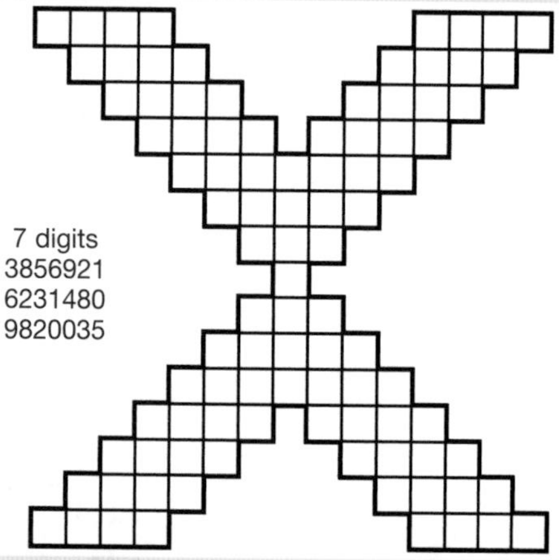

 Turn to page 196 for the solutions

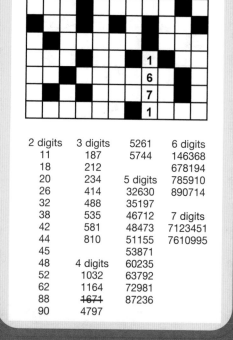

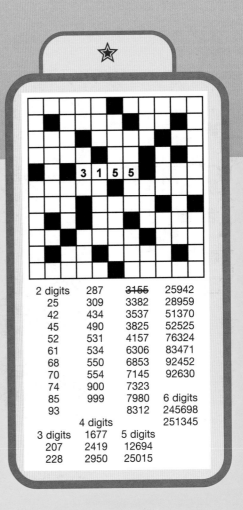

NUMBER CROSS

★

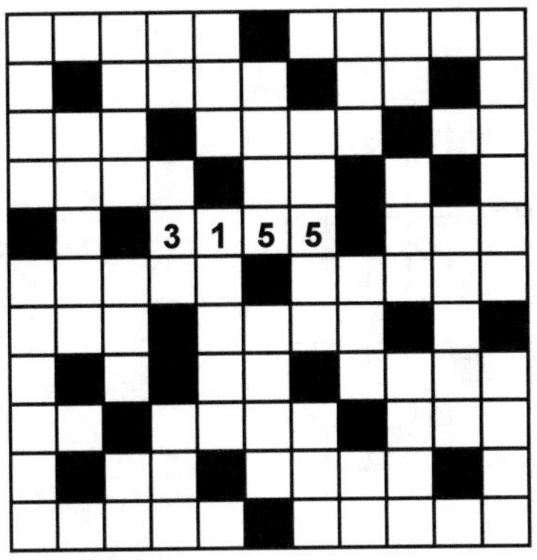

2 digits
25, 42, 45, 52, 61, 68, 70, 74, 85, 93

3 digits
207, 228, 287, 309, 434, 490, 531, 534, 550, 554, 900, 999

4 digits
1677, 2419, 2950, ~~3155~~, 3382, 3537, 3825, 4157, 6306, 6853, 7145, 7323, 7980, 8312

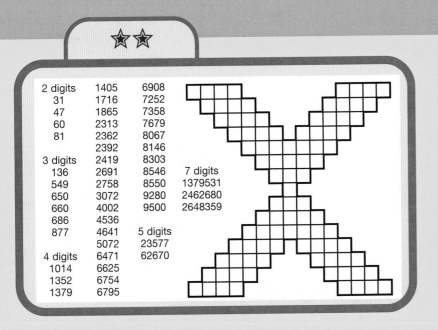

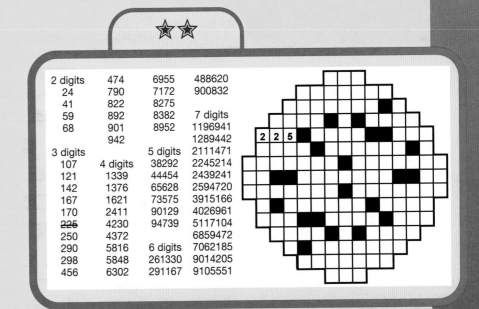

5 digits
12694, 25015, 25942, 28959, 51370, 52525, 76324, 83471, 92452, 92630

6 digits
245698, 251345

★★

2 digits
31, 47, 60, 81

3 digits
136, 549, 650, 660, 686, 877

4 digits
1014, 1352, 1379, 1405, 1716, 1865, 2313, 2362, 2392, 2419, 2691, 2758, 3072, 4002, 4536, 4641, 5072, 6471, 6625, 6754, 6795, 6908, 7252, 7358, 7679, 8067, 8146, 8303, 8546, 8550, 9280, 9500

5 digits
23577, 62670

7 digits
1379531, 2462680, 2648359

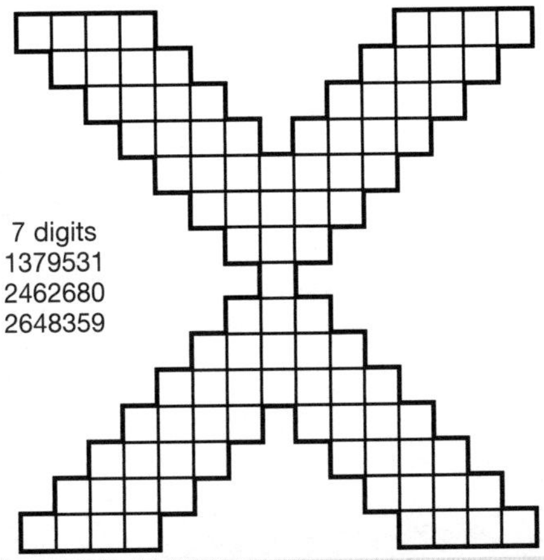

★

2 digits
29, 52, 59, 71

3 digits
116, 123, 132, 140, 224, 243, 425, 427, 441, 518, 608, 624, 637, 654, 678, 682, 697, 721, 726, 801, 817, 900, 901, 961

4 digits
1389, 2074, 3108, 3232, 7279, 7499

5 digits
~~19335~~, 20144, 22427, 42330, 63120, 65141, 72491

6 digits
427276, 469326

7 digits
1031708, 1959746

★★

2 digits
24, 41, 59, 68

3 digits
107, 121, 142, 167, 170, ~~225~~, 250, 290, 298, 456, 474, 790, 822, 892, 901, 942

4 digits
1339, 1376, 1621, 2411, 4230, 4372, 5816, 5848, 6302, 6955, 7172, 8275, 8382, 8952

5 digits
38292, 44454, 65628, 73575, 90129, 94739

6 digits
261330, 291167, 488620, 900832

7 digits
1196941, 1289442, 2111471, 2245214, 2439241, 2594720, 3915166, 4026961, 5117104, 6859472, 7062185, 9014205, 9105551

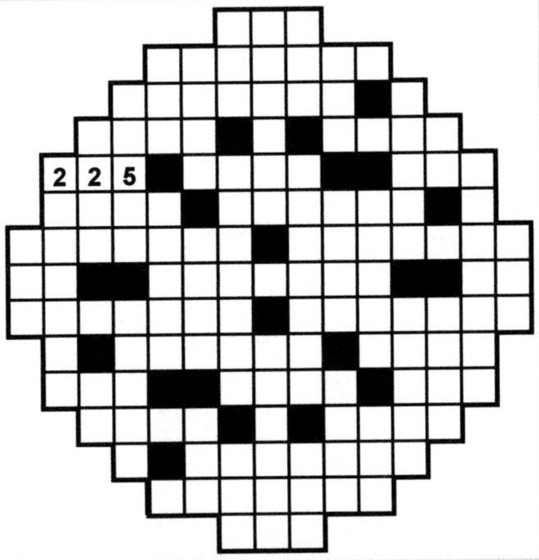

Turn to page 196 for the solutions

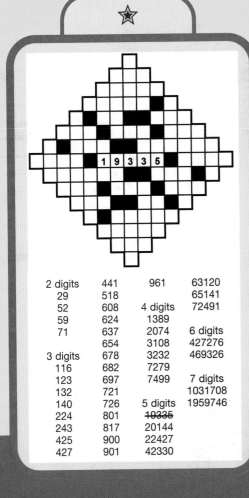

NUMBER CROSS

Can you fit all of the listed numbers into the grid? We have given you a head start in some.

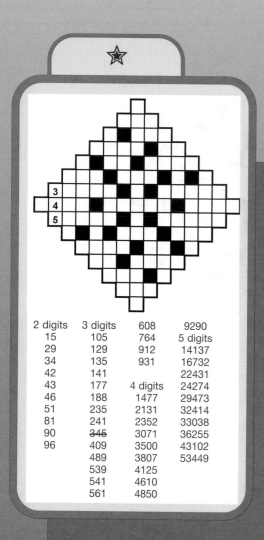

★

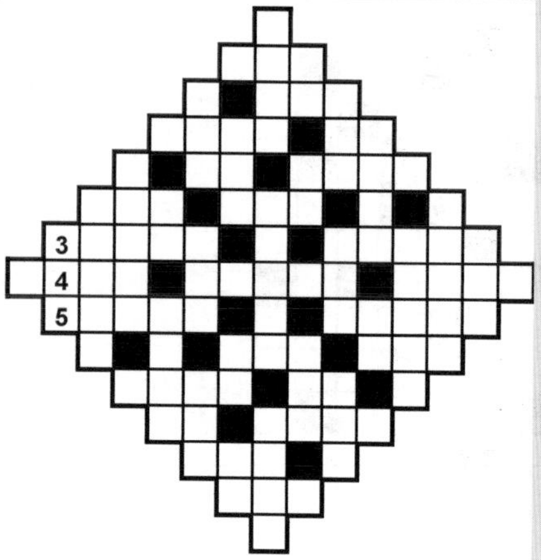

2 digits
15
29
34
42
43
46
51
81
90
96

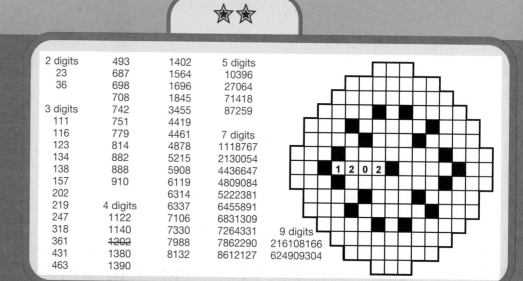

3 digits
105
129
135
141
177
188
235
241
~~345~~
409
489
539
541
561
608
764
912
931

4 digits
1477
2131
2352
3071
3500
3807
4125
4610
4850
9290

5 digits
14137
16732
22431
24274
29473
32414
33038
36255
43102
53449

★★

2 digits
23
36

3 digits
111
116
123
134
138
157
202
219
247
318
361
431
463
493
687
698
708
742
751
779
814
882
888
910

4 digits
1122
1140
~~1202~~
1380
1390
1402
1564
1696
1845
3455
4419
4461
4878
5215
5908
6119
6314
6337
7106
7330
7988
8132

5 digits
10396
27064
71418
87259

7 digits
1118767
2130054
4436647
4809084
5222381
6455891
6831309
7264331
7862290
8612127

9 digits
216108166
624909304

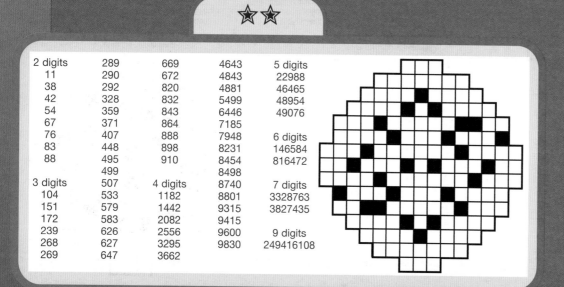

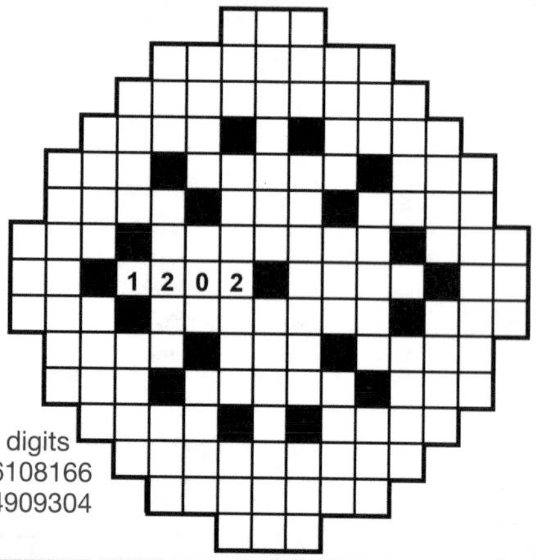

★★

2 digits
11
38
42
54
67
76
83
88

3 digits
104
151
172
239
268
269
289
290
292
328
359
371
407
448
495
499
507
533
579
583
626
627
647
669
672
820
832
843
864
888
898
910

4 digits
1182
1442
2082
2556
3295
3662
4643
4843
4881
5499
6446
7185
7948
8231
8454
8498
8740
8801
9315
9415
9600
9830

5 digits
22988
46465
48954
49076

6 digits
146584
816472

7 digits
3328763
3827435

9 digits
249416108

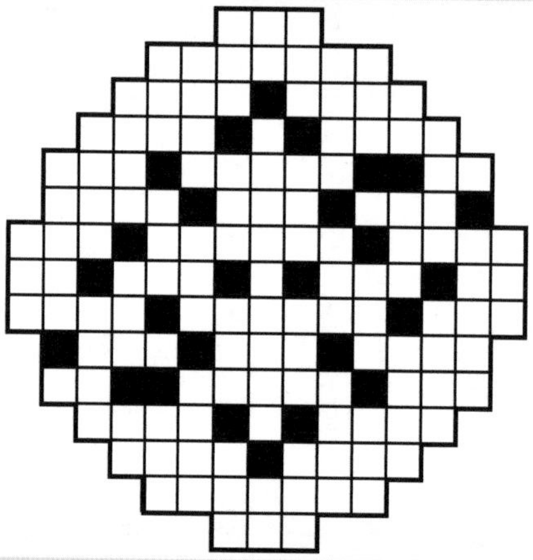

★

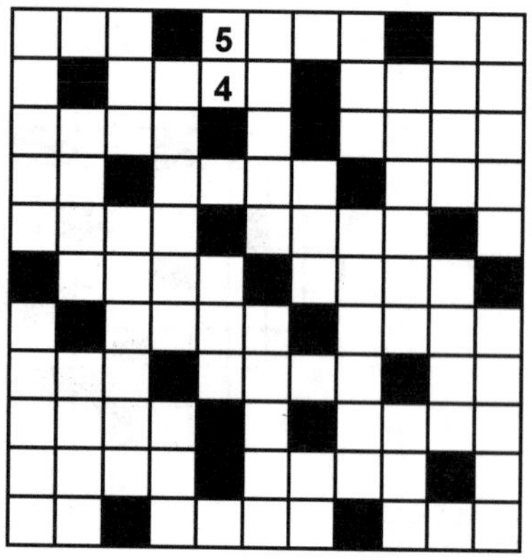

2 digits
18
29
47
~~54~~
61
75

3 digits
107
208
411
502
623
787
830
836
861
994

4 digits
1069
1256
1320
2158
2217
2676
2973
3037
3567
3792
4114
4177
4744
5909
6263
8013
8196
8744
9015
9150
9474
9694

5 digits
19968
30095
75371
78914
94252
94708

6 digits
173965
618795
741640
978612

 Turn to page 196 for the solutions

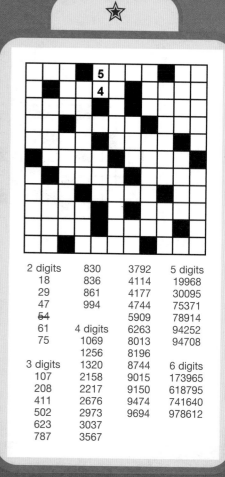

NUMBER CROSS

2 digits
20
29
34
38
39
49
52
54
91
92

3 digits
189
192
197
202
220
256
310
420
456
515
518
601
607
641
654
667
688
696
720
740
797
804
900
910
962

4 digits
~~1261~~
1267
1556
2028
2126
2173
2233
2371
3572
4603
4810
5290
5666
6253
6970
7645
7752
7920
8299
8422
8865
9414
9521
9601

5 digits
13724
15993
17105
19393
26780
35147
37072
47643
55380
61220
61600
76655
87315
90106

6 digits
166064
221380
629163
642006
767837
814673
815602
824585
926574
976326

7 digits
2390458
5522906
6509758

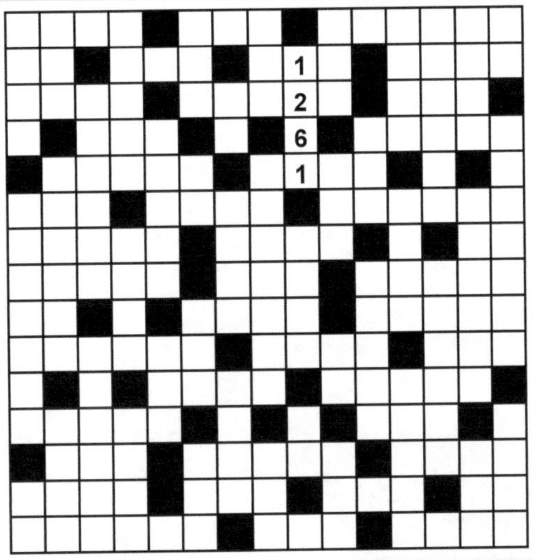

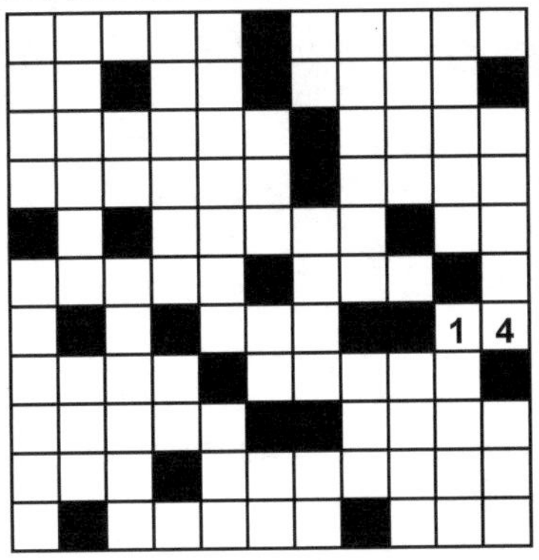

2 digits
~~14~~
26
30
34
39
51
63
73
78
80

3 digits
118
230
284
306
440
519
544
643
691

4 digits
1208
2400
2777
4365
4687
6713
8142
8484
9382

5 digits
10608
26628
26984
29850
40690
48044
52901
53808
79235
99548

6 digits
518285
684529
746193
753710
831724
934711
978184

7 digits
1353804
4991682

2 digits
15
25
30
58

3 digits
142
180
182
722
813
817

4 digits
1009
1203
1606
1735
1901
2325
2379
2420
2752
2839
2928
3876
4232
4753
4902
5184
5194
6061
6083
6309
7021
8109
8392
8435
8520
8720
8755
8990
9091
9230
9350
9501

5 digits
47488
50955

7 digits
2354735
4949145
6725711

2 digits
12
28
30
36
37
40
52
55
59
62
70
71
76
83
86
87
88
95
96
98

3 digits
214
300
345
409
428
494
550
560
566
608
~~631~~
678
691
740
922

4 digits
1100
1355
2037
2310
2970
3000
3210
3904
4047
4212
4512
4929
5325
5489
5949
6262
6359
6605
6870
7922
8231
8855
8880

5 digits
13568
19100
19222
21486
29133
32164
33900
34000
34535
35261
35922
42119
42890
51245
56459
58880
74941
93610

6 digits
103481
132107
250203
298304
421965
513349
752068
892294

7 digits
1500030
4328428

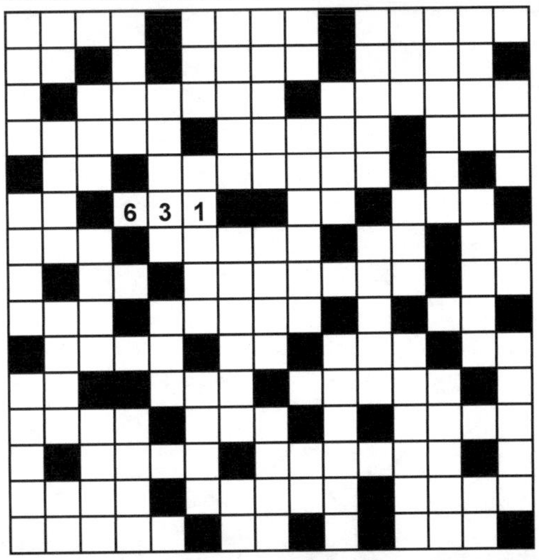

Turn to page 196 for the solutions

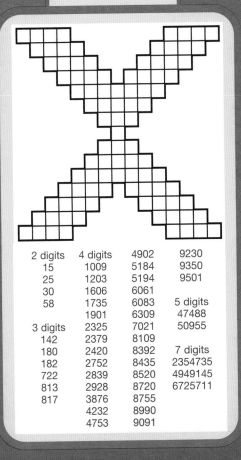

PYRAMIDS

The foundations of this puzzle have been laid down for you. Each brick must contain a number that is the sum total of the two numbers below it. Can you build on the clues to fill in the missing numbers?

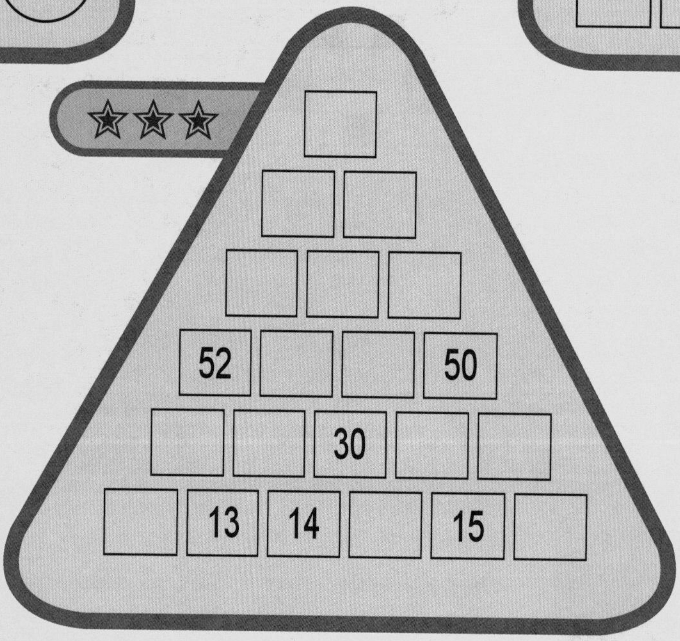

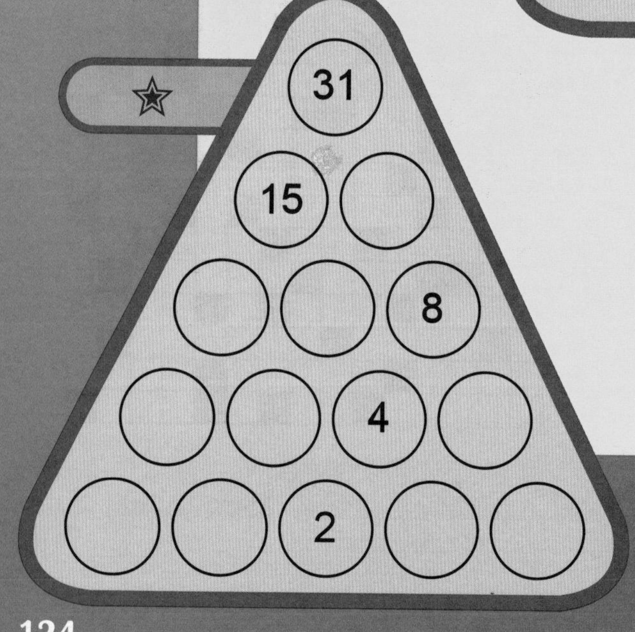

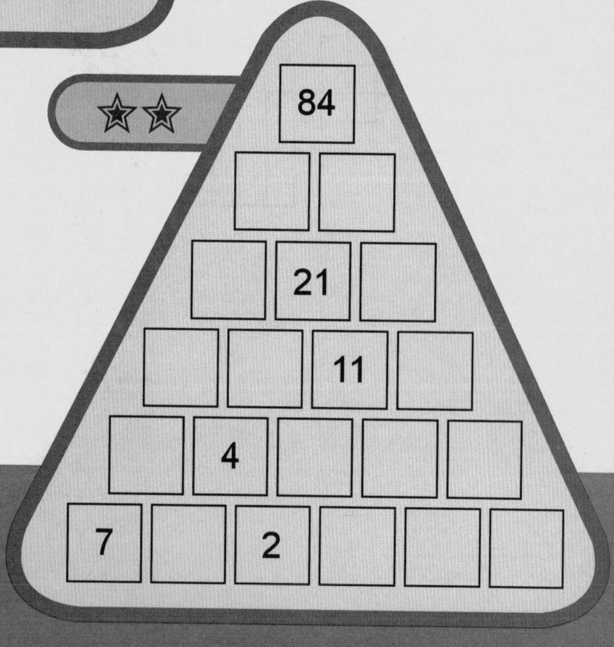

 Turn to page 196 for the solutions

PYRAMIDS

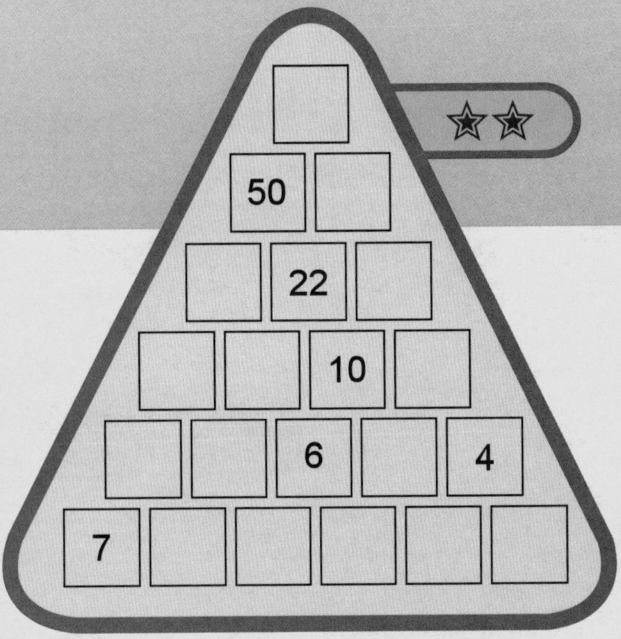

50
22
10
6 4
7

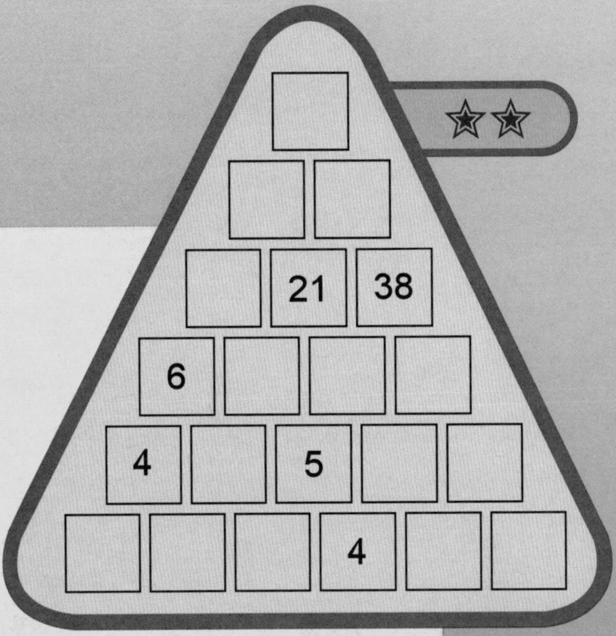

21 38
6
4 5
4

10 17
4
3 3

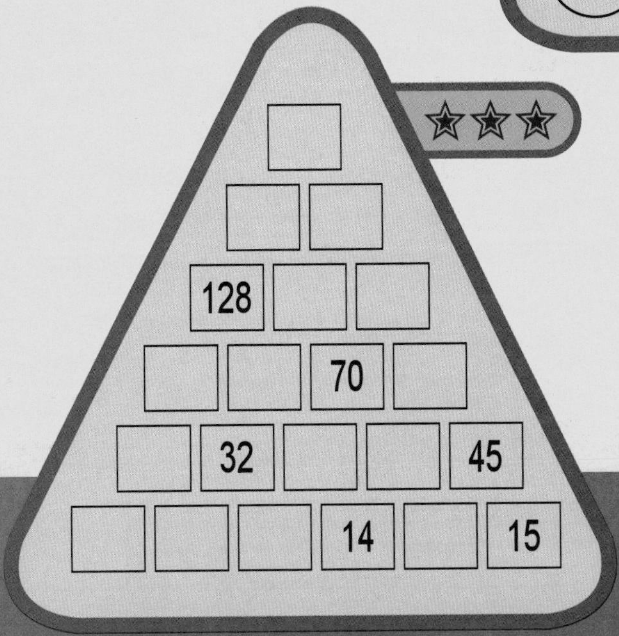

128
70
32 45
14 15

205
116
59
19
8 19

PYRAMIDS

The foundations of this puzzle have been laid down for you. Each brick must contain a number that is the sum total of the two numbers below it. Can you build on the clues to fill in the missing numbers?

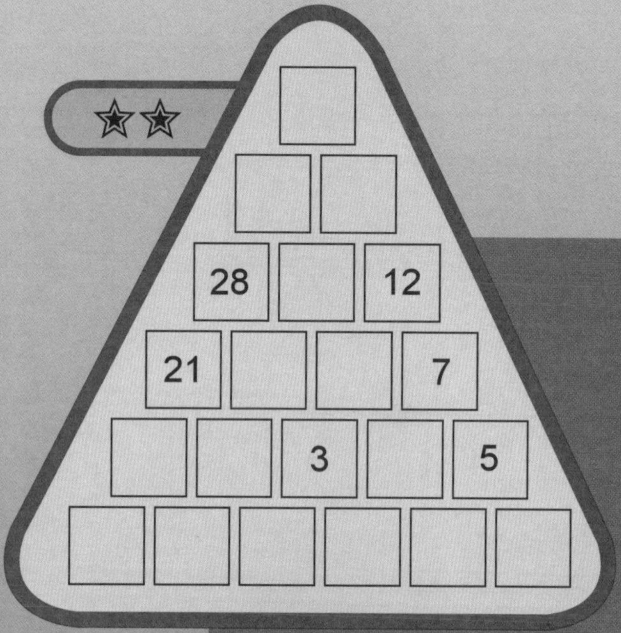

 Turn to page 196 for the solutions

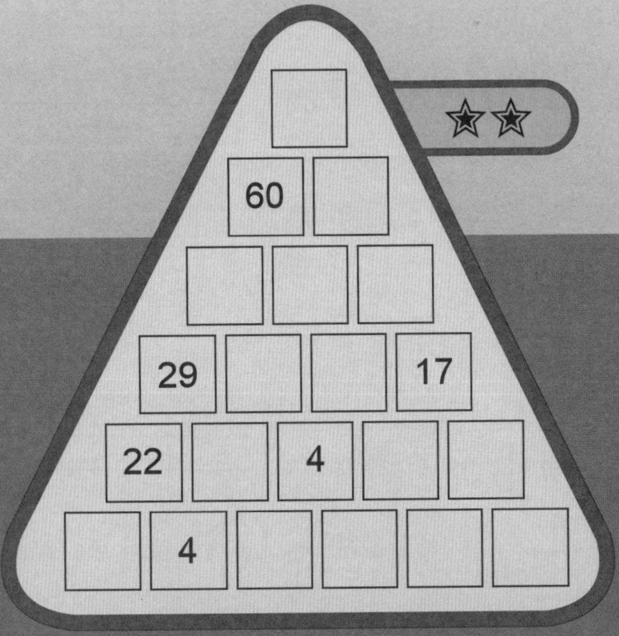

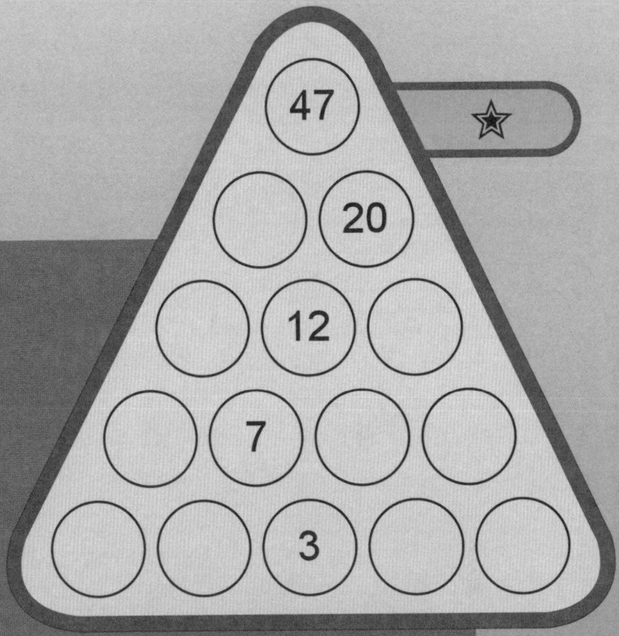

Turn to page 196 for the solutions

PYRAMIDS

The foundations of this puzzle have been laid down for you. Each brick must contain a number that is the sum total of the two numbers below it. Can you build on the clues to fill in the missing numbers?

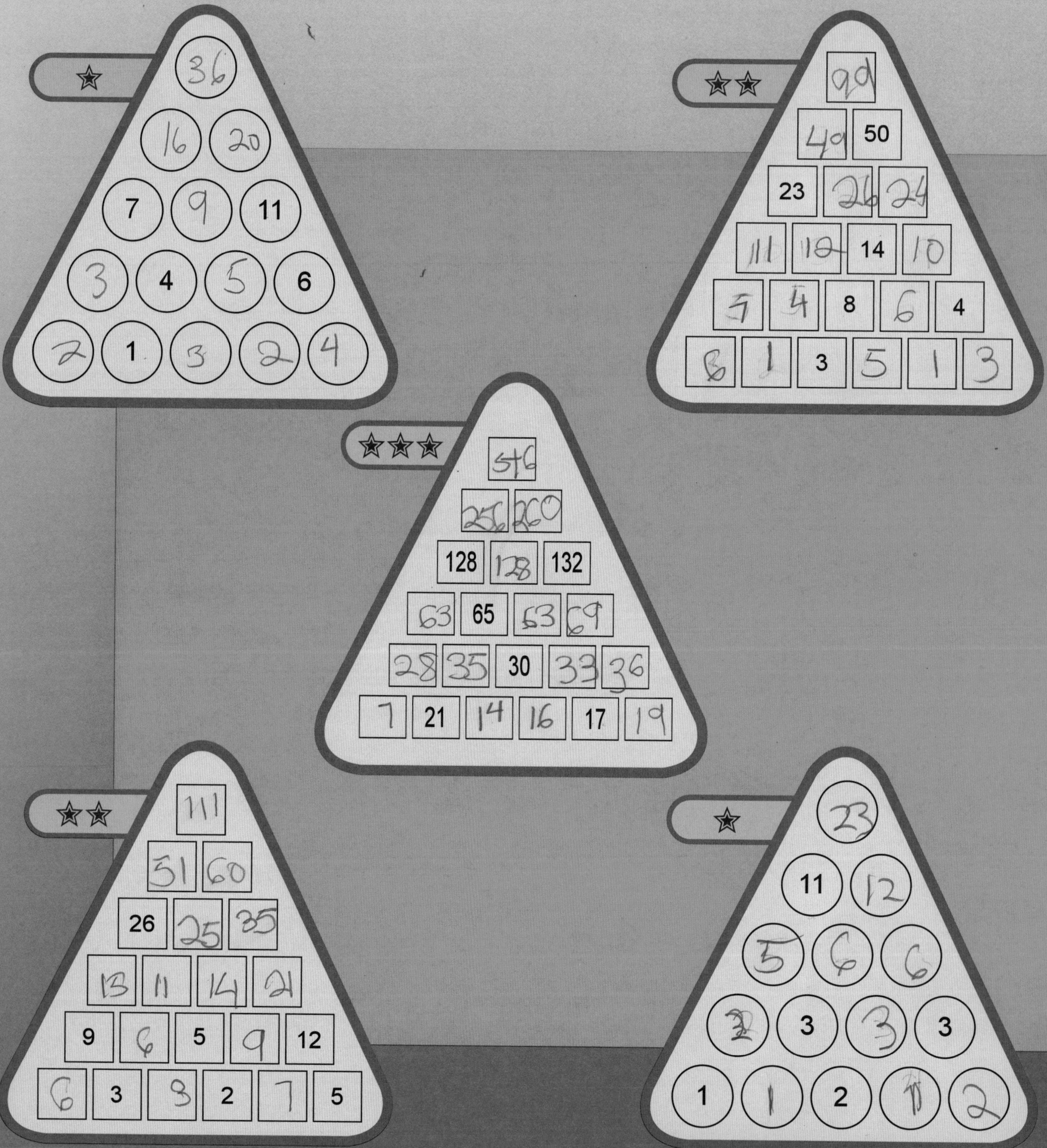

 Turn to page 196 for the solutions

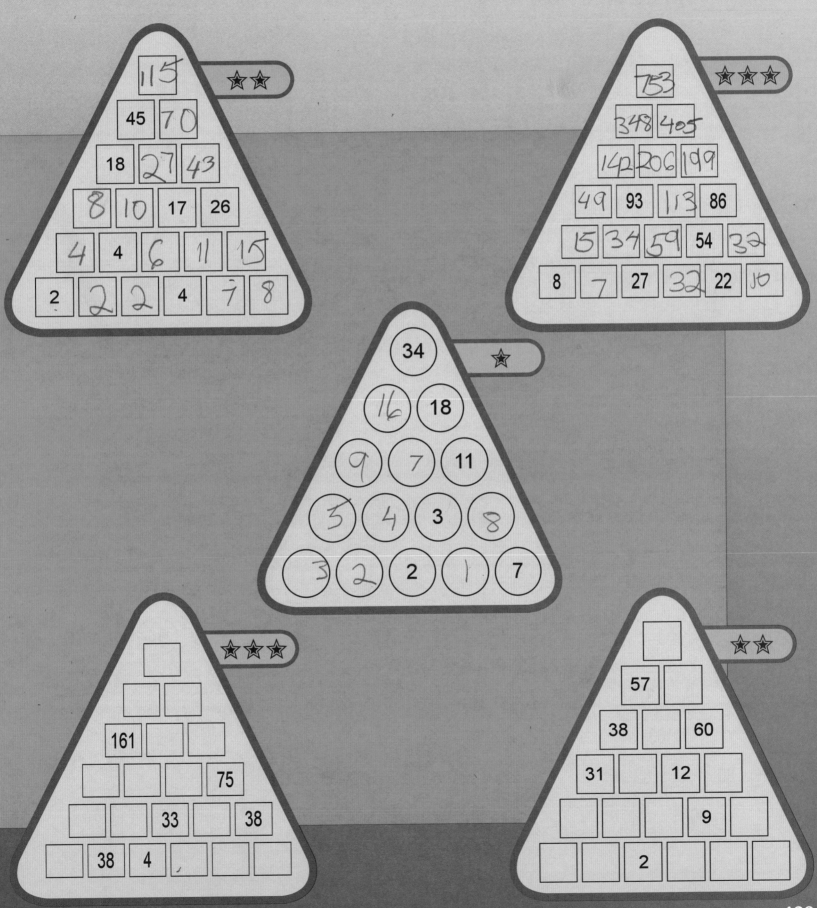

★★

115					
45	70				
18	27	43			
8	10	17	26		
4	4	6	11	15	
2	2	2	4	7	8

★★★

753					
348	405				
142	206	199			
49	93	113	86		
15	34	59	54	32	
8	7	27	32	22	10

★

34				
16	18			
9	7	11		
5	4	3	8	
3	2	2	1	7

★★★

161					
			75		
		33		38	
	38	4			

★★

57					
38		60			
31		12			
			9		
		2			

Turn to page 196 for the solutions

PYRAMIDS

The foundations of this puzzle have been laid down for you. Each brick must contain a number that is the sum total of the two numbers below it. Can you build on the clues to fill in the missing numbers?

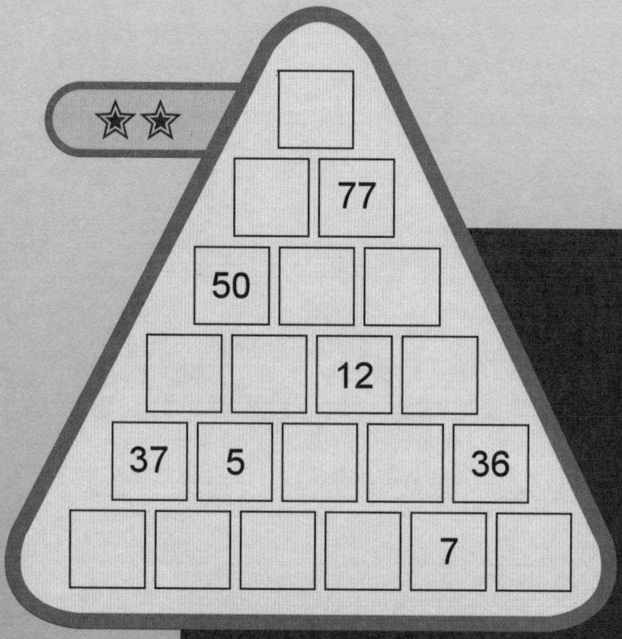

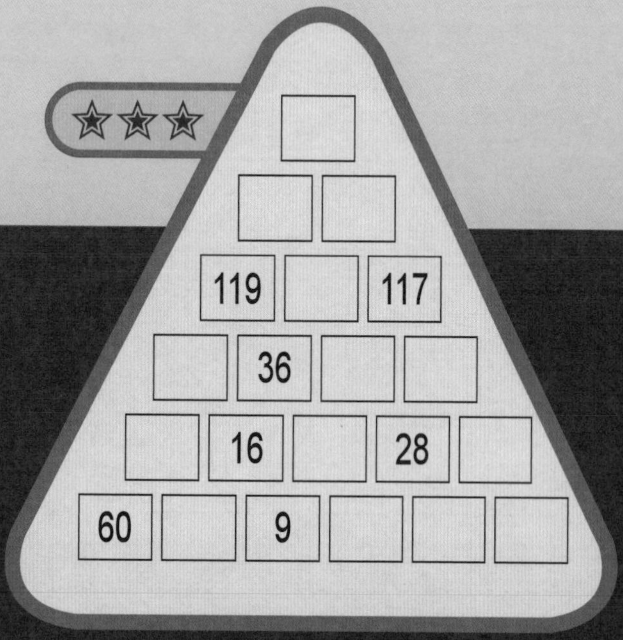

 Turn to page 196 for the solutions

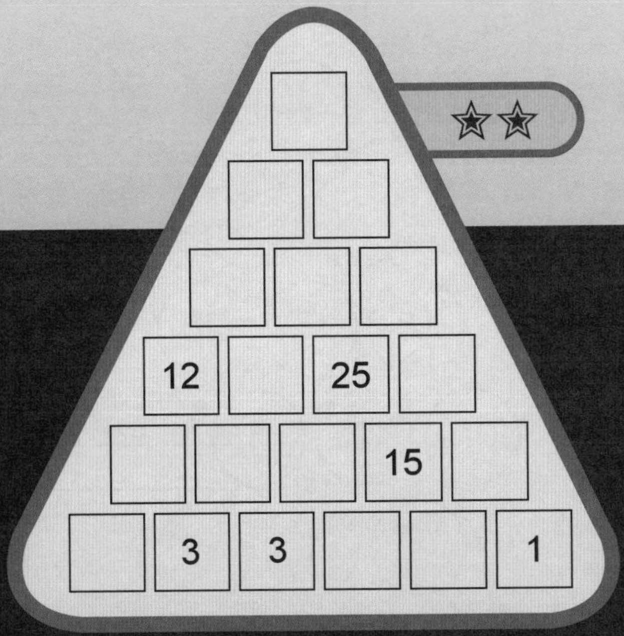
12 25
15
3 3 1

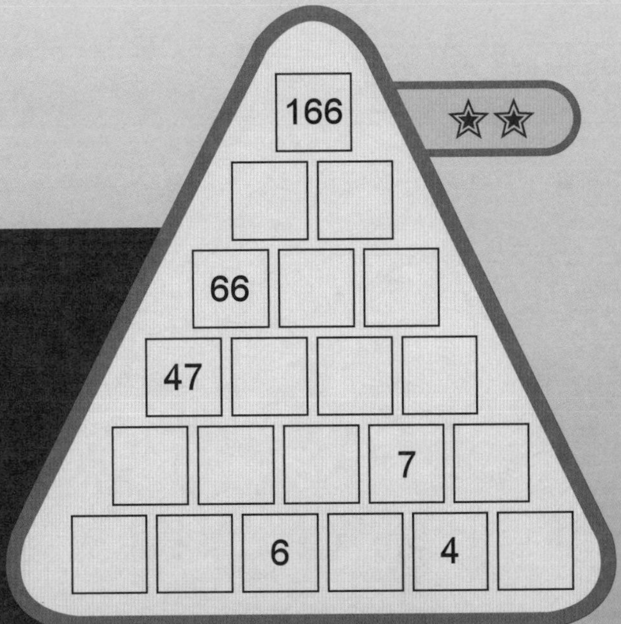
166
66
47
7
6 4

164
76
29 47
13 25 28

171
78 89
51 47
17 19

30
18 7
4
2

PYRAMIDS

The foundations of this puzzle have been laid down for you. Each brick must contain a number that is the sum total of the two numbers below it. Can you build on the clues to fill in the missing numbers?

 Turn to page 196 for the solutions

PYRAMIDS

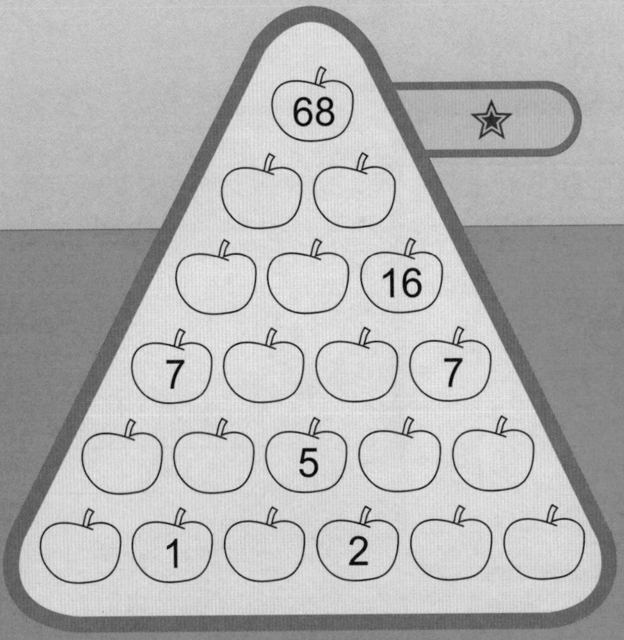

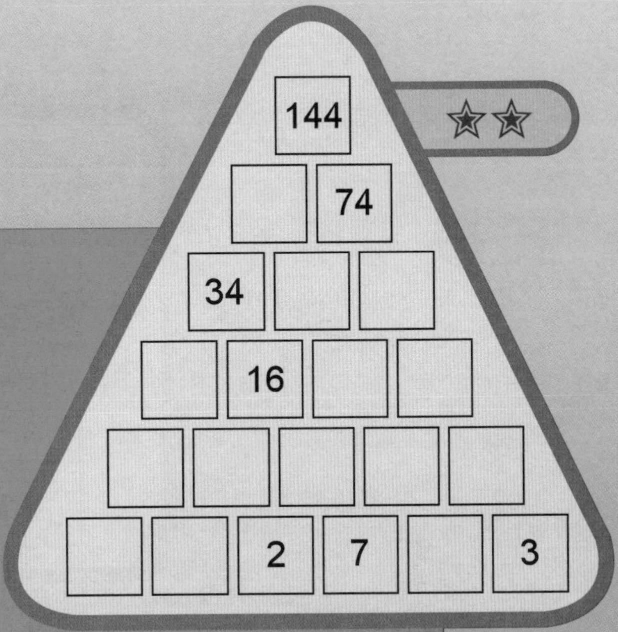

Turn to page 196 for the solutions

HIDDEN ANIMALS

Can you find the different animals hiding in these grids? Spell out the animals by shading the numbers in. Each puzzle has a different instruction. Follow each instruction carefully.

★

Shade in the numbers divisible by 5

10	15	20	16	7	16	6	5	15	5	12
5	13	5	4	12	8	14	10	8	25	4
25	6	25	9	6	17	7	20	5	10	22
10	15	10	8	11	13	19	15	21	9	7
20	8	14	10	7	5	14	10	8	13	23
5	9	4	15	16	25	18	5	17	4	18
10	6	11	5	20	10	7	12	6	8	11

★★

Shade in the numbers that appear 3 times

1	11	6	4	18	9	18	2	14	1	16
14	8	17	2	21	7	10	7	4	17	3
5	10	19	13	21	5	18	12	8	5	7
3	12	9	3	8	12	20	11	21	16	13
12	4	14	15	7	2	8	16	12	19	2
9	6	11	13	20	15	7	17	19	10	15
7	2	15	8	4	13	3	6	8	1	4

★★★

Shade in the numbers whose digits equal 11

29	36	41	58	46	35	53	64	24	68	45
20	48	51	22	31	60	62	42	66	34	69
92	57	38	59	40	43	47	38	49	54	25
38	37	47	32	55	23	65	52	29	71	74
21	50	65	29	38	48	92	56	73	83	91
28	39	83	33	65	61	83	76	38	81	92
30	44	92	56	29	27	74	29	76	26	82

★

Shade in the numbers divisible by 6

27	89	64	130	46	21	119	15	149	72	75	11
10	115	28	16	98	8	26	58	12	102	36	23
78	138	48	83	40	125	32	92	135	42	112	7
108	121	156	106	61	14	142	19	100	90	20	88
6	150	30	70	18	126	54	118	74	66	158	56
60	140	120	67	84	155	114	52	29	86	25	103
132	9	96	152	144	110	24	160	5	128	13	79
22	71	95	17	134	145	35	81	94	68	161	41

★★

Shade in the numbers divisible by 7

21	20	29	42	40	28	13	46	27	22	50
14	6	7	24	43	14	33	6	33	21	25
35	56	41	15	32	49	46	22	48	56	53
28	39	49	31	26	35	20	45	30	28	6
7	23	32	21	37	13	47	7	63	84	85
13	27	18	38	22	34	29	77	57	14	31
25	18	30	6	26	24	15	42	56	63	23

 Turn to page 196 for the solutions

HIDDEN ANIMALS

★★★

Shade in the numbers divisible by 13

74	78	222	39	105	43	25	76	49	120	29
33	86	143	59	37	75	68	104	89	91	99
53	87	52	73	24	56	90	44	117	100	54
169	40	51	60	50	79	27	26	58	130	114
182	101	12	69	93	38	98	95	46	116	67
13	30	55	80	52	78	39	34	81	28	111
156	65	83	36	117	103	65	48	113	66	45

★

Shade in the numbers divisible by 5

21	88	96	35	107	19	41	111	8	44	79	28
67	9	61	60	36	140	110	70	73	63	14	97
33	46	104	105	84	20	109	45	114	5	85	155
69	15	150	40	11	65	90	115	22	160	98	100
27	95	86	135	52	93	32	49	119	125	50	145
71	120	55	10	76	4	101	42	13	56	127	75
3	48	17	89	31	58	7	62	81	83	24	25
37	59	91	26	94	39	77	18	54	30	80	130

★★

Shade in the numbers that appear more than 5 times

5	1	8	4	13	1	5	5	3	11	8
14	13	2	15	3	9	6	5	16	2	13
1	5	15	4	6	9	14	1	7	10	6
9	15	4	15	2	14	12	9	12	17	16
11	7	9	14	9	11	7	8	17	14	17
3	4	1	7	1	16	10	3	17	5	12
11	10	14	5	14	6	2	16	8	1	9

★★★

Shade in the numbers that have 5 letters when written

7	3	7	8	3	1	9	4	7	3	5
8	5	8	15	7	14	5	14	8	4	1
2	9	11	4	6	2	9	1	7	3	13
11	5	3	15	3	10	8	10	7	9	2
4	1	8	7	8	6	3	5	8	3	14
10	6	16	11	2	17	7	10	4	12	6
2	16	9	1	4	11	8	2	9	1	4

★

Shade in the numbers with 2 digits

14	17	16	7	116	8	137	9	10	6	5
15	8	5	3	7	152	7	2	14	7	8
12	123	6	9	13	4	14	8	61	128	2
17	3	9	5	14	2	31	141	12	4	6
15	36	12	134	28	11	43	9	78	27	13
9	6	192	7	164	8	2	5	39	8	81
4	8	5	186	9	108	7	143	89	11	17

Turn to page 196 for the solutions

HIDDEN ANIMALS

Can you find the different animals hiding in these grids? Spell out the animals by shading the numbers in. Each puzzle has a different instruction. Follow each instruction carefully.

★

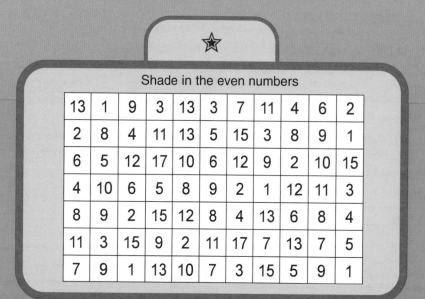

Shade in the even numbers

13	1	9	3	13	3	7	11	4	6	2
2	8	4	11	13	5	15	3	8	9	1
6	5	12	17	10	6	12	9	2	10	15
4	10	6	5	8	9	2	1	12	11	3
8	9	2	15	12	8	4	13	6	8	4
11	3	15	9	2	11	17	7	13	7	5
7	9	1	13	10	7	3	15	5	9	1

★★

Shade in the numbers written with 1 letter in Roman numerals

8	3	27	6	10	1	20	2	9	1	5
2	78	100	20	1	90	3	8	4	10	9
20	7	5	3	10	100	9	100	5	100	11
100	5	10	38	5	9	2	5	110	7	3
10	4	1	7	5	1	11	1	10	39	2
1	10	5	2	6	80	3	100	40	120	12
6	2	75	4	30	2	60	10	1	13	30

★★★

Shade in the prime numbers

2	11	17	6	7	2	13	19	11	12	10
19	6	13	15	11	8	17	12	3	20	4
3	11	5	4	9	15	4	10	6	16	18
13	20	10	16	6	8	9	5	13	2	9
7	14	11	14	3	16	20	19	18	3	20
9	4	13	2	11	12	8	17	13	7	4
6	18	8	15	4	16	10	11	20	19	18

★

Shade in the numbers whose digits add up to 5

32	14	27	59	41	23	32	48	14	5	23
41	37	24	57	5	59	32	42	50	12	50
50	5	6	9	14	50	14	29	41	5	32
41	28	7	69	72	12	39	18	37	17	32
4	7	14	23	26	47	27	7	12	44	23
38	17	5	55	57	8	11	28	23	32	5
6	30	23	49	12	44	38	3	42	43	53

★★

Shade in the numbers that don't appear in every row

2	1	4	5	1	9	6	5	7	9	3
4	3	3	1	9	5	3	6	6	8	8
6	9	2	5	1	9	5	1	5	9	5
5	9	5	7	3	8	1	8	9	7	5
9	5	1	2	5	8	9	8	4	5	1
5	1	9	8	7	2	1	3	3	1	9
9	5	1	3	1	8	5	4	9	2	1

 Turn to page 196 for the solutions

HIDDEN ANIMALS

★★★

Shade in the numbers whose digits equal 15

488	224	62	69	78	926	222	314	98	211	69
98	68	47	861	82	68	118	74	94	107	78
87	474	334	87	294	112	160	163	64	60	249
96	63	17	906	97	29	87	744	69	90	87
339	78	162	96	78	17	375	80	78	74	881
169	69	81	624	100	38	69	834	618	62	207
555	87	783	124	56	47	78	63	96	813	973

★

Shade in the numbers that appear only twice

3	16	15	2	11	6	9	12	4	15	6
10	4	9	6	1	8	2	8	20	1	12
7	17	1	18	14	19	20	4	9	11	4
13	12	6	3	6	16	9	20	12	20	6
5	8	11	18	7	14	20	19	2	13	1
2	1	2	15	9	20	15	8	5	20	1
1	4	8	12	2	6	9	17	11	10	9

★★

Shade in the numbers that begin with the letter 'S'

7	2	6	31	47	2	6	17	92	1	48
6	17	63	5	1	26	16	81	2	4	11
16	13	7	11	89	52	79	46	6	17	80
1	2	12	72	66	7	33	3	60	28	1
4	94	56	16	3	75	4	11	73	7	18
3	43	14	6	68	7	95	36	16	21	4
1	83	2	17	12	16	1	88	6	17	86

★★★

Shade in the numbers that appear in only 3 columns

8	19	8	4	19	6	10	14	13	4	19
9	13	12	11	14	12	7	10	8	15	16
5	7	18	11	18	5	4	14	18	7	9
5	18	6	5	12	15	8	10	5	11	15
9	12	8	12	11	6	7	12	12	7	6
5	4	12	12	9	12	7	4	18	14	18
19	17	15	11	10	6	10	4	12	7	6

★

Shade in the numbers divisible by 9

117	18	171	181	40	179	113	61	134	25	173	70
72	80	158	22	185	63	19	7	87	148	20	90
153	189	36	100	128	16	126	183	99	161	27	12
106	25	142	54	180	108	17	45	21	135	26	35
64	11	132	144	15	198	97	56	29	104	127	4
175	95	177	81	162	9	152	5	91	155	20	150
32	14	85	159	111	187	15	130	10	78	22	93
140	75	13	52	28	102	24	68	145	23	115	30

Turn to page 196 for the solutions

HIDDEN ANIMALS

Can you find the different animals hiding in these grids? Spell out the animals by shading the numbers in. Each puzzle has a different instruction. Follow each instruction carefully.

★★

Shade in the numbers that look the same upside down

8	11	1	66	84	7	14	99	93	103	87
111	186	69	199	181	113	181	102	91	7	13
101	181	8	114	11	9	101	36	8	89	11
69	105	11	196	69	18	8	98	88	1	66
164	7	197	97	1	181	88	48	11	69	87
65	178	115	68	67	71	86	54	8	86	1
108	99	66	77	86	112	45	67	69	72	66

★★

Shade in the even numbers divisible by 3

6	25	14	36	73	12	84	48	32	51	9
24	1	26	47	2	42	74	96	50	4	59
12	30	71	72	68	54	90	18	22	99	31
7	55	13	6	35	58	17	49	61	16	64
8	37	46	24	52	3	62	76	60	72	6
38	5	28	20	43	57	39	10	18	81	102
15	53	29	44	11	67	21	56	78	87	66

★

Shade in the numbers divisible by 3

2	8	4	13	6	5	1	10	1	16	5
3	18	12	16	12	4	19	7	14	2	10
18	11	1	17	3	15	19	6	13	8	9
9	6	14	5	11	14	8	18	19	3	13
15	7	2	13	2	4	5	9	12	11	4
3	12	9	13	8	16	1	15	17	18	1
4	1	10	5	11	2	10	3	7	8	6

★

Shade in the numbers with 1 digit

6	9	8	2	16	5	55	43	28	6	29
1	29	37	8	42	49	8	18	7	17	62
4	14	26	3	23	97	48	1	78	52	57
3	24	13	6	37	87	4	38	7	76	15
5	28	17	4	33	2	47	17	91	2	31
9	16	72	4	66	41	66	24	77	67	88
6	7	9	2	29	58	56	71	43	16	67

★★

Shade in the numbers that are divisible by 8

16	40	8	39	66	13	44	19	71	18	38
72	30	56	14	24	29	61	32	45	48	24
8	80	24	49	72	62	16	68	12	8	14
48	6	28	27	40	88	25	36	51	56	88
32	47	96	58	64	50	32	53	41	64	46
20	23	48	7	8	42	55	96	75	40	16
31	22	16	43	35	11	34	57	15	33	79

 Turn to page 196 for the solutions

★★★

Shade in the numbers divisible by 11

10	41	54	48	14	100	20	30	21	33	88
21	16	28	11	121	44	74	43	96	132	98
58	56	63	99	46	66	23	10	83	11	110
20	42	29	33	110	22	45	78	31	55	23
39	14	30	21	70	25	34	77	90	121	85
22	69	88	72	132	12	82	132	18	89	38
44	99	11	77	33	32	23	22	79	36	17

★★

Shade in the numbers that go into 36 exactly

2	12	4	18	6	7	3	14	5	20	8
6	10	6	13	3	17	4	11	13	2	12
3	16	9	16	18	10	9	14	19	9	8
10	5	11	8	7	15	18	12	17	6	18
8	13	3	18	2	8	19	14	20	4	19
14	11	12	15	6	10	11	13	10	18	9
7	15	4	9	4	13	5	17	16	7	11

★★

Shade in the numbers that appear less than 6 times

5	14	9	15	7	8	17	13	18	8	10
10	15	5	12	9	11	18	6	9	5	16
7	11	15	16	17	8	14	16	19	12	11
12	16	12	13	5	13	16	6	14	16	17
8	13	20	6	6	10	15	12	20	6	13
20	6	16	20	11	7	13	14	8	20	11
6	11	8	20	6	10	11	7	20	13	8

★★★

Shade in the numbers that have 3 letters when written

2	3	9	5	8	4	2	3	7	4	5
10	7	4	7	3	7	6	10	5	8	3
1	5	6	11	13	4	1	4	9	2	10
6	10	9	8	6	12	2	10	3	6	7
2	8	1	12	4	7	4	8	5	10	1
7	3	9	7	10	3	7	11	9	2	3
4	11	5	4	1	8	5	3	7	6	10

★

Shade in the numbers 1 to 5

1	5	3	7	3	4	1	7	9	7	6
4	6	2	8	2	8	5	9	6	8	7
2	1	4	6	4	5	3	6	9	6	9
5	3	9	7	3	8	2	8	3	5	2
1	5	2	6	8	6	9	7	9	1	9
4	7	4	8	9	7	8	9	6	4	7
3	1	5	6	7	9	6	9	7	2	8

Turn to page 196 for the solutions

HIDDEN ANIMALS

Can you find the different animals hiding in these grids? Spell out the animals by shading the numbers in. Each puzzle has a different instruction. Follow each instruction carefully.

★★

Shade in the numbers that only appear once

35	4	47	35	3	21	38	2	39	7	25
27	20	1	43	31	19	18	19	33	4	6
41	12	40	22	9	46	17	49	23	48	52
11	37	16	2	40	8	40	26	44	12	50
10	45	30	26	14	36	47	8	51	24	42
34	15	28	10	45	13	45	35	50	29	52
14	47	6	29	22	32	5	12	49	4	43

★

Shade in the numbers that go into 12

10	5	9	8	10	7	8	9	11	5	11
2	6	4	13	7	4	11	12	2	6	7
12	9	12	7	10	7	5	6	7	4	8
4	3	4	9	7	12	9	4	3	12	5
6	7	5	10	13	4	8	7	10	2	11
2	8	11	5	9	2	11	13	5	6	9
5	10	7	10	7	6	9	2	6	4	7

★★★

Shade in the prime numbers

72	116	131	84	104	93	107	83	108	74	96
115	99	71	118	76	98	97	82	133	90	110
85	117	101	89	109	121	89	137	75	138	81
105	92	103	119	79	86	113	130	149	79	103
101	89	102	87	122	91	73	139	97	112	127
73	95	120	77	114	72	129	88	101	157	71
97	78	106	123	94	126	80	100	83	111	113

★★★

Shade in the prime numbers

21	27	48	37	25	46	33	26	36	22	49
32	25	22	23	27	30	21	38	23	45	33
47	41	34	43	53	59	26	32	59	44	21
59	24	28	29	42	41	39	24	41	25	28
23	39	21	39	33	25	22	30	29	43	47
29	27	30	24	41	40	59	26	53	35	41
43	53	32	22	31	53	23	21	43	59	31

★★

Shade in the numbers divisible by 9

9	27	72	41	20	27	45	9	34	7	53
22	18	25	7	29	63	70	81	28	42	20
8	45	37	22	32	81	40	18	17	57	35
17	31	54	38	9	50	21	25	90	99	36
21	16	63	32	72	16	49	68	27	59	63
30	32	18	99	36	51	20	33	72	81	9
20	28	35	8	47	23	39	92	54	43	99

 Turn to page 196 for the solutions

HIDDEN ANIMALS

★

Shade in the odd numbers

5	1	9	8	2	8	6	3	9	5	2
3	8	4	6	10	4	2	10	1	4	6
7	10	6	9	7	3	10	8	7	6	2
1	2	10	1	8	7	8	2	5	10	8
8	10	4	7	5	9	4	6	8	2	6
2	6	2	3	6	5	2	10	4	10	4
4	8	6	7	4	3	6	8	2	8	2

★

Shade in the odd numbers

35	42	26	15	75	31	14	12	68	77	17	39
21	6	72	47	62	8	70	34	22	9	56	18
55	50	28	57	7	80	22	8	52	41	48	64
29	65	37	25	36	44	71	23	61	3	16	34
73	54	5	43	69	49	1	16	51	40	2	24
13	45	63	76	24	30	33	59	19	66	28	12
32	40	10	4	46	36	53	42	67	38	60	30
10	74	26	20	20	58	11	32	27	46	14	18

★★

Shade in the numbers that only appear twice

7	4	11	10	20	27	2	18	3	12	3
10	16	1	24	14	7	21	12	23	1	16
15	3	19	22	5	27	8	13	8	21	9
6	18	6	11	16	14	18	13	11	17	21
1	16	24	5	26	25	2	9	28	25	21
25	2	4	19	22	11	23	20	23	29	8
14	6	26	28	15	3	8	17	19	12	29

★★★

Shade in the numbers whose digits equal 13

67	49	58	88	54	99	49	94	76	98	47
18	85	47	57	21	78	58	81	94	18	55
39	94	98	76	85	9	85	93	67	83	74
54	55	38	49	29	65	94	67	76	29	97
29	65	81	67	58	93	76	96	49	86	49
74	92	54	85	23	74	87	92	87	96	85
18	38	75	67	94	92	84	83	69	39	67

★★★

Shade in the numbers divisible by 15

90	20	150	115	60	5	140	25	40	10	65
30	45	120	15	135	55	130	35	40	80	50
50	80	25	125	65	45	105	85	30	105	60
35	10	60	135	125	75	5	55	75	25	15
40	95	105	40	160	30	120	40	90	155	120
55	70	15	110	20	135	50	145	45	160	150
20	100	35	65	50	150	75	70	100	5	95

Turn to page 196 for the solutions

HIDDEN ANIMALS

Can you find the different animals hiding in these grids? Spell out the animals by shading the numbers in. Each puzzle has a different instruction. Follow each instruction carefully.

★★★

Shade in the numbers that have 6 letters when written

10	14	22	15	37	13	36	33	9	89	14
11	12	13	8	21	38	12	15	19	30	96
20	16	11	80	12	13	17	34	10	11	18
11	23	20	18	11	27	80	14	76	12	8
21	15	12	13	20	10	20	8	78	12	91
17	22	20	12	11	17	12	17	13	11	10
14	19	11	17	20	8	79	9	81	60	9

★★

Shade in the numbers that appear only once

6	26	13	27	46	7	38	3	43	16	42
35	27	1	11	20	39	29	49	38	32	52
19	37	34	14	3	29	30	22	51	5	9
41	18	2	21	45	5	14	11	24	47	24
7	25	40	50	8	22	50	17	23	4	52
25	13	10	28	36	34	1	12	43	48	47
3	20	31	18	15	9	14	44	16	33	9

★

Shade in the numbers from 6 to 10

6	2	1	3	6	4	2	5	8	1	7
3	7	13	8	12	1	4	11	6	9	12
2	11	6	5	5	3	13	1	10	3	1
5	14	10	2	10	8	7	4	7	8	5
3	1	7	14	6	4	9	2	9	13	6
4	12	8	4	9	10	8	12	3	1	5
11	2	3	5	7	2	6	1	14	2	11

★★★

Shade in the numbers divisible by 9

9	8	51	40	18	99	63	55	42	27	81
36	20	41	8	72	22	9	13	79	54	74
63	27	54	30	36	90	54	58	45	18	7
81	10	9	31	27	59	63	7	35	71	44
18	45	90	7	53	19	37	66	24	36	108
60	11	21	38	8	12	49	14	67	72	86
62	7	50	17	32	28	16	64	45	9	89

★★

Shade in the numbers that begin with the letter 'F'

14	39	10	5	78	52	74	27	34	13	5
43	9	54	65	18	28	22	6	26	82	6
4	44	60	3	29	4	67	12	64	21	14
56	23	15	71	19	47	63	7	73	84	50
15	61	35	40	30	68	8	38	3	52	7
24	11	6	31	70	4	33	41	66	15	37
3	36	20	62	8	14	15	42	5	48	25

 Turn to page 196 for the solutions

HIDDEN ANIMALS

★★★

Shade in the numbers divisible by 13

30	11	49	14	51	36	17	58	26	91	52
21	50	22	13	65	39	60	24	45	13	27
26	43	30	52	57	78	62	11	33	65	83
65	16	47	44	31	25	59	64	27	39	37
39	56	78	15	54	104	78	91	69	71	25
91	13	27	51	40	26	67	13	34	12	87
52	35	26	32	18	39	104	65	46	29	38

★

Shade in the numbers below 12

6	11	5	15	13	16	13	17	5	14	10
7	16	10	13	17	18	14	13	8	15	7
3	1	8	15	3	7	1	17	9	18	4
14	18	9	16	2	17	8	18	11	6	9
17	15	10	13	11	18	4	13	17	14	16
7	4	2	17	19	18	16	15	16	18	14
13	16	18	14	17	16	15	18	17	19	13

★★

Shade in the numbers that begin with the letter 'T'

3	12	8	10	29	12	4	7	17	3	29
10	1	5	2	16	28	11	5	1	10	9
2	20	8	26	13	3	61	6	18	2	13
6	15	7	3	15	27	7	19	11	12	53
48	4	9	43	4	7	62	12	51	17	4
7	9	1	5	1	57	5	2	8	6	49
14	6	19	11	9	6	18	21	10	17	11

★★★

Shade in the numbers that appear more than once in a row

4	9	1	10	6	16	9	4	20	26	29
11	21	19	3	8	23	11	25	13	1	6
7	14	1	23	16	6	7	20	14	7	14
19	3	5	18	5	25	10	1	5	27	18
1	8	22	21	24	3	12	6	22	24	22
6	21	2	17	17	20	16	23	2	1	28
8	1	15	10	15	3	19	12	15	13	6

★

Shade in the numbers divisible by 4

10	85	57	13	81	66	3	72	104	8	88	40
42	12	60	28	43	11	35	90	7	120	27	77
31	56	1	65	16	84	128	51	83	48	69	39
74	44	70	14	64	93	36	2	58	92	53	6
45	96	30	97	100	4	116	75	3	24	114	73
9	20	79	50	52	101	68	67	71	76	59	29
63	80	124	32	112	55	108	113	23	110	47	126
34	87	41	5	82	62	21	38	86	18	78	118

Turn to page 196 for the solutions

SUM SQUARES

Following the instructions given with each puzzle, fill in the spaces in the grid to complete the sums.

Use the numbers 1-9 to fill in the spaces in the grid and complete each sum. Each number can only be used once. The sum totals are shown below and to the right of each grid. For each equation the multiplication and division is completed before the addition and subtraction.

8	+	6	X		20
-	■	-	■	-	
	+	1	+	9	15
-	■	-	■	X	
	-		+		8
-4		2		-34	

Use the numbers 1-9 to fill in the spaces in the grid and complete each sum. Each number can only be used once. The sum totals are shown below and to the right of each grid. For each equation the multiplication and division is completed before the addition and subtraction.

	+	5	X		42
+	■	+	■	-	
	X		+		16
X	■	X	■	+	
4	-	6	+		1
38		11		4	

Use the numbers 1-9 to fill in the spaces in the grid and complete each sum. Each number can only be used once. The sum totals are shown below and to the right of each grid. For each equation the multiplication and division is completed before the addition and subtraction.

	X	5	-		26
+	■	-	■	-	
	-		-		1
+	■	+	■	-	
	+		-		11
17		10		6	

Use the numbers 1-9 to fill in the spaces in the grid and complete each sum. Each number can only be used once. The sum totals are shown below and to the right of each grid. For each equation the multiplication and division is completed before the addition and subtraction.

	+	9	+		23
+	■	+	■	-	
	-		X	5	-31
+	■	+	■	-	
	X	2	+		5
11		18		0	

Use the numbers 1-9 to fill in the spaces in the grid and complete each sum. Each number can only be used once. The sum totals are shown below and to the right of each grid. For each equation the multiplication and division is completed before the addition and subtraction.

	-		+		5
+	■	X	■	-	
	+		+		17
+	■	-	■	+	
	+	3	+		19
13		13		11	

 Turn to page 196 for the solutions

Use the numbers 1-9 to fill in the spaces in the grid and complete each sum. Each number can only be used once. The sum totals are shown below and to the right of each grid. For each equation the multiplication and division is completed before the addition and subtraction.

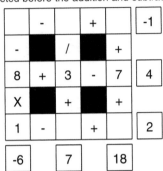

	-		+		-1
-	■	/	■	+	
8	+	3	-	7	4
X	■	+	■	+	
1	-		+		2
-6		7		18	

Use the numbers 1-9 to fill in the spaces in the grid and complete each sum. Each number can only be used once. The sum totals are shown below and to the right of each grid. For each equation the multiplication and division is completed before the addition and subtraction.

	-		-		-10
-	■	-	■	+	
	-	4	X	1	2
+	■	-	■	-	
	-	3	-		0
6		2		7	

Use the numbers 1-9 to fill in the spaces in the grid and complete each sum. Each number can only be used once. The sum totals are shown below and to the right of each grid. For each equation the multiplication and division is completed before the addition and subtraction.

	-		+		6
+	■	-	■	-	
	+		+		14
+	■	+	■	-	
4	-		-		-11
19		7		-13	

Use the numbers 1-9 to fill in the spaces in the grid and complete each sum. Each number can only be used once. The sum totals are shown below and to the right of each grid. For each equation the multiplication and division is completed before the addition and subtraction.

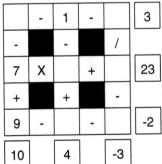

	-	1	-		3
-	■	-	■	/	
7	X		+		23
+	■	+	■	-	
9	-		-		-2
10		4		-3	

Use the numbers 1-9 to fill in the spaces in the grid and complete each sum. Each number can only be used once. The sum totals are shown below and to the right of each grid. For each equation the multiplication and division is completed before the addition and subtraction.

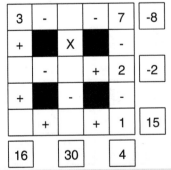

3	-		-	7	-8
+	■	X	■	-	
	-		+	2	-2
+	■	-	■	-	
	+		+	1	15
16		30		4	

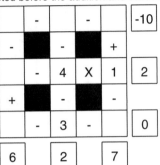

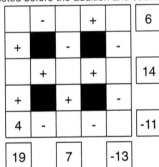

Turn to page 196 for the solutions

SUM SQUARES

Following the instructions given with each puzzle, fill in the spaces in the grid to complete the sums.

★

Use the numbers 1-9 to fill in the spaces in the grid and complete each sum. Each number can only be used once. The sum totals are shown below and to the right of each grid. For each equation the multiplication and division is completed before the addition and subtraction.

4	X	6	-		15
+	■	/	■	X	
	-		+		6
X	■	-	■	-	
	X	8	-	5	19
7		-5		58	

★★

Use the numbers 1-9 to fill in the spaces in the grid and complete each sum. Each number can only be used once. The sum totals are shown below and to the right of each grid. For each equation the multiplication and division is completed before the addition and subtraction.

	+	9	-		10
/	■	+	■	X	
	-		X		-38
+	■	+	■	+	
	+	6	-	1	12
9		20		25	

★★★

Use the numbers 1-9 to fill in the spaces in the grid and complete each sum. Each number can only be used once. The sum totals are shown below and to the right of each grid. For each equation the multiplication and division is completed before the addition and subtraction.

	-		-		-10
-	■	+	■	+	
	-		-		-5
-	■	-	■	+	
	-		X	6	-49
-6		-4		21	

★★

Use the numbers 1-9 to fill in the spaces in the grid and complete each sum. Each number can only be used once. The sum totals are shown below and to the right of each grid. For each equation the multiplication and division is completed before the addition and subtraction.

4	-	9	+		-4
-	■	X	■	X	
	-	2	+		9
-	■	+	■	-	
	-		+		12
-9		21		-1	

★★★

Use the numbers 1-9 to fill in the spaces in the grid and complete each sum. Each number can only be used once. The sum totals are shown below and to the right of each grid. For each equation the multiplication and division is completed before the addition and subtraction.

	-		-		-14
-	■	-	■	-	
	-		X		-27
-	■	-	■	-	
6	-		-		2
-9		0		0	

 Turn to page 196 for the solutions

SUM SQUARES

Use the numbers 1-9 to fill in the spaces in the grid and complete each sum. Each number can only be used once. The sum totals are shown below and to the right of each grid. For each equation the multiplication and division is completed before the addition and subtraction.

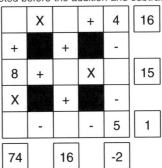

5	-		X		-7
+		/		+	
9	-	3	+		13
X		+		+	
	-		+	4	-3
14		10		13	

Use the numbers 1-9 to fill in the spaces in the grid and complete each sum. Each number can only be used once. The sum totals are shown below and to the right of each grid. For each equation the multiplication and division is completed before the addition and subtraction.

	X		+	4	16
+		+		-	
8	+		X		15
X		+		-	
	-		-	5	1
74		16		-2	

Use the numbers 1-9 to fill in the spaces in the grid and complete each sum. Each number can only be used once. The sum totals are shown below and to the right of each grid. For each equation the multiplication and division is completed before the addition and subtraction.

	+		-		3
/		+		/	
2	+		-		6
+		+		-	
	X		+		31
7		21		2	

Use the numbers 1-9 to fill in the spaces in the grid and complete each sum. Each number can only be used once. The sum totals are shown below and to the right of each grid. For each equation the multiplication and division is completed before the addition and subtraction.

	-		-		-13
-		+		/	
	-	9	-		-10
+		X		X	
2	-		+	7	4
0		51		14	

Use the numbers 1-9 to fill in the spaces in the grid and complete each sum. Each number can only be used once. The sum totals are shown below and to the right of each grid. For each equation the multiplication and division is completed before the addition and subtraction.

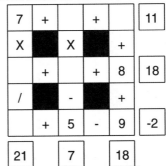

7	+		+		11
X		X		+	
	+		+	8	18
/		-		+	
	+	5	-	9	-2
21		7		18	

Turn to page 196 for the solutions

SUM SQUARES

Following the instructions given with each puzzle, fill in the spaces in the grid to complete the sums.

★

Use the numbers 1-9 to fill in the spaces in the grid and complete each sum. Each number can only be used once. The sum totals are shown below and to the right of each grid. For each equation the multiplication and division is completed before the addition and subtraction.

	+	8	X		37
+	■	X	■	+	
1	-	6	X	9	-53
+	■	/	■	-	
	-		-		-6
9		24		6	

★★

Use the numbers 1-9 to fill in the spaces in the grid and complete each sum. Each number can only be used once. The sum totals are shown below and to the right of each grid. For each equation the multiplication and division is completed before the addition and subtraction.

2	X		-	6	8
+	■	-	■	+	
3	+		X		75
X	■	-	■	-	
	-		-		-2
14		-7		13	

★★★

Use the numbers 1-9 to fill in the spaces in the grid and complete each sum. Each number can only be used once. The sum totals are shown below and to the right of each grid. For each equation the multiplication and division is completed before the addition and subtraction.

	+		+		21
+	■	+	■	+	
	-		+		5
-	■	-	■	+	
	-	4	-		-3
6		7		18	

★★

Use the numbers 1-9 to fill in the spaces in the grid and complete each sum. Each number can only be used once. The sum totals are shown below and to the right of each grid. For each equation the multiplication and division is completed before the addition and subtraction.

	-		-		-8
+	■	+	■	-	
	X		-		-1
+	■	+	■	X	
	+		-	7	5
12		18		-40	

★★★

Use the numbers 1-9 to fill in the spaces in the grid and complete each sum. Each number can only be used once. The sum totals are shown below and to the right of each grid. For each equation the multiplication and division is completed before the addition and subtraction.

	-		-		-11
X	■	X	■	-	
	-		+		6
-	■	+	■	+	
	X	1	-		3
37		37		7	

 Turn to page 196 for the solutions

SUM SQUARES

Use the numbers 1-9 to fill in the spaces in the grid and complete each sum. Each number can only be used once. The sum totals are shown below and to the right of each grid. For each equation the multiplication and division is completed before the addition and subtraction.

5	+	1	X		13
X	■	+	■	/	
	+		+	2	11
+	■	-	■	+	
7	X		-		19
22		3		13	

Use the numbers 1-9 to fill in the spaces in the grid and complete each sum. Each number can only be used once. The sum totals are shown below and to the right of each grid. For each equation the multiplication and division is completed before the addition and subtraction.

3	X		+		11
+	■	-	■	+	
6	X	7	+		47
/	■	-	■	+	
	X		-		14
6		-15		17	

Use the numbers 1-9 to fill in the spaces in the grid and complete each sum. Each number can only be used once. The sum totals are shown below and to the right of each grid. For each equation the multiplication and division is completed before the addition and subtraction.

	-		+	1	5
X	■	X	■	+	
	+		X		35
-	■	+	■	+	
	-		X		-13
41		23		8	

Use the numbers 1-9 to fill in the spaces in the grid and complete each sum. Each number can only be used once. The sum totals are shown below and to the right of each grid. For each equation the multiplication and division is completed before the addition and subtraction.

2	+	1	X		6
-	■	X	■	-	
	+		+	3	16
X	■	+	■	-	
	+		+		22
-28		17		-6	

Fill in the missing squares in the grid to complete the sums. Use numbers from 1-9 and the symbols +, -, x, /.

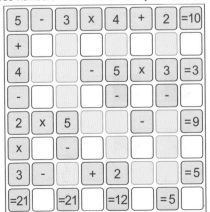

5	-	3	x	4	+	2	=10
+							
4			-	5	x	3	=3
-				-		-	
2	x	5			-		=9
x		-					
3	-		+	2			=5
=21		=21		=12		=5	

Turn to page 196 for the solutions

SUM SQUARES

Following the instructions given with each puzzle, fill in the spaces in the grid to complete the sums.

Fill in the missing squares in the grid to complete the sums. Use numbers from 1-9 and the symbols +, -, x, /.

2	+	5	x	1	-	7	=0
x				+			
1	x	7	+			5	=4
-				x		+	
7			+	5			=22
+		+					
5			-	7	+	1	=4
=0		=36		=8		=4	

Use the numbers 1-9 to fill in the spaces in the grid and complete each sum. Each number can only be used once. The sum totals are shown below and to the right of each grid. For each equation the multiplication and division is completed before the addition and subtraction.

3	+		X		8
-	■	-	■	-	
2	-		-		-15
-	■	X	■	/	
6	+		-		9
-5		-62		3	

Use the numbers 1-9 to fill in the spaces in the grid and complete each sum. Each number can only be used once. The sum totals are shown below and to the right of each grid. For each equation the multiplication and division is completed before the addition and subtraction.

	-		+	5	-1
X	■	-	■	-	
	X		-		0
+	■	+	■	-	
	+		+		14
12		6		-10	

Use the numbers 1-9 to fill in the spaces in the grid and complete each sum. Each number can only be used once. The sum totals are shown below and to the right of each grid. For each equation the multiplication and division is completed before the addition and subtraction.

	-		-		-1
-	■	-	■	X	
4	+		+		16
-	■	-	■	+	
	+	5	+	8	14
2		-6		62	

Use the numbers 1-9 to fill in the spaces in the grid and complete each sum. Each number can only be used once. The sum totals are shown below and to the right of each grid. For each equation the multiplication and division is completed before the addition and subtraction.

	X		-		53
+	■	-	■	-	
	+		X		11
X	■	X	■	-	
	+	4	-		11
62		3		-4	

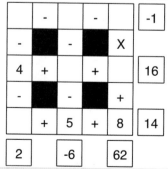

 Turn to page 196 for the solutions

SUM SQUARES

★

Fill in the missing squares in the grid to complete the sums. Use numbers from 1-9 and the symbols +, -, x, /.

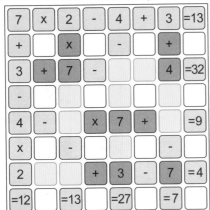

7	x	2	-	4	+	3	=13
+		x		-		+	
3	+	7	-			4	=32
-							
4	-		x	7	+		=9
x		-				-	
2			+	3	-	7	=4
=12		=13		=27		=7	

★★

Use the numbers 1-9 to fill in the spaces in the grid and complete each sum. Each number can only be used once. The sum totals are shown below and to the right of each grid. For each equation the multiplication and division is completed before the addition and subtraction.

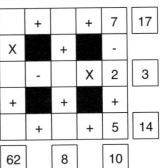

	+		+	7	17
X	■	+	■	-	
	-		X	2	3
+	■	+	■	+	
	+		+	5	14
62		8		10	

★★★

Use the numbers 1-9 to fill in the spaces in the grid and complete each sum. Each number can only be used once. The sum totals are shown below and to the right of each grid. For each equation the multiplication and division is completed before the addition and subtraction.

	-		+		14
/	■	+	■	+	
	-		-	8	-11
-	■	+	■	+	
	-		X		-1
-1		9		20	

★★

Use the numbers 1-9 to fill in the spaces in the grid and complete each sum. Each number can only be used once. The sum totals are shown below and to the right of each grid. For each equation the multiplication and division is completed before the addition and subtraction.

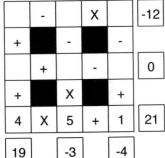

	-		X		-12
+	■	-	■	-	
	+		-		0
+	■	X	■	+	
4	X	5	+	1	21
19		-3		-4	

★

Fill in the missing squares in the grid to complete the sums. Use numbers from 1-9 and the symbols +, -, x, /.

6	+	1	x	5	-	7	=28
-		+					
1	x	5		7	+		=4
x				+			
7			+	1	x	5	=10
+						+	
5	+	7		6		1	=6
=40		=0		=30		=6	

Turn to page 196 for the solutions

SUM SQUARES

Following the instructions given with each puzzle, fill in the spaces in the grid to complete the sums.

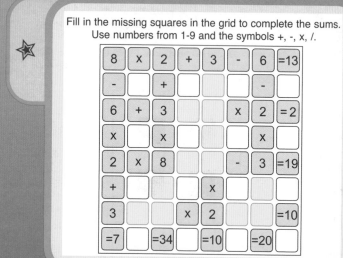

Fill in the missing squares in the grid to complete the sums.
Use numbers from 1-9 and the symbols +, -, x, /.

8	x	2	+	3	-	6	=13
-		+				-	
6	+	3			x	2	=2
x		x				x	
2	x	8			-	3	=19
+				x			
3			x	2			=10
=7		=34		=10		=20	

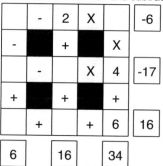

Use the numbers 1-9 to fill in the spaces in the grid and complete each sum. Each number can only be used once. The sum totals are shown below and to the right of each grid. For each equation the multiplication and division is completed before the addition and subtraction.

	-	2	X		-6
-	■	+	■	X	
	-		X	4	-17
+	■	+	■	+	
	+		+	6	16
6		16		34	

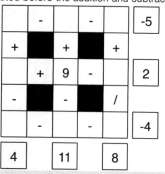

Use the numbers 1-9 to fill in the spaces in the grid and complete each sum. Each number can only be used once. The sum totals are shown below and to the right of each grid. For each equation the multiplication and division is completed before the addition and subtraction.

	-		-		-5
+	■	+	■	+	
	+	9	-		2
-	■	-	■	/	
	-		-		-4
4		11		8	

Fill in the missing squares in the grid to complete the sums.
Use numbers from 1-9 and the symbols +, -, x, /.

9	+	2	-	5	x	7	=42
-		x		+		-	
7		5			+	2	=20
x				-		x	
2			+	7	-		=20
+		+				+	
5	+	7		2			=15
=9		=8		=14		=34	

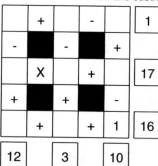

Use the numbers 1-9 to fill in the spaces in the grid and complete each sum. Each number can only be used once. The sum totals are shown below and to the right of each grid. For each equation the multiplication and division is completed before the addition and subtraction.

	+		-		1
-	■	-	■	+	
	X		+		17
+	■	+	■	-	
	+		+	1	16
12		3		10	

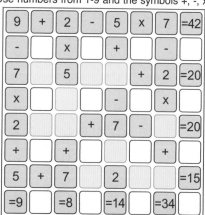

 Turn to page 196 for the solutions

SUM SQUARES

Fill in the missing squares in the grid to complete the sums. Use numbers from 1-9 and the symbols +, -, x, /.

6	x	3	+	2	-	4	=16
-						-	
2	+	6			-	3	=29
x		-		-			
4			-	3	x	6	=18
+							
3	x	4	+		-		=16
=19		=20		=18		=8	

Use the numbers 1-9 to fill in the spaces in the grid and complete each sum. Each number can only be used once. The sum totals are shown below and to the right of each grid. For each equation the multiplication and division is completed before the addition and subtraction.

	+		+		6
X	■	-	■	X	
7	+		-		5
+	■	X	■	+	
	-		-		-12
19		-31		27	

Use the numbers 1-9 to fill in the spaces in the grid and complete each sum. Each number can only be used once. The sum totals are shown below and to the right of each grid. For each equation the multiplication and division is completed before the addition and subtraction.

	+		+		12
-	■	+	■	X	
	X		-		46
+	■	+	■	+	
5	-		-		0
-2		17		25	

Use the numbers 1-9 to fill in the spaces in the grid and complete each sum. Each number can only be used once. The sum totals are shown below and to the right of each grid. For each equation the multiplication and division is completed before the addition and subtraction.

	-		+		5
+	■	X	■	+	
	+		X		33
+	■	-	■	+	
	+	1	+		12
16		31		16	

Fill in the missing squares in the grid to complete the sums. Use numbers from 1-9 and the symbols +, -, x, /.

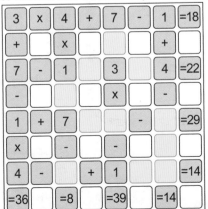

3	x	4	+	7	-	1	=18
+		x				+	
7	-	1		3		4	=22
-				x		-	
1	+	7			-		=29
x		-		-			
4	-		+	1			=14
=36		=8		=39		=14	

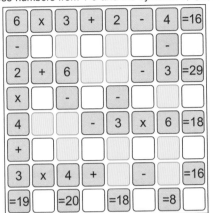

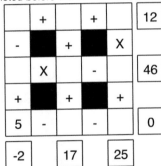

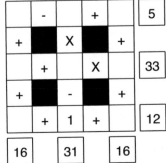

Turn to page 196 for the solutions

FIGURE IT OUT

Each of the 36 squares in the grid is filled with a single digit number from 1 to 9 – each of those numbers being used four times. Use the clues to complete the square, bearing in mind that the same number must not appear in two adjacent (touching) squares either across or down. If the same number is used more than once in any row across or column down it is stated in the relevant clue.

★

	1	2	3
1			
2			
3			

Across

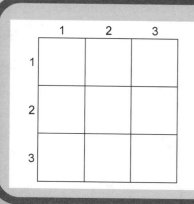

1. One of each number.
2. Smallest number in the middle.
3. Numbers go from highest to lowest.

Down

1. Numbers go from lowest to highest.
2. Highest number first.
3. Highest number second.

★★

	1	2	3	4
1				
2				
3				
4				

Across

1. Four different numbers.
2. Two twos.
3. Two fours. Total eleven.
4. Two threes. Total eleven.

Down

1. Two fours. Total thirteen.
2. Two twos.
3. Four different numbers.
4. Two ones. Two threes.

★★

	1	2	3	4
1				
2				
3				
4				

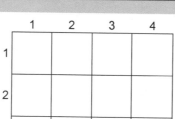

Across

1. Two twos. Total eleven.
2. Two ones.
3. Two threes separated by only one number.
4. Four different numbers.

Down

1. Two twos. Total eight.
2. Two fours. No three.
3. Two threes.
4. First two numbers add up to three.

★★★

	1	2	3	4	5
1					
2					
3			5		
4					
5					

1. Two fives. No twos
2. Two fours. Two twos.
3. Two ones. Two threes. All odd.
4. Five different numbers.
5. Two twos. No ones. First two numbers total eight.

Down

1. Two fives. No threes
2. Three threes. Total twelve.
3. Two fours separated by more that one number.
4. Total fifteen. Last two numbers total seven.
5. Five different numbers.

★

	1	2	3
1			
2			
3			

Across

1. Two twos. Total five.
2. Two threes.
3. Two ones. Total five

Down

1. Two twos.
2. Contains each number.
3. Two threes.

 Turn to page 196 for the solutions

★

	1	2	3
1			
2			
3			

Across

1. Numbers decrease each time.
2. Two twos.
3. Two threes.

Down

1. Two threes.
2. Two ones.
3. Total is six.

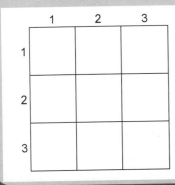

★★★

	1	2	3	4	5
1					
2					
3			2		
4					
5					

Across

1. Two ones. No fives
2. Last two numbers total four.
3. First three numbers total six.
4. Two fives. No threes
5. Two threes. Total seventeen.

Down

1. Two threes and a pair of twos.
2. Two ones. Total fourteen.
3. Two twos. No three. First two numbers total six.
4. First three numbers total nine.
5. Two fours. Last two numbers total eight.

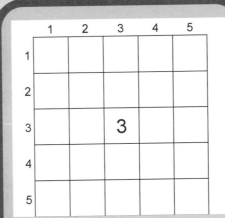

★★★

	1	2	3	4	5
1					
2					
3			3		
4					
5					

Across

1. Two ones. No fives. Last two numbers total six.
2. Two fives. Total nineteen.
3. First three numbers total six.
4. Two twos. First two numbers total six.
5. Two threes. No twos.

Down

1. Two fives. Last two numbers total nine.
2. Two twos. Two threes.
3. Two fours. No twos.
4. Two twos. No threes.
5. Two threes. Total sixteen.

★★

	1	2	3	4
1				
2				
3				
4				

Across

1. Two threes.
2. Two fours.
3. Last two numbers total seven.
4. Highest number first.

Down

1. Middle two numbers total three.
2. Two ones.
3. Two threes. No ones.
4. Four different numbers.

★

	1	2	3
1			
2			
3			

Across

1. Two ones.
2. Two twos.
3. Numbers decrease each time.

Down

1. Three threes.
2. Two twos. Total five.
3. Two ones.

Turn to page 196 for the solutions

FIGURE IT OUT

Each of the 36 squares in the grid is filled with a single digit number from 1 to 9 – each of those numbers being used four times. Use the clues to complete the square, bearing in mind that the same number must not appear in two adjacent (touching) squares either across or down. If the same number is used more than once in any row across or column down it is stated in the relevant clue.

★

	1	2	3
1			
2			
3			

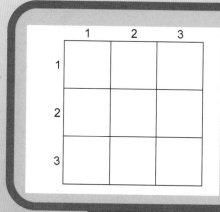

Across

1. Two twos.
2. Two threes.
3. Two ones. Total five.

Down

1. Lowest number last.
2. Numbers increase each time.
3. Highest number in the middle.

★★

	1	2	3	4
1				
2				
3				
4				

Across

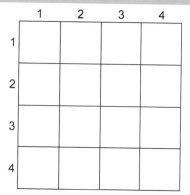

1. Alternate even and odd numbers.
2. Two fours. Numbers total thirteen.
3. Two ones. No four.
4. First two numbers total three.

Down

1. Four different numbers.
2. Two ones.
3. Two twos. No ones.
4. Two threes.

★★

	1	2	3	4
1				
2				
3				
4				

Across

1. Four different numbers.
2. Two fours. Total twelve.
3. Two ones and two twos.
4. Two threes. No ones.

Down

1. Two twos.
2. Last two numbers total three.
3. Two fours. No one.
4. Two ones. No twos.

★★★

	1	2	3	4	5
1					
2					
3			4		
4					
5					

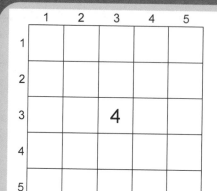

Across

1. Two ones. No threes.
2. Two fives. Total nineteen.
3. Two threes. No fives
4. Two fives. Total seventeen.
5. Two threes. No fives

Down

1. First two numbers total seven.
   Last two numbers total five.
2. Two threes. No ones.
3. Two fours. No three.
4. Two ones. Two threes. No five.
5. Pair of ones and a pair of threes.

★

	1	2	3
1			
2			
3			

Across

1. Two ones. Total four.
2. Contains each number.
3. Two threes.

Down

1. Contains each number.
2. Lowest number in the middle.
3. Numbers increase each time.

 Turn to page 196 for the solutions

FIGURE IT OUT

★

	1	2	3
1			
2			
3			

Across

1. Two threes.
2. Two ones.
3. Numbers add up to six.

Down

1. Two threes.
2. Numbers decrease each time.
3. Two twos. Total five.

★★★

	1	2	3	4	5
1					
2					
3			1		
4					
5					

Across

1. Two twos. Total twelve.
2. Two threes.
3. Two fives. Total seventeen.
4. Two fours and two twos.
5. Two threes. Two fives. Three is not the first number.

Down

1. Two fours. No fives
2. Two twos. Total thirteen.
3. Two fives
4. Two twos. Total sixteen.
5. Two ones. No twos.

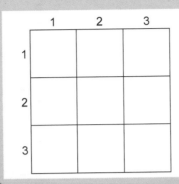

★★★

	1	2	3	4	5
1					
2					
3			4		
4					
5					

Across

1. Last two numbers total three.
2. First two numbers total three.
3. First two numbers total eight.
4. Two ones.
5. Two twos.

Down

1. Two threes. No fours.
2. Two fives. Middle three numbers total six.
3. Three fours and two fives
4. Two ones and two twos.
5. Two fours.

★★

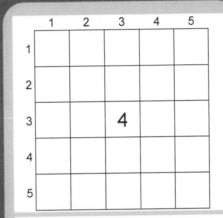

	1	2	3	4
1				
2				
3				
4				

Across

1. Two threes.
2. Two twos. Total eleven.
3. Two fours.
4. Two ones.

Down

1. Four different numbers.
2. Two ones.
3. Two twos.
4. Numbers decrease each time.

★

	1	2	3
1			
2			
3			

Across

1. Two threes.
2. Two ones.
3. Numbers decrease each time.

Down

1. Two threes.
2. Two twos.
3. Numbers decrease each time.

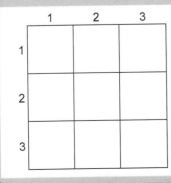

Turn to page 196 for the solutions

FIGURE IT OUT

Each of the 36 squares in the grid is filled with a single digit number from 1 to 9 – each of those numbers being used four times. Use the clues to complete the square, bearing in mind that the same number must not appear in two adjacent (touching) squares either across or down. If the same number is used more than once in any row across or column down it is stated in the relevant clue.

★

	1	2	3
1			
2			
3			

Across

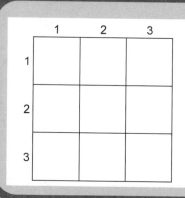

1. Numbers add up to six.
2. Highest number in the middle.
3. Lowest number last.

Down

1. Two twos. No three.
2. Two threes.
3. Two ones.

★★

	1	2	3	4
1				
2				
3				
4				

Across

1. Two ones separated only by a four. Total eight.
2. Two twos.
3. Two ones. No twos.
4. Two threes.

Down

1. Two ones.
2. Two fours.
3. Two ones.
4. Two fours.

★★

	1	2	3	4
1				
2				
3				
4				

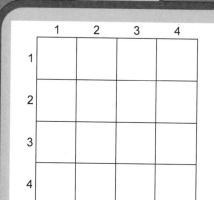

Across

1. Two threes.
2. Two fours.
3. Two ones.
4. Two threes. Total twelve.

Down

1. Four different numbers.
2. Two fours.
3. Two twos. Total eight.
4. Last two numbers total three.

★★★

	1	2	3	4	5
1					
2					
3			1		
4					
5					

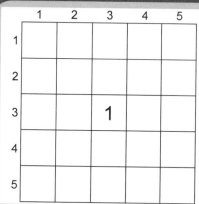

Across

1. Two twos. No ones.
2. Two ones. Two threes separated by only one number.
3. Two fours. Two fives
4. Two twos separated by more that one number. No five.
5. First three numbers total seven.

Down

1. Two ones. Total twelve.
2. Two fours. No ones.
3. Two fours. Last two numbers total six.
4. Two twos. No fours.
5. Two fives. Total eighteen.

★

	1	2	3
1			
2			
3			

Across

1. Three twos.
2. Two threes.
3. Two ones.

Down

1. Three different numbers.
2. Two ones.
3. Two threes.

 Turn to page 196 for the solutions

★

	1	2	3
1			
2			
3			

Across

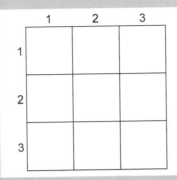

1. Two twos.
2. Two ones.
3. Two threes. Total seven.

Down

1. Two threes.
2. Contains each of the numbers.
3. Two ones.

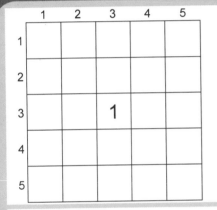

★★★

	1	2	3	4	5
1					
2					
3			1		
4					
5					

Across

1. First two numbers total three.
2. Two threes. No fives
3. Two fives. Total seventeen.
4. Two ones. Middle three numbers total nine.
5. Two fives. No ones

Down

1. Two fives. No threes
2. Two threes. Total thirteen.
3. Two twos. Two fives
4. Two threes. Two fours. No five.
5. Last two numbers total three.

★★★

	1	2	3	4	5
1					
2					
3			2		
4					
5					

Across

1. Two threes. Two fours. No five.
2. Three ones and two fives
3. Two twos and two threes.
4. Two fives. Total sixteen.
5. Two fours. No three. First two numbers total six.

Down

1. Two fours. Middle three numbers total eight.
2. Two threes. No fours.
3. Two ones. No threes.
4. Two fours. Total eighteen.
5. Two threes. Last two numbers total seven.

★★

	1	2	3	4
1				
2				
3				
4				

Across

1. Two threes.
2. Numbers increase each time.
3. Numbers decrease each time.
4. Two twos.

Down

1. Four different numbers.
2. First two numbers total six.
3. Last two numbers total six.
4. Total ten.

★

	1	2	3
1			
2			
3			

Across

1. Two threes.
2. Contains each number.
3. Two ones.

Down

1. Two twos.
2. Two threes.
3. Numbers decrease each time.

Turn to page 196 for the solutions

FIGURE IT OUT

Each of the 36 squares in the grid is filled with a single digit number from 1 to 9 – each of those numbers being used four times. Use the clues to complete the square, bearing in mind that the same number must not appear in two adjacent (touching) squares either across or down. If the same number is used more than once in any row across or column down it is stated in the relevant clue.

★

	1	2	3
1	1	3	3
2	2	3	1
3	3	1	2

Across

1. Contains each number.
2. Two twos.
3. Two ones.

Down

1. Two twos.
2. Two ones.
3. Three threes.

★★

	1	2	3	4
1	1	2	3	4
2	2	3	4	1
3	4	1	2	3
4	3	4	1	2

Across

1. Two twos. Two ones.
2. Two fours. Total thirteen.
3. Last two numbers total three.
4. Two threes. No twos.

Down

1. Two fours. No ones.
2. Middle two numbers total six.
3. Two twos. No fours.
4. Two ones.

★★

	1	2	3	4
1				
2				
3				
4				

Across

1. Two threes.
2. Two twos. Two ones.
3. Last two numbers total three.
4. Two fours.

Down

1. Two fours. Total thirteen.
2. First two numbers total four.
3. Two ones.
4. Two threes. Total nine.

★★★

	1	2	3	4	5
1					
2					
3			3		
4					
5					

Across

1. First two numbers total three.
2. Two twos. No threes.
3. Two threes and two fours.
4. Two ones. Two fives.
   First two numbers total six.
5. Two threes. Total seventeen.

Down

1. Two ones and two threes.
2. Two twos. No threes.
3. Two twos. Two fives
4. Two threes. No twos.
5. Two fours. Total sixteen.

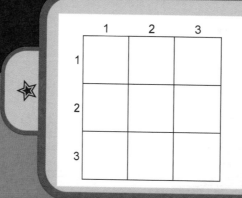

★

	1	2	3
1			
2			
3			

Across

1. Contains each number.
2. Two threes.
3. Two ones.

Down

1. Numbers decrease each time
2. Two ones.
3. Two twos. Total seven.

 Turn to page 196 for the solutions

FIGURE IT OUT

★

	1	2	3
1			
2			
3			

Across

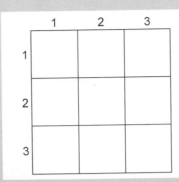

1. Two twos.
2. Three ones.
3. Two threes.

Down

1. Highest number first.
2. Highest number last.
3. Same as 2 down.

★★★

	1	2	3	4	5
1					
2					
3			2		
4					
5					

Across

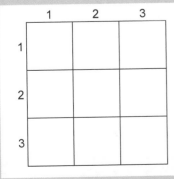

1. Two threes separated by only one number. No one.
2. Two ones. No fours.
3. Two twos and two fours.
4. Two fives. Total seventeen.
5. Two ones. Middle three numbers total twelve.

Down

1. First two numbers total eight.
2. Two ones. Total thirteen.
3. Two fives. Two threes.
4. Three fours. Two twos.
5. Two threes. Two ones. Total thirteen.

★★★

	1	2	3	4	5
1					
2					
3			3		
4					
5					

Across

1. Two ones. Two fives. Total fourteen.
2. Two fours. No ones.
3. Two threes. Total seventeen.
4. Two twos. No five.
5. Two ones. No twos.

Down

1. Two twos. No fives
2. Two fours. Last two numbers total six.
3. Two fives. No fours
4. Two threes. Total sixteen.
5. Numbers decrease each time.

★★

	1	2	3	4
1				
2				
3				
4				

Across

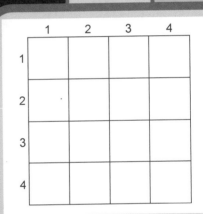

1. Two ones.
2. Two threes.
3. Middle numbers total three.
4 Two twos. Total eleven.

Down

1. Two fours.
2. Last two numbers total three.
3. Two twos. No fours.
4. First two numbers total four.

★

	1	2	3
1			
2			
3			

Across

1. Two ones.
2. Two twos.
3. Two threes. Total seven.

Down

1. Two twos.
2. Two ones.
3. Numbers increase each time.

Turn to page 196 for the solutions

FIGURE IT OUT

Each of the 36 squares in the grid is filled with a single digit number from 1 to 9 – each of those numbers being used four times. Use the clues to complete the square, bearing in mind that the same number must not appear in two adjacent (touching) squares either across or down. If the same number is used more than once in any row across or column down it is stated in the relevant clue.

	1	2	3	4
1				
2				
3				
4				

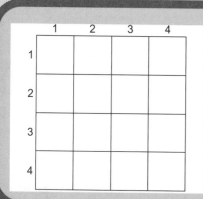

Across

1. Two threes. No one.
2. Two ones separated only by a four.
3. Last two numbers total five
4. Last two numbers total five

Down

1. First two numbers total four.
2. Four different numbers.
3. Two threes. No twos.
4. Two twos.

	1	2	3	4
1				
2				
3				
4				

Across

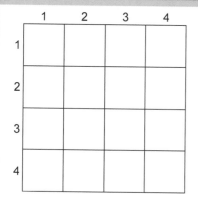

1. Two ones. Two fours.
2. Two twos.
3. Two ones. No fours.
4. Two threes.

Down

1. Four different numbers.
2. First two numbers total four.
3. Middle two numbers total three.
4. Last two numbers total five

	1	2	3	4
1				
2				
3				
4				

Across

1. Two ones.
2. Two fours. No threes.
3. Two twos. Two threes.
4. Two fours.

Down

1. Four different numbers.
2. Middle two numbers total four.
3. Last two numbers total three.
4. Numbers increase each time.

	1	2	3	4	5
1					
2					
3			2		
4					
5					

Across

1. Two fours. No twos.
2. Two twos. Last two numbers total five.
3. Two twos. Total fourteen.
4. Two threes and two fours.
5. Two fives. No fours

Down

1. Three ones.
2. Two ones. Total fourteen.
3. Two fives.
4. Two twos. Two fours.
5. Two fives.

	1	2	3	4	5
1					
2					
3			1		
4					
5					

Across

1. Two threes. No fives.
2. Two fours. Total sixteen.
3. Two twos. No fours.
4. Last three numbers total nine.
5. Two fives. No twos.

Down

1. First two numbers total eight.
2. Middle three numbers total nine.
3. Last two numbers total eight.
4. Two ones. Two fives.
5. Two fours. Two threes.

 Turn to page 196 for the solutions

FIGURE IT OUT

	1	2	3	4
1				
2				
3				
4				

Across

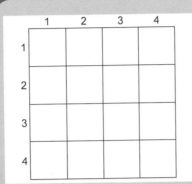

1. Two fours. Total twelve.
2. Two twos.
3. Two threes. No ones.
4. Two ones. Total seven.

Down

1. Two twos.
2. Two ones. Middle two numbers total three.
3. Two fours. Total thirteen.
4. Two ones.

	1	2	3	4	5
1					
2					
3			3		
4					
5					

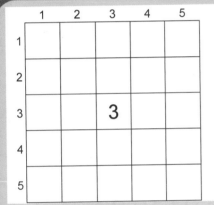

Across

1. Last two numbers total six.
2. Two fives. No threes
3. Two twos. Two threes.
4. Two ones. No threes.
5. Two threes. Total sixteen.

Down

1. Two ones. Two fours.
2. Two fives separated only by a four.
3. Two twos. Two threes.
4. Two fours. Two fives
5. Two ones. Two threes. No two.

	1	2	3	4	5	6
1						
2						
3						
4						
5						
6						

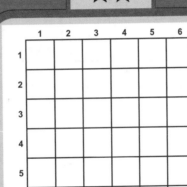

Across

1 No eight.

2 Six different numbers.

3 No one.

4 Two sevens. No even numbers.

5 Two eights. Two nines.

6 Total thirty-nine.

Down

1 Two threes. No even numbers.

2 Total twenty-one.

3 Two ones.

4 Three twos. No seven. No eight.

5 Two fours. Two eights. No six.

6 Two nines. Total forty-two.

	1	2	3	4	5	6
1		5				
2						
3						
4						
5						
6						

Across

1 Consecutive numbers placed in order.

2 Two twos. No three. No six.

3 Six is the highest number.

4 Total thirty-nine.

5 Two eights.

6 The lowest number is adjacent to the highest number.

Down

1 No two. No seven. No eight.

2 Two fives. Two sixes.

3 Two sevens, with only a one between them. No eight.

4 Consecutive numbers placed in order.

5 Two nines. No four.

6 Two ones.

	1	2	3	4	5	6
1						
2						
3						
4						2
5						
6						

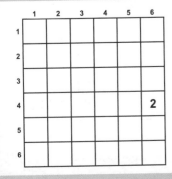

Across

1 Eight is the only even number.

2 A one is next to and between two fours.

3 Consecutive numbers placed in order.

4 Two sixes.

5 Two sevens. Two is the only even number.

6 Two nines. No one. No three.

Down

1 Total twenty-one.

2 Two nines. No three. Four is the only even number.

3 Consecutive numbers placed in order.

4 Two twos. No five. No nine.

5 Total thirty.

6 Two eights. No one.

Turn to page 196 for the solutions

NUMBER SQUARES

The numbers in each row below should add up to the totals in the boxes on the right. Those in each column should add up to the totals in the boxes along the bottom. Try to fill in the gaps using whole numbers; for easy and moderate puzzles use numbers 1-10, for challenging puzzles use numbers 1-9. Here's a hint: the numbers placed diagonally across the grid add up to the total in the bottom or top right-hand corner.

★

Diagonal total: 19

		4	4	20
		4	1	22
	7	3	10	24
4	9		8	28
19	34	18	23	21

★★

Diagonal total: 27

	8	1	4	18
	8			24
10		10		36
	5		1	16
31	29	18	16	24

★★★

Diagonal total: 16

				16
	9	1		23
4		3		21
4			1	19
13	24	19	23	14

★

Diagonal total: 27

	3	6	5	24
2	6			24
		2	6	22
	7	6	4	23
22	26	20	25	22

★★

Diagonal total: 17

		5	3	27
	8			27
	2	5	8	16
5		10		27
23	28	27	19	26

★★★

Diagonal total: 17

		2	9	27
			2	11
		1		13
3			4	19
19	22	10	19	19

 Turn to page 196 for the solutions

NUMBER SQUARES

★

				22
5		5	9	26
	9	8		33
			2	17
3	7	3	8	21
24	25	22	26	28

★★

				21
		3	8	20
2			3	18
		7	2	14
	4	10		26
16	18	25	19	26

★★★

				22
			7	27
		6		18
	3		1	12
6	1			13
21	15	16	18	15

★

				19
	9		6	21
8	8	4		24
1	2		5	11
7		7		33
18	28	18	25	23

★★

				12
	8			26
6	8		4	21
		5		9
3	5		1	11
20	22	13	12	24

Turn to page 196 for the solutions

NUMBER SQUARES

The numbers in each row below should add up to the totals in the boxes on the right. Those in each column should add up to the totals in the boxes along the bottom. Try to fill in the gaps using whole numbers; for easy and moderate puzzles use numbers 1-10, for challenging puzzles use numbers 1-9. Here's a hint: the numbers placed diagonally across the grid add up to the total in the bottom or top right-hand corner.

★

				14
	7		3	22
	3	6		21
		10	5	28
1	4	5	7	17
23	18	29	18	24

★★

				17
	1	9		19
8				31
		10	8	25
	6	4	1	17
26	14	30	22	23

★★★

				16
		5		22
	9		7	19
			5	19
7			8	22
21	27	12	22	27

★

				12
1			3	21
1		3	3	13
	2	5		18
4	1		6	14
11	16	21	18	18

★★

				28
	6		9	24
	1			17
	10	1	1	21
4		1		18
21	25	9	25	14

★★★

				17
	7	2		22
5				21
9				20
6		3		18
27	22	11	21	22

 Turn to page 196 for the solutions

★★★

				19
			7	16
	6	6		23
	1			16
5			8	25
19	18	17	26	17

★★

				26
	7	7		22
	10	7	9	28
8		1		21
	6			30
25	31	21	24	26

★★★

				26
		1		22
2		2		17
6	8		3	25
				27
24	27	19	21	29

★

				27
	4		6	22
		9	10	25
8		4	5	24
	5	3	9	22
20	21	22	30	24

★★

				29
		1		17
	8			27
	8	2	6	18
6		10	3	25
22	27	21	17	17

Turn to page 196 for the solutions

NUMBER SQUARES

The numbers in each row below should add up to the totals in the boxes on the right. Those in each column should add up to the totals in the boxes along the bottom. Try to fill in the gaps using whole numbers; for easy and moderate puzzles use numbers 1-10, for challenging puzzles use numbers 1-9. Here's a hint: the numbers placed diagonally across the grid add up to the total in the bottom or top right-hand corner.

★

				29
2	6		10	27
10	6		1	23
			2	22
5	8		10	28
19	28	30	23	28

★★

				29
		6		16
9			4	21
		7	10	35
10	5	3		22
32	18	21	23	18

★★★

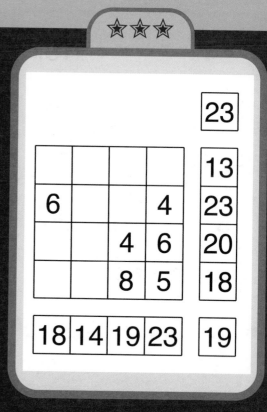

				23
				13
6			4	23
		4	6	20
		8	5	18
18	14	19	23	19

★

				16
5		7		21
	8	1	8	27
	2	8	5	22
9			9	25
31	21	17	26	30

★★

				24
		10	3	26
4	10			31
9		8		24
	8	2		26
28	27	30	22	35

★★★

				22
2				20
	7			20
	4	9		22
9			8	30
16	20	24	32	26

 Turn to page 196 for the solutions

NUMBER SQUARES

★

				27
4	4	3		16
			9	25
	5		2	21
8	5	4	5	22
26	17	20	21	16

★★

				18
4			9	27
8		3		23
8			2	17
	5		7	20
21	21	19	26	17

★★★

				20
2				19
1		5		16
	5	7		23
			5	16
13	14	27	20	20

★

				18
2	2	9		22
	3	2		13
		10	4	18
6	2		4	13
13	8	22	23	19

★★★

				24
			8	16
			4	19
6		5		22
	7	8		23
18	22	20	20	19

Turn to page 196 for the solutions

NUMBER SQUARES

The numbers in each row below should add up to the totals in the boxes on the right. Those in each column should add up to the totals in the boxes along the bottom. Try to fill in the gaps using whole numbers; for easy and moderate puzzles use numbers 1-10, for challenging puzzles use numbers 1-9. Here's a hint: the numbers placed diagonally across the grid add up to the total in the bottom or top right-hand corner.

★

				10
	5	2	3	12
	2		2	19
		3	9	23
1	3		4	14
23	11	16	18	11

★★

				28
		2		30
	6	5	5	26
2				24
6	8	10		28
27	32	22	27	24

★★★

				11
	4			13
5	9	1		21
		9		22
5				30
17	23	21	25	30

★

					12
	2	2	4		15
		5	1	5	16
1	2		3	1	11
4	1		1		9
	4	1		5	18
15	11	14	14	15	16

★★

				25
10				29
		5	8	26
	7		5	23
6	9		8	30
25	30	25	28	33

★★★

				27
			9	25
	3	3		17
3			8	25
7				24
17	19	25	30	18

 Turn to page 196 for the solutions

NUMBER SQUARES

★

					41
6	10	9			43
9		7	9		41
	10	7	6	7	40
10		6	8	6	37
			7	10	43
45	44	38	40	37	41

★★★

				21
4			1	11
			4	22
	8			28
	8	5		20
23	20	25	13	17

★★

				21
	1			26
	10	1	2	18
7		10		26
		10	1	23
29	17	27	20	30

★

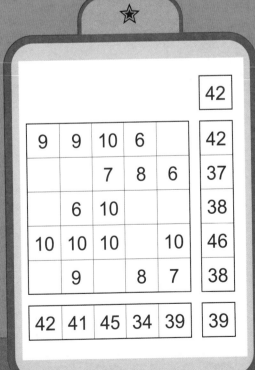

					42
9	9	10	6		42
		7	8	6	37
	6	10			38
10	10	10		10	46
	9		8	7	38
42	41	45	34	39	39

★★

				22
	4	5		28
	3		7	19
	4		3	15
5		7		26
26	21	17	24	18

Turn to page 196 for the solutions

NUMBER SQUARES

The numbers in each row below should add up to the totals in the boxes on the right. Those in each column should add up to the totals in the boxes along the bottom. Try to fill in the gaps using whole numbers; for easy and moderate puzzles use numbers 1-10, for challenging puzzles use numbers 1-9. Here's a hint: the numbers placed diagonally across the grid add up to the total in the bottom or top right-hand corner.

★

					42
	6			10	37
6	7		9	8	38
6	6		6		34
	7	10	7		40
10		10	7	10	43
34	32	42	36	48	36

★★

				12
	4	7	1	21
7	5		9	27
	4			15
		2		14
24	23	18	12	18

★★★

				29
			9	26
8		8		23
		1		18
		3	3	18
30	15	18	22	12

★

					42
8	7				41
9			10	10	47
		8	10	9	43
	8		9	8	45
9	10	6	7	8	40
43	43	43	45	42	42

★★★

				23
5			1	15
		8		24
	7			27
		8	3	25
28	22	32	9	23

★★★

				28
				23
		9		28
2	2			15
8		5	1	18
23	21	18	22	20

 Turn to page 196 for the solutions

NUMBER SEQUENCES

Make a note of the numbers below. Each puzzle has a sequence. Can you work out what these are and fill in the missing number in each one? Remember you can add, subtract, multiply and divide to solve the puzzle.

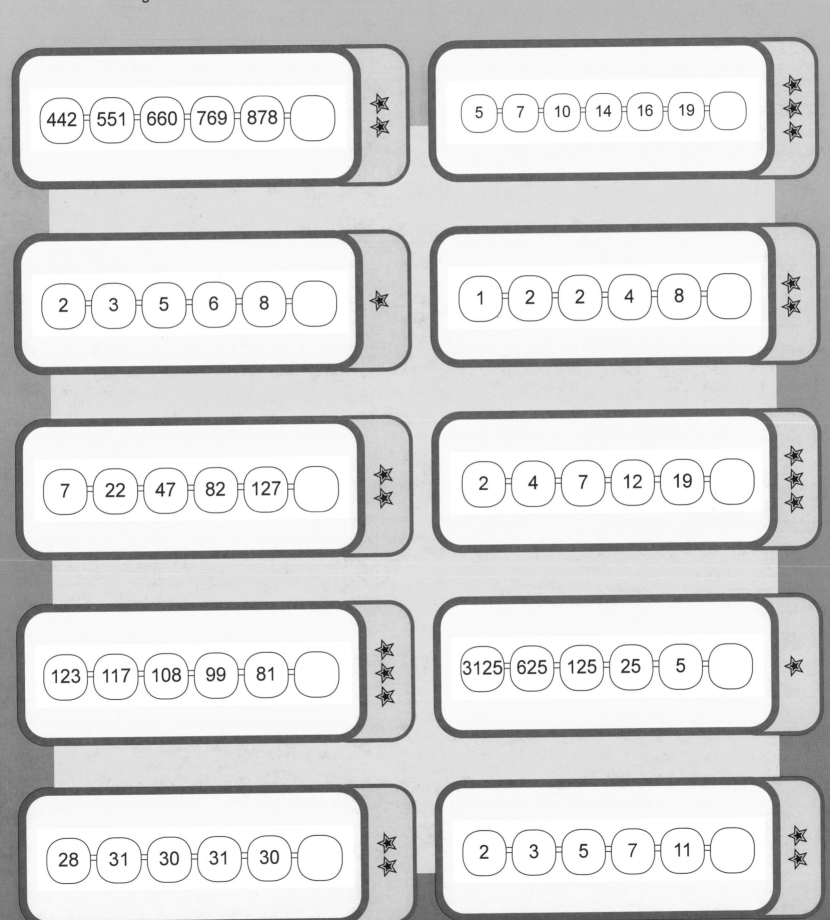

442	551	660	769	878	
2	3	5	6	8	
7	22	47	82	127	
123	117	108	99	81	
28	31	30	31	30	

5	7	10	14	16	19	
1	2	2	4	8		
2	4	7	12	19		
3125	625	125	25	5		
2	3	5	7	11		

Turn to page 196 for the solutions

NUMBER SEQUENCES

Make a note of the numbers below. Each puzzle has a sequence. Can you work out what these are and fill in the missing number in each one? Remember you can add, subtract, multiply and divide to solve the puzzle.

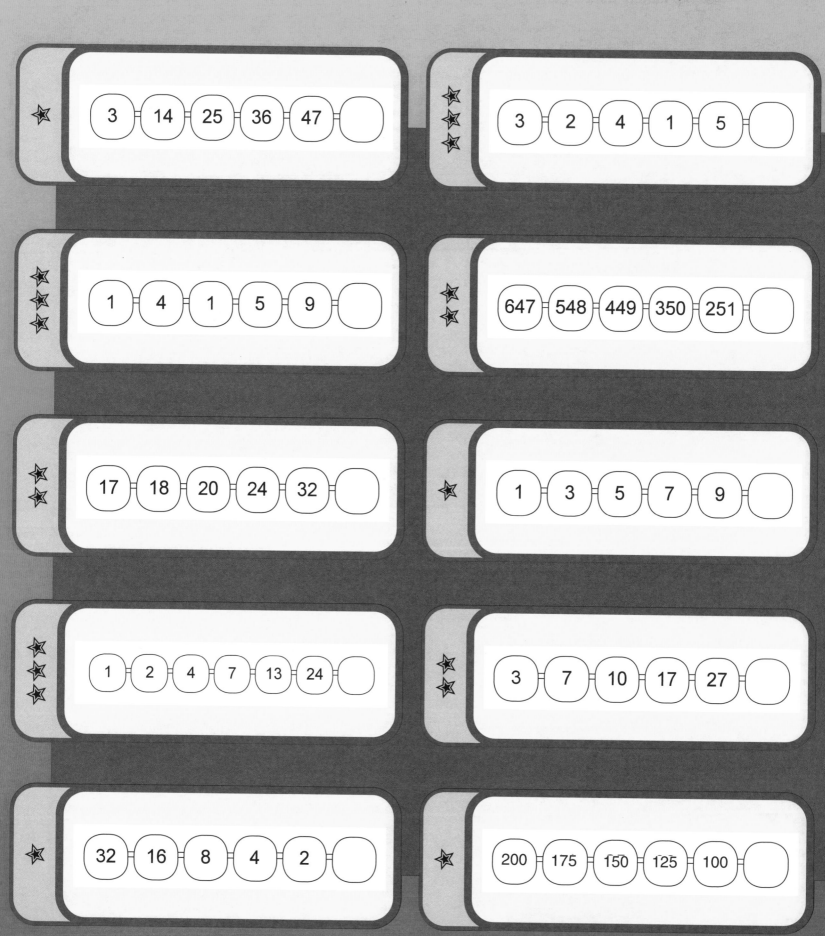

★ 3 – 14 – 25 – 36 – 47 – ___

★★★ 3 – 2 – 4 – 1 – 5 – ___

★★★ 1 – 4 – 1 – 5 – 9 – ___

★★ 647 – 548 – 449 – 350 – 251 – ___

★★ 17 – 18 – 20 – 24 – 32 – ___

★ 1 – 3 – 5 – 7 – 9 – ___

★★★ 1 – 2 – 4 – 7 – 13 – 24 – ___

★★ 3 – 7 – 10 – 17 – 27 – ___

★ 32 – 16 – 8 – 4 – 2 – ___

★ 200 – 175 – 150 – 125 – 100 – ___

 Turn to page 196 for the solutions

NUMBER SEQUENCES

II – IV – VI – VIII – X – ☐ ★

200 – 196 – 180 – 116 – ☐ ★★★

80 – 160 – 240 – 320 – 400 – ☐ ★★

32 – 29 – 26 – 23 – 20 – ☐ ★

55 – 89 – 144 – 233 – 377 – ☐ ★★★

1 – 8 – 16 – 25 – 35 – ☐ ★★

0 – 1 – 3 – 6 – 10 – ☐ ★

5 – 9 – 16 – 29 – 54 – ☐ ★★★

6 – 11 – 15 – 18 – 20 – ☐ ★★

6 – 6 – 7 – 9 – 8 – 6 – ☐ ★★★

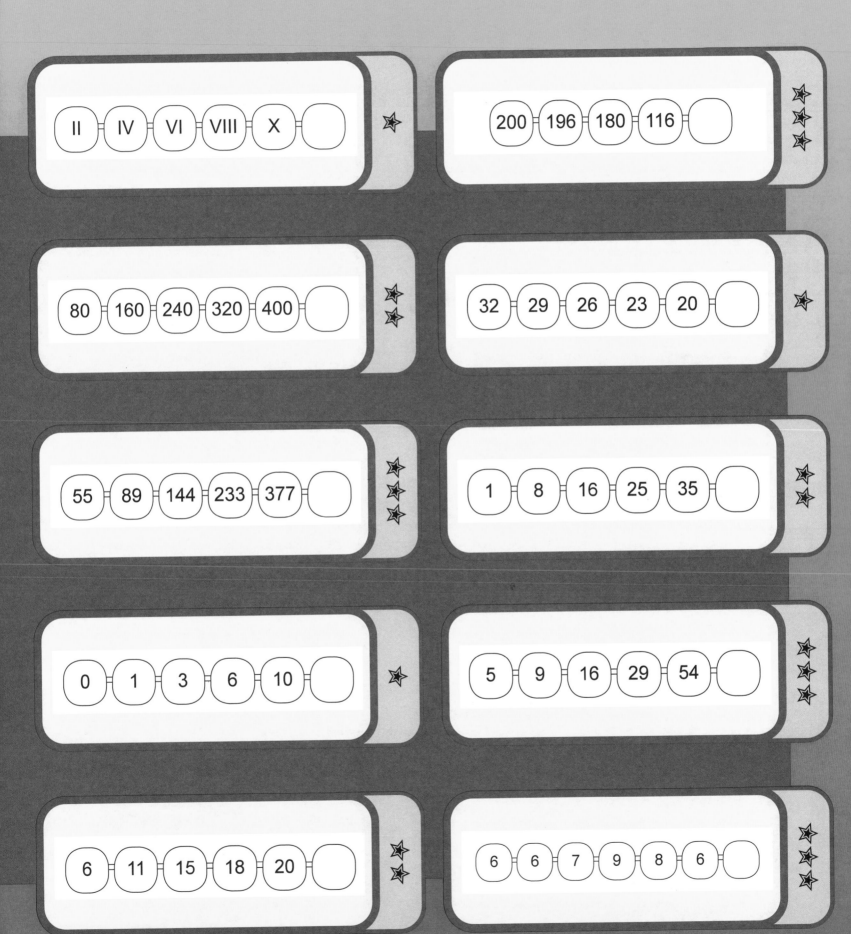

Turn to page 196 for the solutions

NUMBER SEQUENCES

Make a note of the numbers below. Each puzzle has a sequence. Can you work out what these are and fill in the missing number in each one? Remember you can add, subtract, multiply and divide to solve the puzzle.

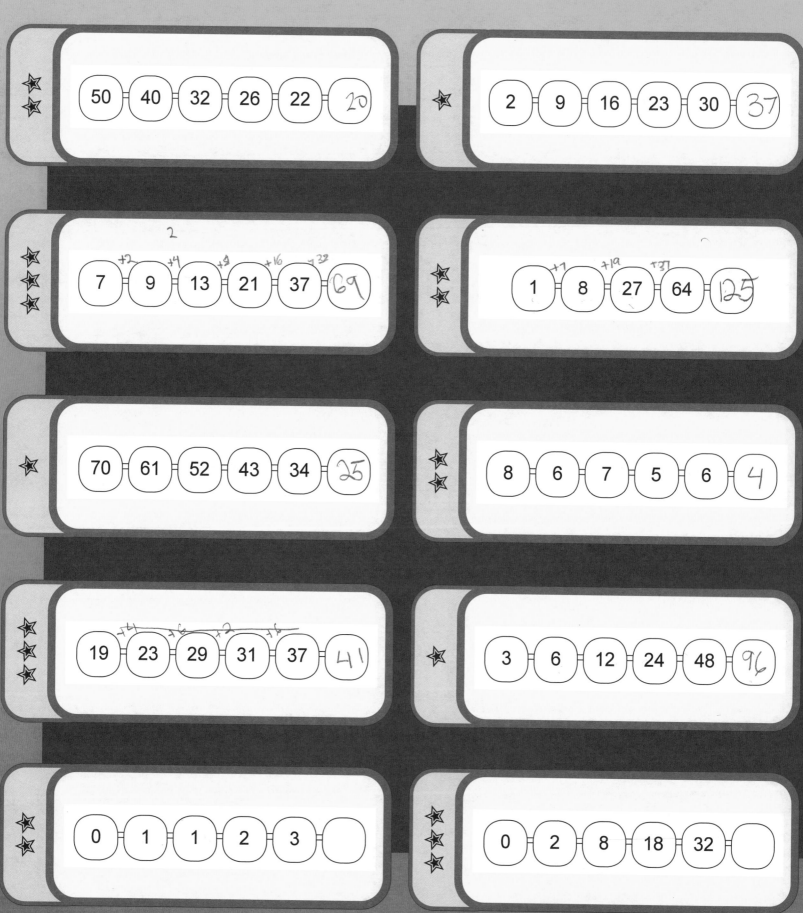

★★ 50 – 40 – 32 – 26 – 22 – 20

★ 2 – 9 – 16 – 23 – 30 – 37

★★★ 7 – 9 – 13 – 21 – 37 – 69

★★ 1 – 8 – 27 – 64 – 125

★ 70 – 61 – 52 – 43 – 34 – 25

★★ 8 – 6 – 7 – 5 – 6 – 4

★★★ 19 – 23 – 29 – 31 – 37 – 41

★ 3 – 6 – 12 – 24 – 48 – 96

★★ 0 – 1 – 1 – 2 – 3 –

★★★ 0 – 2 – 8 – 18 – 32 –

 Turn to page 196 for the solutions

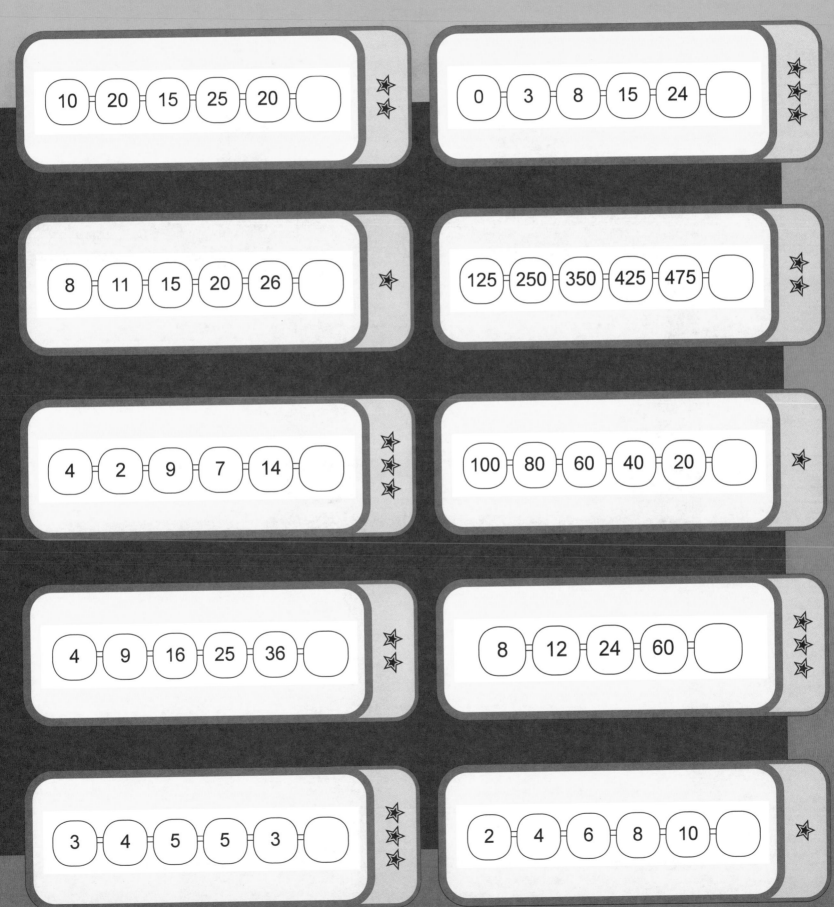

NUMBER SEQUENCES

10	20	15	25	20		★★
8	11	15	20	26		★
4	2	9	7	14		★★★
4	9	16	25	36		★★
3	4	5	5	3		★★★
0	3	8	15	24		★★★
125	250	350	425	475		★★
100	80	60	40	20		★
8	12	24	60			★★★
2	4	6	8	10		★

Turn to page 196 for the solutions

CHAIN LINK

Draw a single continuous loop, by connecting the dots. No line may cross the path of another. The figure inside each set of any four surrounding dots indicates the total number of surrounding lines.

★

2	2	1	2
3	0	1	1
2	2	3	3
1	3	1	1

★

3	2	3	2
2	2	3	2
2	1	2	2
2	3	2	1

★

1	2	2	2
1	2	3	2
2	2	2	3
3	2	1	1

★★

1	2	2	1	1	1
2	1	0	1	1	2
2					1
1	0		1	0	1
2	1	2	3	1	1
1	1	1	1	2	2

★★

2	3	2	2	2	2
3	1	1	1	0	1
1	2	1			1
1	2	1		1	2
2	1		1	3	1
2	1	1	1	3	1

★★★

1		2				
1	1	1	2	2	3	
2	2	3		2	2	
3		1	1		1	2
2			1		1	1
	2	3	1	1	2	2
	2	3	1			3

★★★

2		2		1		2
2	2	2	1		1	2
	1		1		2	
3		1			1	
2	1	2	1	1		
2	1	1	0		2	
2		1		1	3	1

 Turn to page 196 for the solutions

CHAIN LINK

1	2	1	3
2	1	1	3
2	1	1	2
3	2	2	3

2	2	2	3
2	3	2	2
1	1	1	3
2	1	2	2

2	3	2	1
2	0	1	2
2	0	1	1
2	3	3	3

	1	2	1	1	2
	1	1		0	2
1	2	1		1	2
2	2	1	1	1	1
2	2	1	2	2	2
3	1		1	2	3

2	1	1	1	1	2
2	1	1	1	1	1
1	2	1	1	2	2
2	3	2	1	2	2
2	0	1	1	1	1
2	1	1	1	1	2

		3	3	3	2	1
2	2		1	0	1	2
2			1			
1		2	3	1		1
	2	2		1		2
3	2	0	1		3	1
1			1	2	3	

		2	2	1	2	2
	3	1	1		1	3
	2	2	3	2	2	
	1	1	1	2	1	2
	2	1	1	3	1	1
	2			2	2	2
	2	1	2	1	1	1

Turn to page 196 for the solutions

CHAIN LINK

Draw a single continuous loop, by connecting the dots. No line may cross the path of another. The figure inside each set of any four surrounding dots indicates the total number of surrounding lines.

2	3	3	3
2	1	2	2
2	3	2	1
2	2	3	1

1	3	2	2
0	2	3	2
2	2	2	2
3	2	2	1

2	2	2	2	3	1
2	3	2	2	2	1
1	2	2	1	1	2
2	2	2			1
3	1	1	1		1
1			2	1	2

3	2	2	2	2	
2	2	2	3	2	1
2	1	1		1	2
2	1	1	1		2
1	2	2	3	1	1
	3	2	2		2

	1		2	2	3	
	2	1	1	3	2	1
1	1		1	2	2	3
2	1	1	3	2	2	1
2	0		1	1	2	
2	1	1		0	1	
1		2	2		2	

2	2	1	2	1	1	3
3	3		1	2		2
2	2	1		1	1	
3	1				1	1
2					3	2
	1	0		1	2	2
1	2		1	2	2	3

 Turn to page 196 for the solutions

★

2	2	1	2
3	3	2	1
1	1	3	2
1	3	2	2

★

3	2	1	3
2	3	2	3
2	1	0	2
2	1	1	2

★★

		2	2	2	2
1	3	2	1	3	2
0		2	2		3
1		2	2	1	1
3	2	2	1	2	
1	1	2	2	2	3

★★

	1	2	2	2	1
1	1	1		1	2
3	2	1	0		1
2	3	1			1
2	2	0	1	0	2
1	2	3	3	3	2

★★★

		2		2	1	
	2	1	0			
2	1			1	2	1
2	1	0			1	2
1	2				1	2
	1	1	1	2		1
	1	2	2	1	0	

★★★

2	1	1	2	2	3	1
	0	1	2		1	0
1			1	0		
1		1	2		1	0
	1		1		2	
1	2	1		0	1	
	1	2	1		2	1

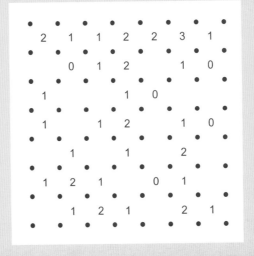

Turn to page 196 for the solutions

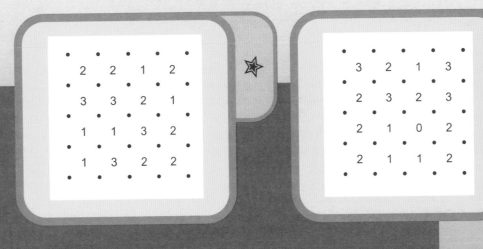

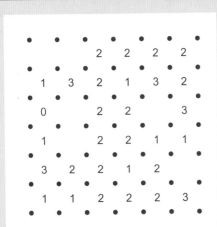

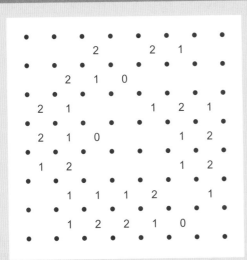

CHAIN LINK

Draw a single continuous loop, by connecting the dots. No line may cross the path of another. The figure inside each set of any four surrounding dots indicates the total number of surrounding lines.

★

1	3	2	3
2	2	3	2
3	1	1	1
1	2	2	2

★

3	1	3	1
3	2	3	1
3	1	1	3
1	2	3	2

★★

0	2	2	1	2	2
2	2	0	0	1	3
2		1	1	2	1
2	2	3	2	1	
1	2	2	2	2	1
1	3	2	1	2	3

★★

	2	1	2	2	3
2	0	1	2	1	1
1		1	2	1	
1			1	1	2
2	1	1	1		1
1	1	1	1	2	3

★★★

1		2	2	1	3	1
2		2			2	
1		3		1	2	1
	1		1	0	1	2
1		2			0	
	2	1		2		1
1	1			1	2	2

★★★

	2	2		1	2	1
1	2		0		1	
	1		0	1	2	
2				2	1	0
2	1		1		1	
	3	1	0	1		1
3	2		1		2	

 Turn to page 196 for the solutions

CHAIN LINK

★

0	2	2	2
2	2	0	1
3	0	0	2
2	2	2	2

★

3	1	2	2
2	1	0	2
1	1	0	2
1	2	2	2

★★

2	2	2	2	1	1
2	2	2	2	3	3
3	1		1	1	
1	1	2	1		1
1	2	2	1	1	2
	3	2	1		1

★★

1	2	1	3	1	
1	1	1	3	1	1
2	1	0	1		2
3	1			1	1
1	2	2	3	2	3
	1	2	3	1	1

★★★

3		2		2		2
	2		2		3	2
2	2	1	1		1	1
	0	1		1		2
1	1	3	2		1	1
1	0	2		3	1	
2		2	1	1		

★★★

	1	2		1		2
1		1	0		0	
2	2		1	0		1
	2	1		1	0	
3	1		2	1		2
1	1	2		0	1	
	1	2	1		2	1

Turn to page 196 for the solutions

CHAIN LINK

Draw a single continuous loop, by connecting the dots. No line may cross the path of another. The figure inside each set of any four surrounding dots indicates the total number of surrounding lines.

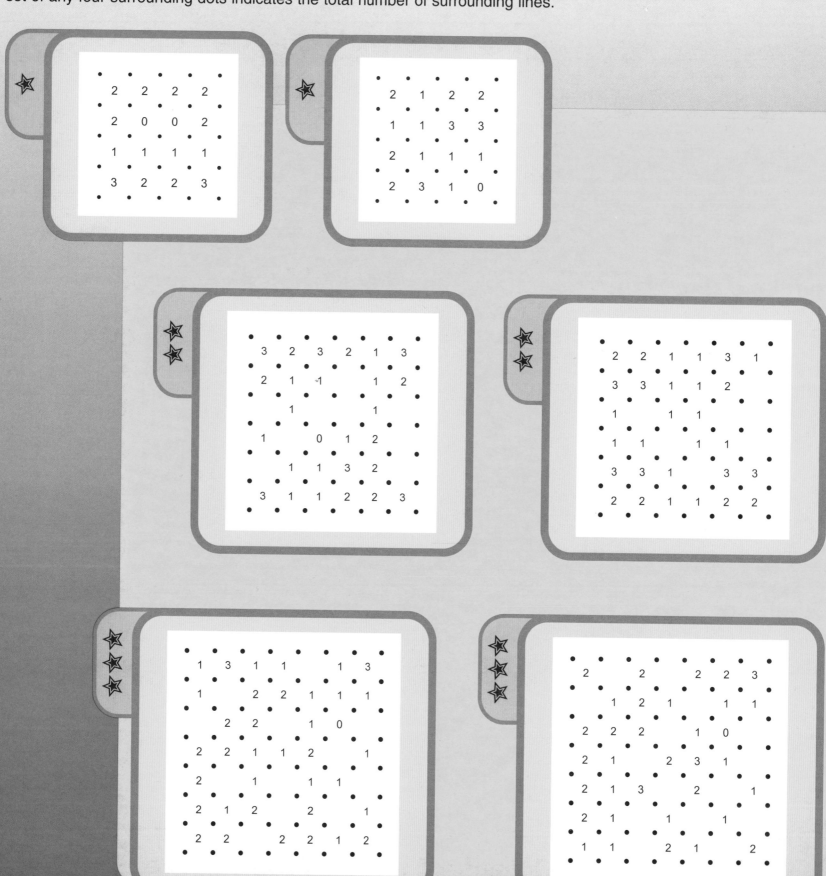

2	2	2	2
2	0	0	2
1	1	1	1
3	2	2	3

2	1	2	2
1	1	3	3
2	1	1	1
2	3	1	0

3	2	3	2	1	3
2	1	1		1	2
	1			1	
1		0	1	2	
	1	1	3	2	
3	1	1	2	2	3

2	2	1	1	3	1
3	3	1	1	2	
1		1	1		
1	1		1	1	
3	3	1		3	3
2	2	1	1	2	2

1	3	1	1		1	3
1		2	2	1	1	1
	2	2		1	0	
2	2	1	1	2		1
2		1		1	1	
2	1	2		2		1
2	2		2	2	1	2

2		2		2	2	3
	1	2	1		1	1
2	2	2		1	0	
2	1		2	3	1	
2	1	3		2		1
2	1		1		1	
1	1		2	1		2

 Turn to page 196 for the solutions

CHAIN LINK

3	2	3	3
2	1	1	1
2	1	0	2
3	1	2	2

2	2	2	2
3	1	3	2
3	2	2	3
3	2	1	1

	1	2	2	2	1
1	2	1	0	1	2
2	1			1	2
1			1	3	2
2	1	1	0	1	3
1	1	2	2	2	2

2	2	2	1		3
1	1	1	2	3	2
2	3	1	1	2	2
2	2	2	2	1	1
3	2	2	2	1	
1	1	2	2	3	1

3		2		2	3	1
1	1		2	3	2	1
1		2		1	1	2
2	1	1	0	1		1
2		0		3	1	
1	2		1	2		2
		2	2	1	1	1

	3	2		2		2
2	1	2	2	1		1
2	1	3		2	1	
1		2	1	1	2	2
	0	1	2		2	2
2		1	2			2
	1		2	2	1	2

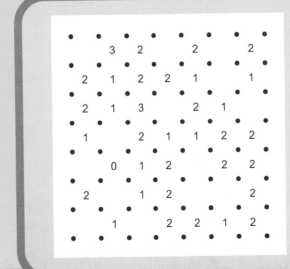

Turn to page 196 for the solutions

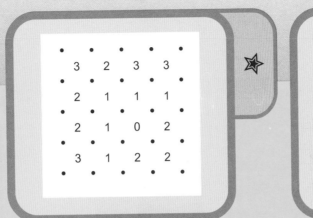

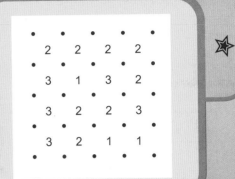

NAME SUMS

In the names below, each letter has been given a value of 1-6. The total value for each name is reached by adding up the individual values of the letters in the name. No two different alphabetical letters can have the same number in any one puzzle. Start by working out what each letter is worth. Some of the numbers have been inserted to get you started.

★

M	A	Y	= 6
1		3	

M	I	A	= 7
1			

E	D	A	= 13
5			

E	M	M	A	=
5	1	1		

★★★

L	A	R	R	Y	= 21
				4	

C	A	R	L	= 16
5				

M	A	R	C	= 14
			5	

M	A	L	= 6

A	M	Y	= 7
		4	

M	A	R	L	A	=

★

J	U	D	= 6
3	2		

J	O	Y	= 12
3		5	

J	O	E	= 13
3			

J	U	D	Y	=

★★

M	A	L	= 11
2	5		

G	I	L	L	= 12

L	I	A	M	= 14
		5	2	

G	A	I	L	=
	5			

★★

J	A	N	= 6
2	3		

A	N	N	E	= 9
3				

E	N	A	= 8
		3	

J	A	N	E	=
2	3			

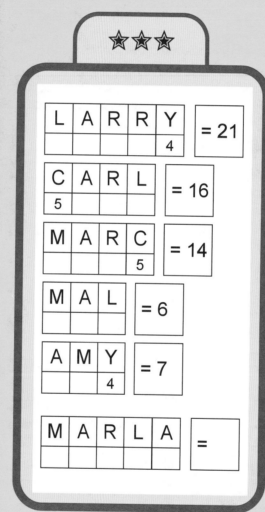

 Turn to page 196 for the solutions

NAME SUMS

★

A	V	A	= 4
	2		

V	A	L	= 6
2		3	

R	A	E	= 10
4			

V	E	R	A	=
2		4		

★★

R	H	O	N	A	= 15
			4		

R	O	N	= 12
		4	

A	N	N	= 10
	4	4	

N	O	R	A	=
4				

★★★

J	I	L	L	= 19

M	O	L	L	Y	= 20
	1			2	

M	I	M	I	= 18

J	I	M	= 12

J	I	M	M	Y	=
				2	

★

B	O	B	= 11
	5		

J	I	L	L	= 9
4	1			

L	I	B	= 6
	1		

B	I	L	L	=
	1			

★★★

D	A	R	Y	L	= 19
1	3				

R	O	D	= 9
		1	

L	O	R	A	= 16
			3	

A	L	L	Y	= 17
3				

L	L	O	Y	D	=
				1	

Turn to page 196 for the solutions

NAME SUMS

In the names below, each letter has been given a value of 1-6. The total value for each name is reached by adding up the individual values of the letters in the name. No two different alphabetical letters can have the same number in any one puzzle. Start by working out what each letter is worth. Some of the numbers have been inserted to get you started.

★

A	N	N	
4			= 10

I	N	A	
2		4	= 9

A	N	N	I	E	
4			2		= 13

N	I	N	A	
	2		4	=

★★★

R	U	B	Y	
		3	1	= 12

B	U	D	D	Y	
3				1	= 16

B	U	R	T	
3				= 15

B	U	D	
3			= 10

T	R	U	D	Y	
				1	=

★

J	I	M	
		3	= 14

M	A	C	
3		2	= 9

M	I	C	K	
3		2	1	= 11

J	A	C	K	
		2	1	=

★★

T	A	R	A	
		3		= 10

R	A	Y	
3		2	= 6

H	A	R	R	Y	
		3	3	2	= 13

T	Y	R	A	
	2	3		=

★★

R	O	S	S	
				= 16

R	O	S	A	
			6	= 18

S	E	R	G	E	
	2			2	= 12

R	O	S	E	
			2	=

Turn to page 196 for the solutions

NAME SUMS

★

R	O	S	= 10
		1	

I	R	A	= 9
3		2	

C	R	I	S	= 14
		3	1	

I	R	I	S	=
3		3	1	

★★

S	A	L	= 9

S	L	Y	= 10
		4	

L	I	L	I	= 14

L	I	S	A	=

★★★

P	E	T	A	= 16
5				

T	R	E	V	= 10
			4	

E	V	E	= 10
	4		

P	A	T	= 13
5			

P	E	T	E	R	=
5					

★

L	O	U	= 8
1		3	

C	O	L	= 10
		1	

S	L	Y	= 9
6	1		

L	U	C	Y	=
1	3			

★★★

G	L	E	N	= 17
		5		

L	E	N	A	= 16
	5			

G	L	E	N	D	A	= 21
		5		3		

D	E	A	N	= 13
3	5			

A	N	G	E	L	=
			5		

Turn to page 196 for the solutions

NAME SUMS

In the names below, each letter has been given a value of 1-6. The total value for each name is reached by adding up the individual values of the letters in the name. No two different alphabetical letters can have the same number in any one puzzle. Start by working out what each letter is worth. Some of the numbers have been inserted to get you started.

★

N	Y	E	= 11
4		6	

N	A	T	= 11
4			

T	O	Y	A	= 11
	3			

T	O	N	Y	=
	3	4		

★

P	E	L	E	= 10
	1		1	

P	A	T	= 9
	4	2	

P	E	T	A	= 10
	1	2	4	

P	E	T	E	=
	1	2	1	

★★★

S	O	N	N	Y	= 15
	1			6	

R	O	S	E	= 13
	1			

R	E	E	S	E	= 18

R	E	N	E	E	= 16

O	R	S	O	N	=
1			1		

★★

R	A	B	= 10
		2	

R	E	B	A	= 14
		2		

B	E	R	T	= 12
2				

B	A	R	T	=
2				

★★

G	U	S	= 13
		6	

D	O	T	= 8
		1	

D	U	D	= 10

D	O	U	G	=

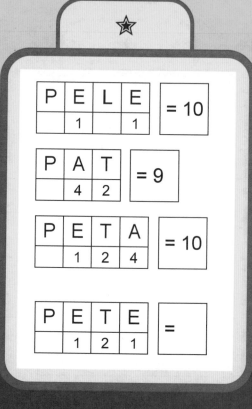

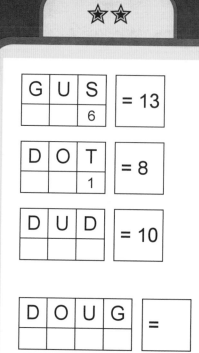

 Turn to page 196 for the solutions

NAME SUMS

★

S	A	M		= 8
	3	4		
L	I	A	M	=15
2		3	4	
L	I	S	A	=12
2			3	
S	I	A	N	=15
		3		
L	A	N	A	=
2	3		3	

★★

N	A	T			= 10
S	T	U			= 13
		6			
T	A	N	I	A	= 13
			1		
S	T	A	N		=

★★★

M	I	L	E	S		= 15
3						
E	L	S	I	E		= 14
L	E	E				= 9
E	M	M	I	E		= 11
	3	3				
M	I	L	L	I	E	=
3						

★

K	E	N		= 9
		2		
A	N	N	E	=12
	2	2		
L	E	N		= 6
1		2		
N	E	I	L	=12
2			1	
L	E	E		=
1				

★★★

E	L	L	A		= 12
6					
C	E	R	I		= 16
	6		5		
L	A	R	A		= 12
C	A	R	L	A	= 14
C	E	L	I	A	=
	6		5		

Turn to page 196 for the solutions

NAME SUMS

In the names below, each letter has been given a value of 1-6. The total value for each name is reached by adding up the individual values of the letters in the name. No two different alphabetical letters can have the same number in any one puzzle. Start by working out what each letter is worth. Some of the numbers have been inserted to get you started.

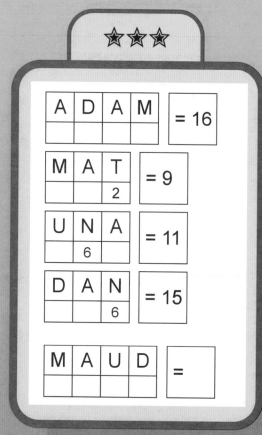

★★★

A	D	A	M	= 16

M	A	T	= 9
		2	

U	N	A	= 11
	6		

D	A	N	= 15
		6	

M	A	U	D	=

★★

W	I	L	L	= 12
3				

F	I	N	= 8
		5	

F	I	F	I	= 6

W	I	L	F	=
3				

★

A	N	N	= 7
	3	3	

S	O	N	I	A	=17
5		3			

I	A	N	= 6
		3	

L	I	S	A	=12
		5		

S	A	L	=10
5			

A	L	I	S	O	N	=
			5		3	

★

I	A	N	= 7
	2		

A	N	N	= 4
2			

T	I	N	A	=10
			2	

A	N	I	T	A	=
2				2	

★★

A	D	A	= 8

L	E	E	= 7
	3	3	

A	L	D	A	= 9

D	A	L	E	=

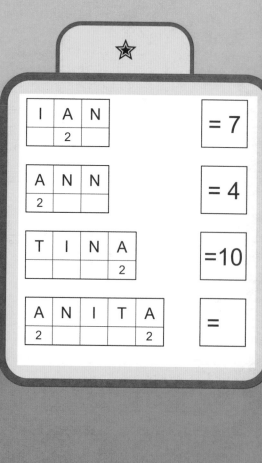

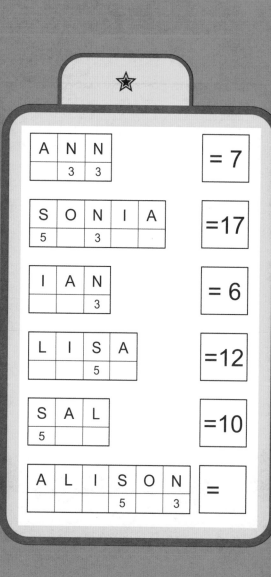

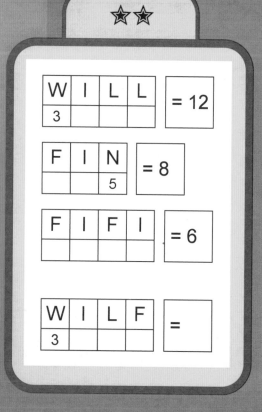

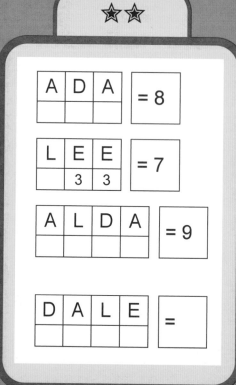

 Turn to page 196 for the solutions

NAME SUMS

★

E	M	M	A	=10
	1	1	3	

M	A	R	Y	=12
1	3			

M	A	R	K	=13
1	3			

R	A	Y	=11
	3		

K	I	M	=12
		1	

M	I	K	E	=17
1				

K	E	R	R	Y	=

★★

B	I	L	L	= 9

L	I	B	B	Y	= 11

B	O	B	= 7
	5		

L	I	L	Y	=

★★★

B	Y	R	O	N	= 25
				7	

R	O	B	I	N	= 21
			1	7	

S	O	N	N	Y	= 24
		7	7		

B	R	Y	N	= 22
			7	

N	O	R	R	I	S	= 25
7				1		

B	O	R	I	S	=
			1		

★

R	O	Y	=11
2		6	

J	O	Y	=10
		6	

R	O	N	=10
2			

R	A	Y	=12
2		6	

J	O	A	N	N	A	=

★★★

G	E	R	R	Y	= 11
				4	

R	O	R	Y	= 11
	5		4	

G	A	R	Y	= 13
			4	

G	R	E	G	= 8

R	O	G	E	R	=
	5				

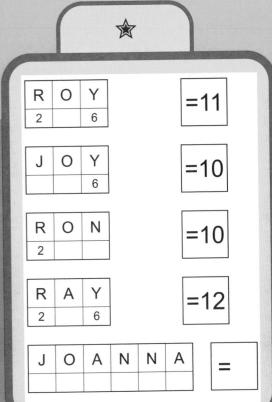

Turn to page 196 for the solutions

NAME SUMS

In the names below, each letter has been given a value of 1-6. The total value for each name is reached by adding up the individual values of the letters in the name. No two different alphabetical letters can have the same number in any one puzzle. Start by working out what each letter is worth. Some of the numbers have been inserted to get you started.

☆☆

D	A	N	
		4	= 10

A	D	A	M	
			3	= 10

D	E	E	
			= 9

D	E	A	N	
			4	=

☆☆

A	N	N	
			= 5

I	N	A	
5			= 8

N	A	T	H	A	N	
			4			= 13

T	I	N	A	
	5			=

☆☆☆

D	E	A	N	
			1	= 14

S	A	D	E	
				= 16

I	N	D	I	A	
	1				= 16

S	I	N	E	A	D	
		1				= 21

D	E	N	N	I	S	
		1	1			=

☆☆

E	V	E	
3		3	= 7

A	V	A	
			= 9

A	D	A	
			= 10

D	A	V	E	
			3	=

☆☆☆

S	E	A	N	
3				= 11

S	A	U	L	
3			4	= 18

A	N	N	E	
				= 10

L	E	N	
4			= 7

S	U	S	A	N	
3		3			=

 Turn to page 196 for the solutions

NAME SUMS

★★

K	A	T	= 7
		1	

K	A	T	I	E	= 15
		1	3		

K	I	T	= 8
	3	1	

K	A	T	E	=
		1		

★★★

D	A	V	I	D	= 12
		2			

N	A	D	I	A	= 16

N	I	N	A	= 16

D	A	N	A	= 11

V	I	V	= 9
2		2	

V	I	V	I	A	N	=
2		2				

★★

Z	O	R	A	= 14
			5	

Z	A	R	A	= 15
	5		5	

L	A	R	A	= 13
	5		5	

Z	O	L	A	=
			5	

★★★

M	A	D	G	E	= 16
				4	

M	E	G	= 8
	4		

M	A	D	D	I	E	= 26
				5	4	

G	E	M	M	A	= 13
	4				

M	A	G	G	I	E	=
				5	4	

★★★

J	O	N	N	Y	= 18
3				6	

L	E	N	N	Y	= 21
				6	

N	E	L	L	= 13

L	E	O	N	= 12

J	O	L	E	N	E	=
3						

Turn to page 196 for the solutions

SOLUTIONS

P4

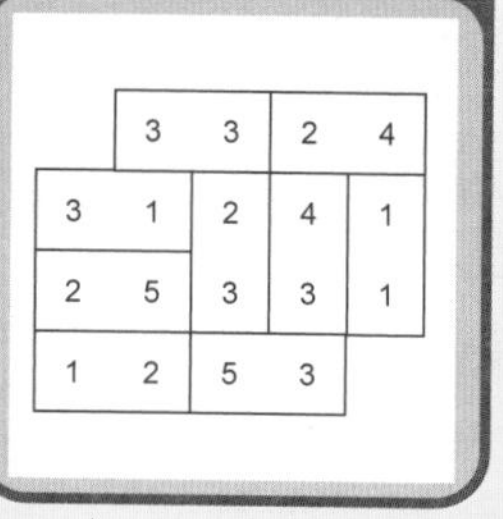

P4

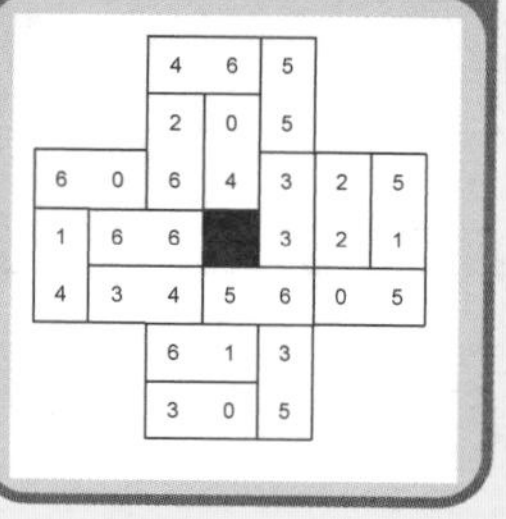

P4

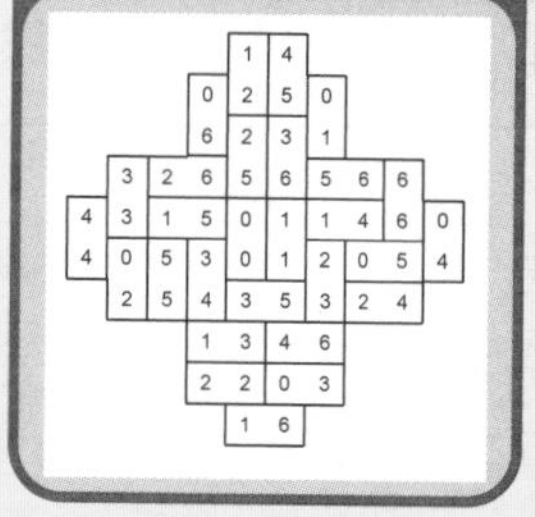

P4

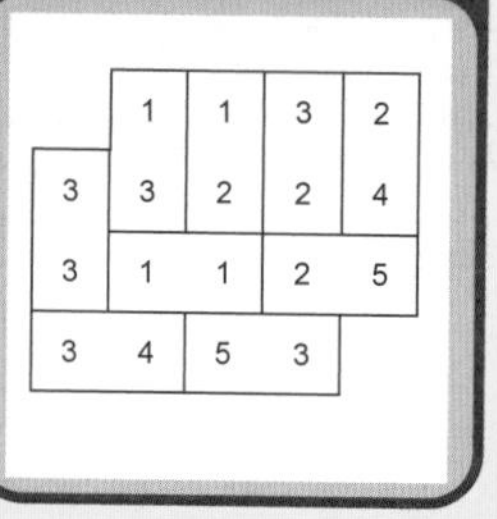

P4

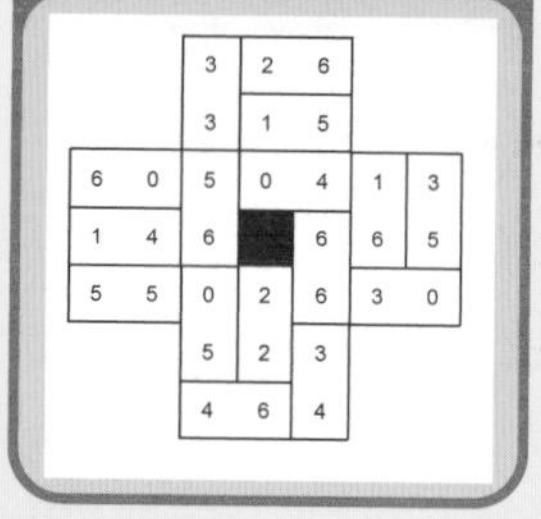

P5

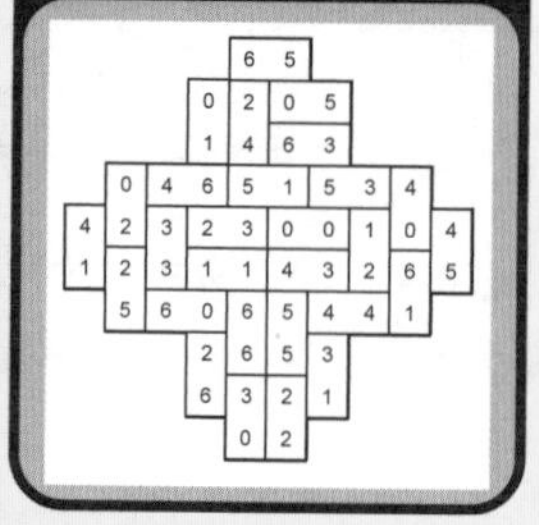

P5

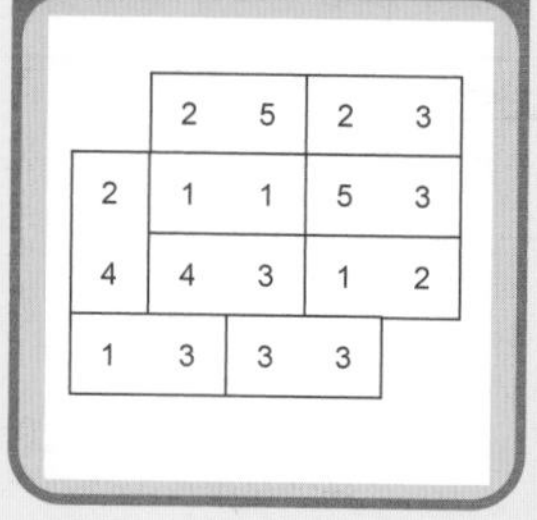

P5

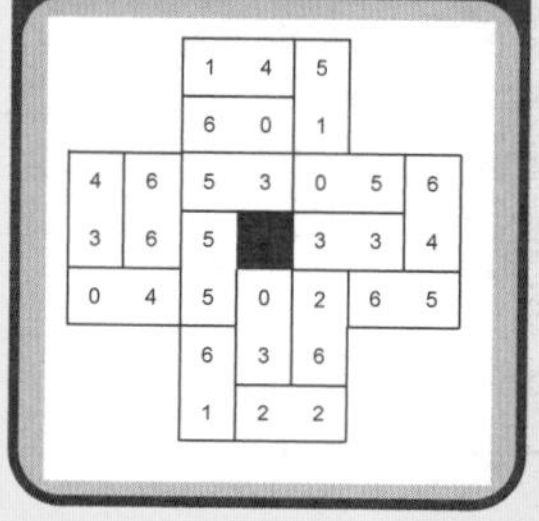

P5

P5

P6

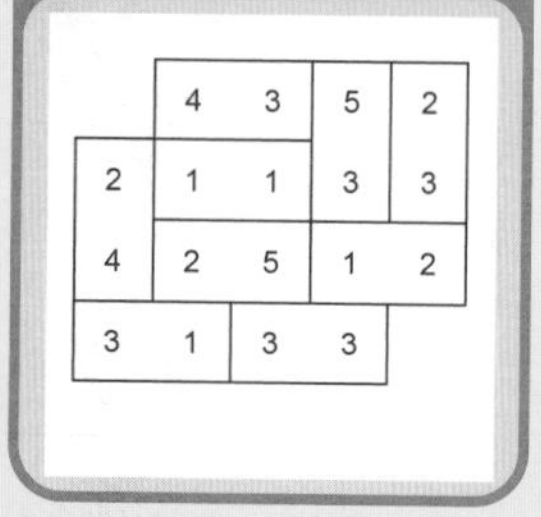

P6

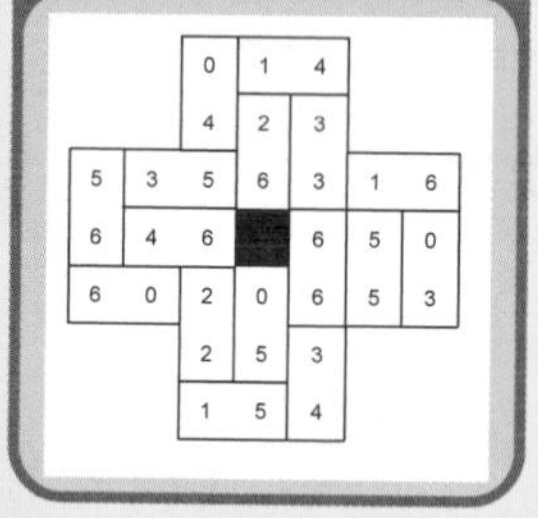

P6

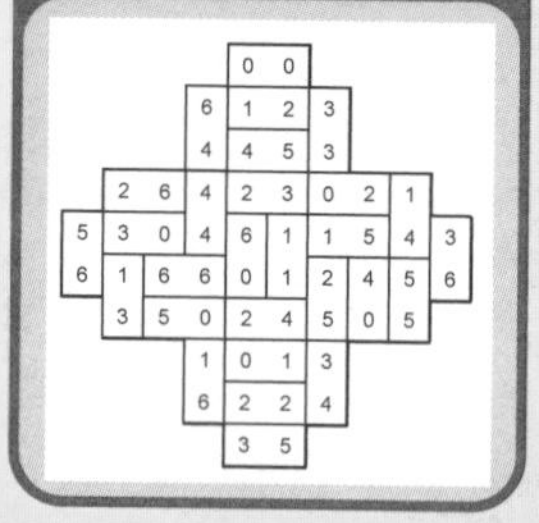

P6

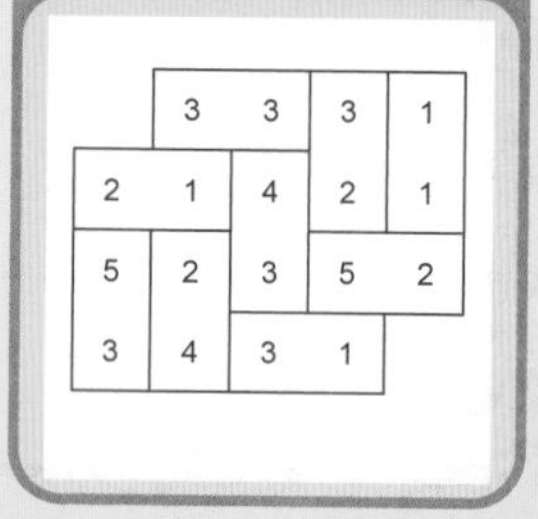

P6

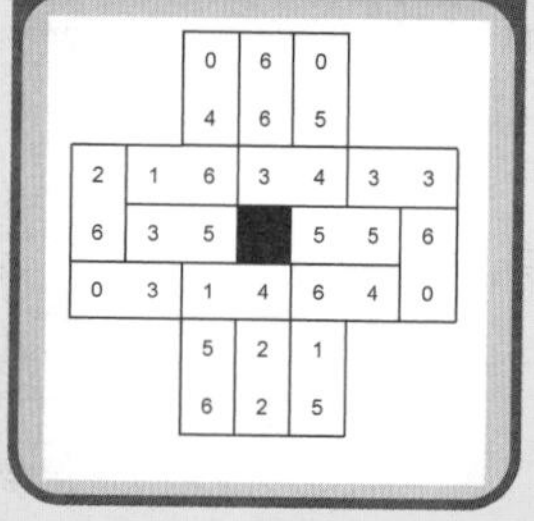

P7

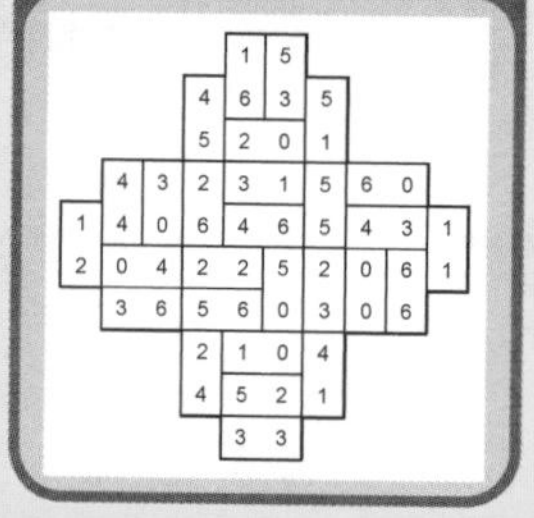

P7

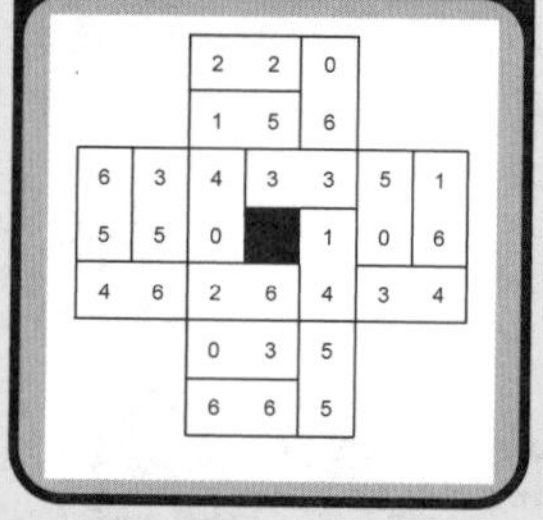

P7

P7

P7

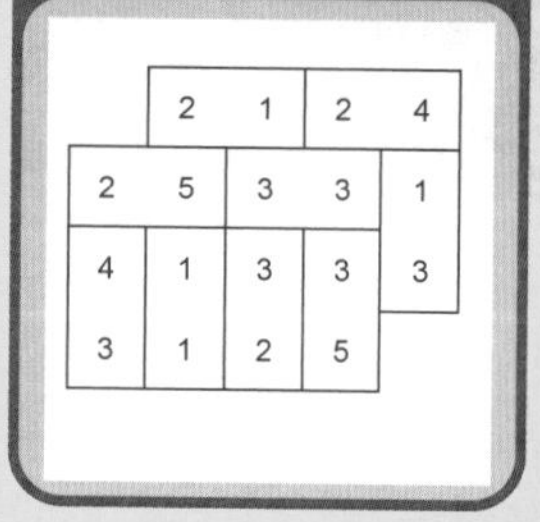

P8

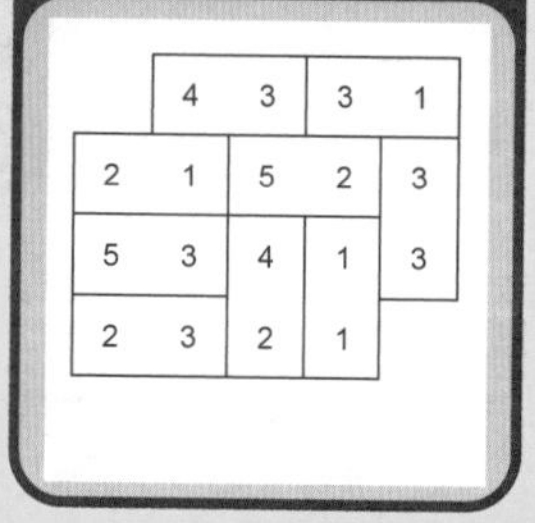

P8

P8

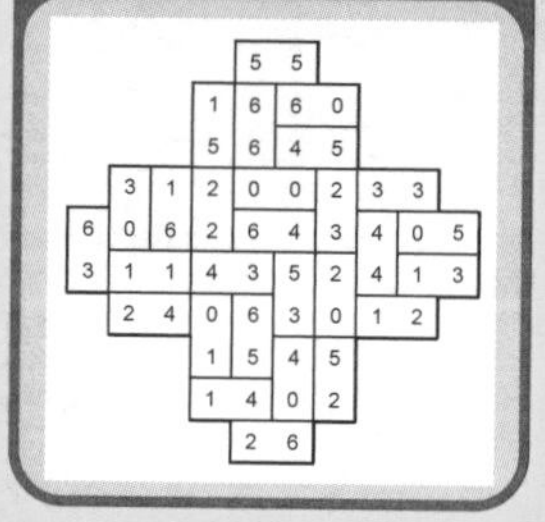

P8

P8

P9

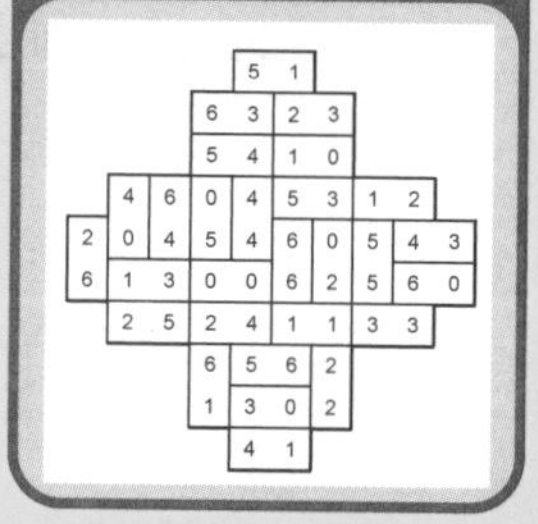

P9

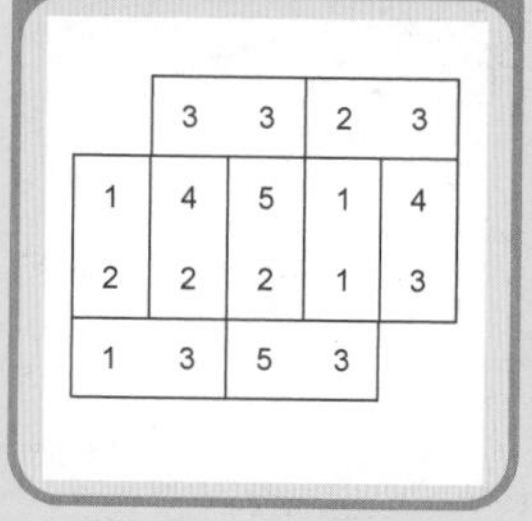

P9

P9

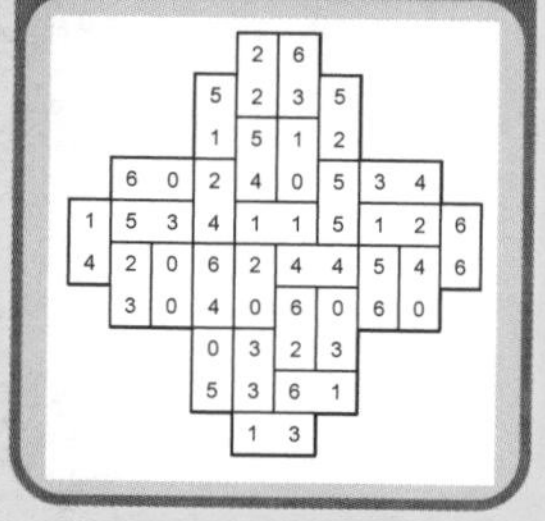

P9

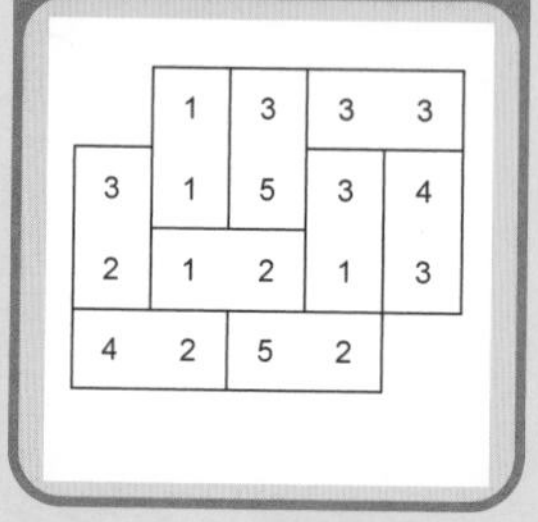

P10

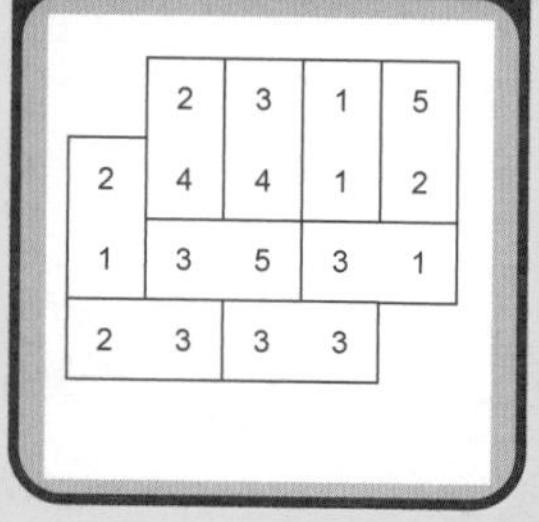

P10

P10

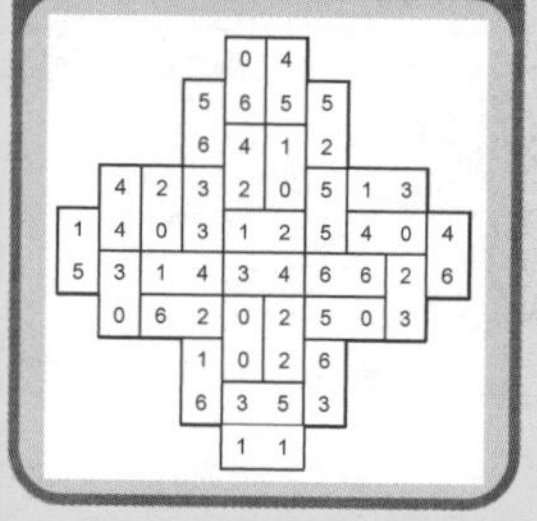

P10

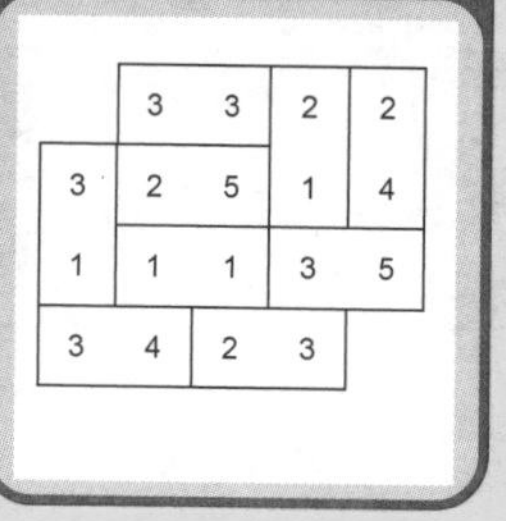

P10

P11

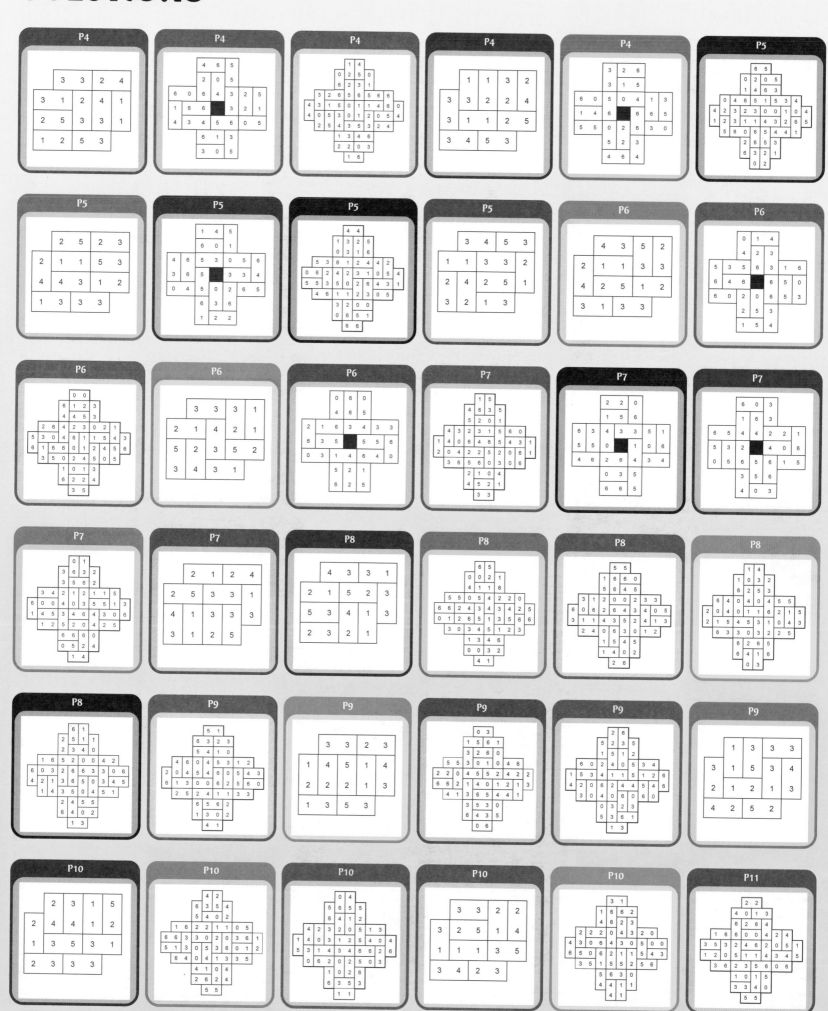

The answers correspond to the questions when read from left to right, and from top to bottom

SOLUTIONS

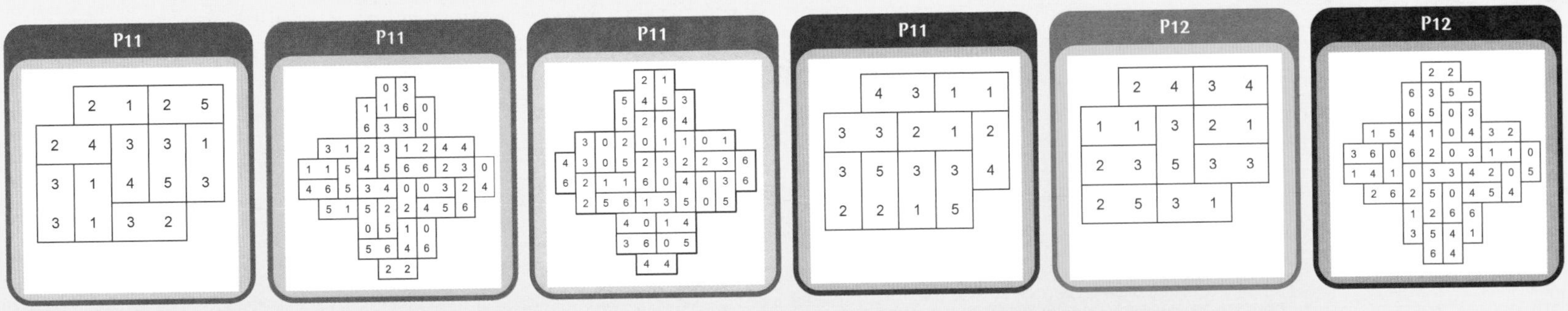
P11
P11
P11
P11
P12
P12

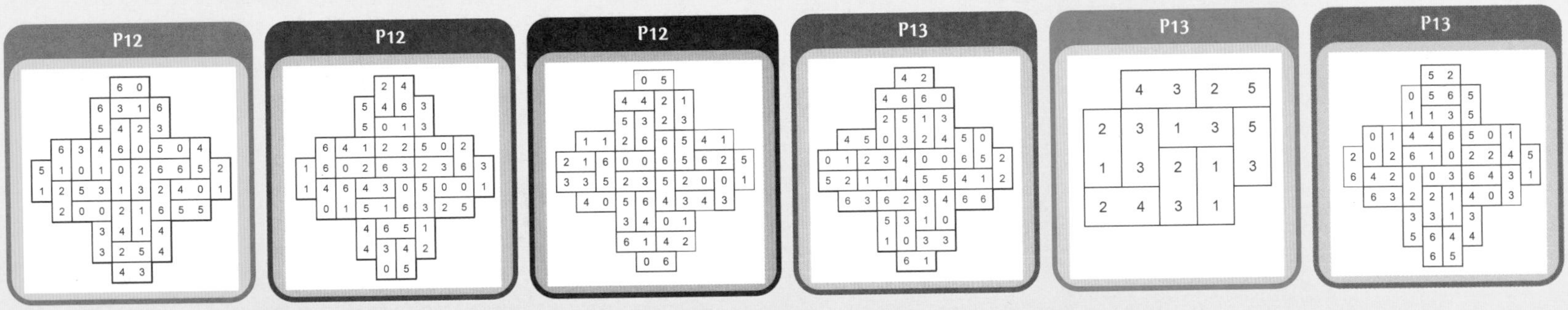
P12
P12
P12
P13
P13
P13

P13
P13
P14
P14
P14
P14

P14
P15
P15
P15
P15
P15

P16
P16
P16
P16
P16
P17

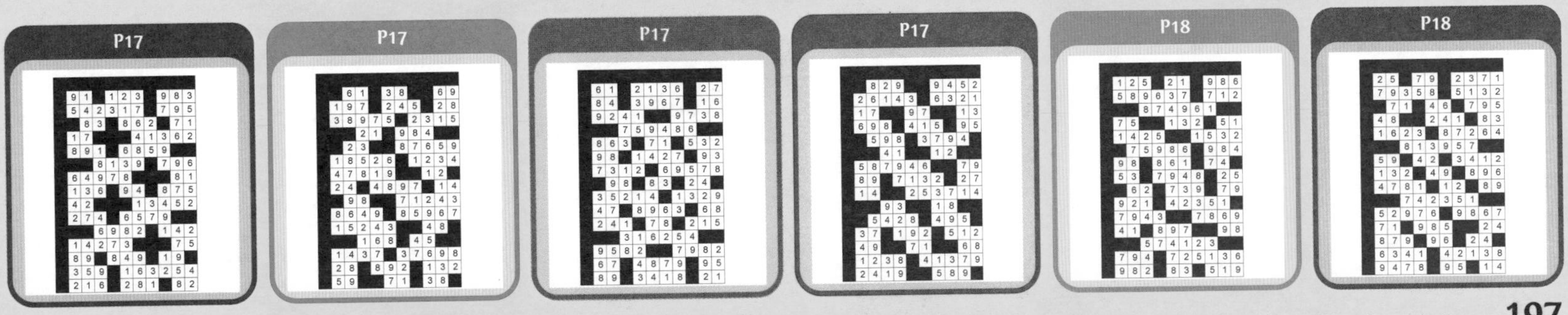
P17
P17
P17
P17
P18
P18

SOLUTIONS

P18

P18

P18

P19

P19

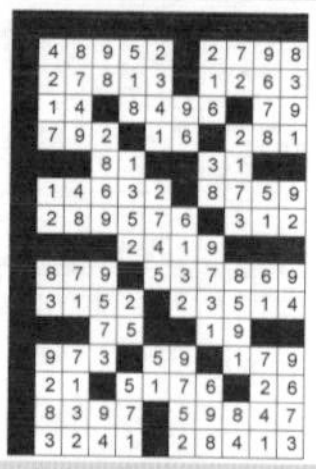

P19

P19

P19

P20

P20

P20

P20

P20

P21

P21

P21

P21

P21

P22

P22

P22

P22

P22

P23

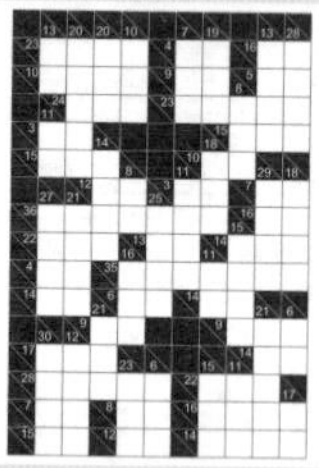

P23

P23

P23

P23

P24

B

Each square adds up to 64

P24

C

Each circle adds up to 10

P24

C

The squares add up to 25, 50, 75 and finally 100

P24

A

The diagonals in each square add up to the same

P24

B

The numbers rotate clockwise by one segment

P25

B

The central number increases by 1, the others by 2

P25

C

Multiply all the numbers in a square. They equal 100

P25

A

The top two segments, when added, equal the bottom segment

 The answers correspond to the questions when read from left to right, and from top to bottom

SOLUTIONS

P25
B
The numbers in the small squares increase by 1, 2, 3 and 4, thus the total increases by 10 each time

P25
A
The top row of each square adds up to 12, the middle row 15, and the bottom 18

P26
C
The top two numbers add up to the same as the bottom two

P26
A
The numbers increase by 2 clockwise starting from the left segment

P26
B
Each row has two numbers which multiply together to give the third

P26
B
Moving clockwise from the top right the numbers decrease by 7, thus the top two numbers add up to the same as the bottom two

P26
B
The right segment divided by the bottom segment equals the left segment

P27
C
The odd numbers are doubled, even numbers halved, along the squares

P27
A
The total of the segments equals 25

P27
B
The bottom number is the total of the other two

P27
A
The digits of the numbers in each small square add up to 8

P27
A
The total of the top row minus the total of the bottom row equals the total of the middle row

P28
A
In each square you can add three of the segments together to give the fourth

P28
C
Each number increases by 5 each time

P28
A
Each square contains the same nine numbers

P28
C
The number 6 moves clockwise two spaces, the 4 moves four spaces and the 3 moves clockwise one

P28
B
The number 4 can go into all the numbers exactly

P29
D
Multiply each corner number by the central number to give the remaining four numbers in the grid

P29
C
Each number increases by 9 moving along the boxes, thus the total increases by 36 each time

P29
C
The total of each circle increases by 2 each time

P29
B
Multiply three numbers in each square to give the bottom left number

P29
A
The diagonals in each grid add up to 20

P30
A
Moving clockwise from the bottom left, the numbers double each time

P30
B
Each segment increases by 1 each time

P30
C
The numbers in column one increase by 1, column two by 2 and column three by 3

P30
C
Moving clockwise from the top left, multiply by 1, 2, 3 and 4 to give the next square

P30
A
The left segment multiplied by the bottom number equals the right segment

P31
D
In each column subtract the second number from the top one to give the bottom number

P31
A
Each number moves anti-clockwise by one place each time

P31
B
The left number is 6 higher than the right and 2 more than the bottom

P31
B
When multiplied the two left numbers equal the two right ones

P31
D
The outer numbers all move clockwise round the grid two spaces

P32
C
Each grid adds up to 15, 30, 45 then 60

P32
A
The numbers decrease by 3 each time

P32
C
The numbers increase by 9 across the rows

P32
B
One pair of diagonal numbers, when added, is six times larger than the sum of the other pair

The answers correspond to the questions when read from left to right, and from top to bottom

SOLUTIONS

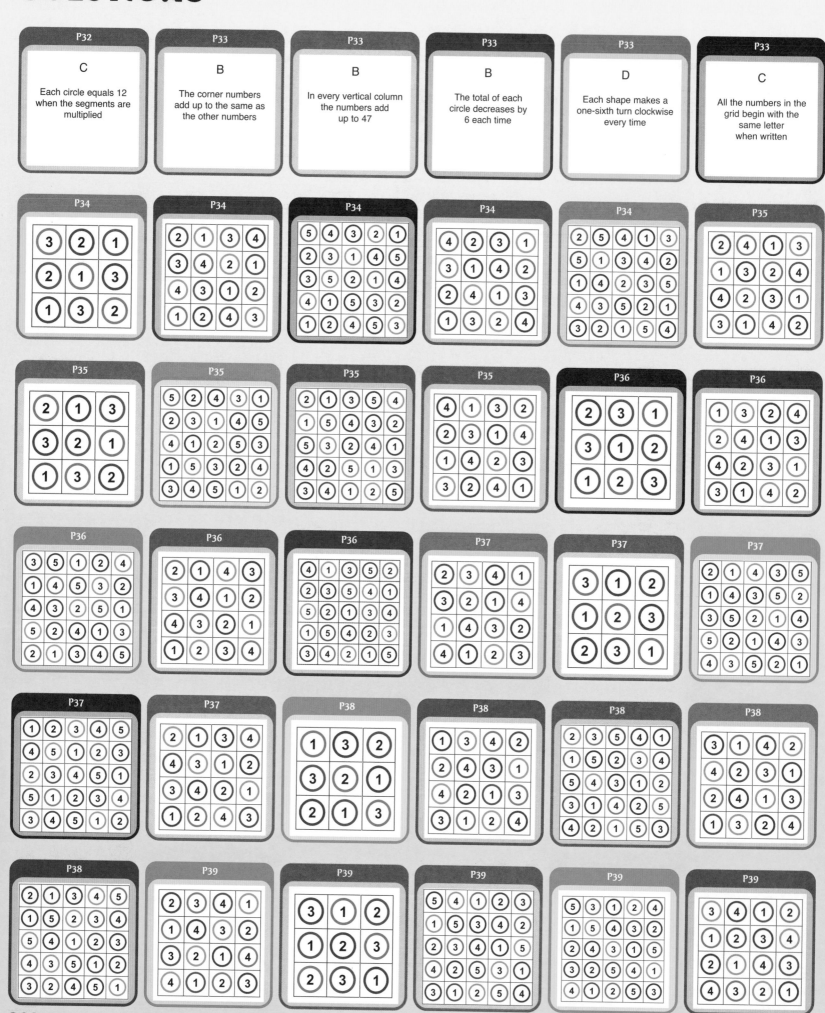

P32

C

Each circle equals 12 when the segments are multiplied

P33

B

The corner numbers add up to the same as the other numbers

P33

B

In every vertical column the numbers add up to 47

P33

B

The total of each circle decreases by 6 each time

P33

D

Each shape makes a one-sixth turn clockwise every time

P33

C

All the numbers in the grid begin with the same letter when written

P34

3	2	1
2	1	3
1	3	2

P34

2	1	3	4
3	4	2	1
4	3	1	2
1	2	4	3

P34

5	4	3	2	1
2	3	1	4	5
3	5	2	1	4
4	1	5	3	2
1	2	4	5	3

P34

4	2	3	1
3	1	4	2
2	4	1	3
1	3	2	4

P34

2	5	4	1	3
5	1	3	4	2
1	4	2	3	5
4	3	5	2	1
3	2	1	5	4

P35

2	4	1	3
1	3	2	4
4	2	3	1
3	1	4	2

P35

2	1	3
3	2	1
1	3	2

P35

5	2	4	3	1
2	3	1	4	5
4	1	2	5	3
1	5	3	2	4
3	4	5	1	2

P35

2	1	3	5	4
1	5	4	3	2
5	3	2	4	1
4	2	5	1	3
3	4	1	2	5

P35

4	1	3	2
2	3	1	4
1	4	2	3
3	2	4	1

P36

2	3	1
3	1	2
1	2	3

P36

1	3	2	4
2	4	1	3
4	2	3	1
3	1	4	2

P36

3	5	1	2	4
1	4	5	3	2
4	3	2	5	1
5	2	4	1	3
2	1	3	4	5

P36

2	1	4	3
3	4	1	2
4	3	2	1
1	2	3	4

P36

4	1	3	5	2
2	3	5	4	1
5	2	1	3	4
1	5	4	2	3
3	4	2	1	5

P37

2	3	4	1
3	2	1	4
1	4	3	2
4	1	2	3

P37

3	1	2
1	2	3
2	3	1

P37

2	1	4	3	5
1	4	3	5	2
3	5	2	1	4
5	2	1	4	3
4	3	5	2	1

P37

1	2	3	4	5
4	5	1	2	3
2	3	4	5	1
5	1	2	3	4
3	4	5	1	2

P37

2	1	3	4
4	3	1	2
3	4	2	1
1	2	4	3

P38

1	3	2
3	2	1
2	1	3

P38

1	3	4	2
2	4	3	1
4	2	1	3
3	1	2	4

P38

2	3	5	4	1
1	5	2	3	4
5	4	3	1	2
3	1	4	2	5
4	2	1	5	3

P38

3	1	4	2
4	2	3	1
2	4	1	3
1	3	2	4

P38

2	1	3	4	5
1	5	2	3	4
5	4	1	2	3
4	3	5	1	2
3	2	4	5	1

P39

2	3	4	1
1	4	3	2
3	2	1	4
4	1	2	3

P39

3	1	2
1	2	3
2	3	1

P39

5	4	1	2	3
1	5	3	4	2
2	3	4	1	5
4	2	5	3	1
3	1	2	5	4

P39

5	3	1	2	4
1	5	4	3	2
2	4	3	1	5
3	2	5	4	1
4	1	2	5	3

P39

3	4	1	2
1	2	3	4
2	1	4	3
4	3	2	1

The answers correspond to the questions when read from left to right, and from top to bottom

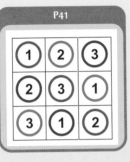

SOLUTIONS

P40

2	1	3
3	2	1
1	3	2

P40

2	4	1	3
3	1	4	2
1	3	2	4
4	2	3	1

P40

5	2	3	1	4
4	5	1	2	3
2	1	4	3	5
3	4	2	5	1
1	3	5	4	2

P40

2	4	1	3
1	3	2	4
4	2	3	1
3	1	4	2

P40

1	3	5	4	2
2	1	4	3	5
4	5	1	2	3
3	4	2	5	1
5	2	3	1	4

P41

1	2	3	4
4	3	2	1
3	4	1	2
2	1	4	3

P41

1	2	3
2	3	1
3	1	2

P41

2	4	3	5	1
1	3	2	4	5
4	1	5	2	3
3	5	4	1	2
5	2	1	3	4

P41

2	5	1	3	4
1	4	5	2	3
3	1	2	4	5
4	2	3	5	1
5	3	4	1	2

P41

2	4	1	3
1	3	2	4
4	2	3	1
3	1	4	2

P42

3	2	1
1	3	2
2	1	3

P42

2	1	4	3
3	4	1	2
4	3	2	1
1	2	3	4

P42

1	4	2	5	3
4	5	1	3	2
2	1	3	4	5
5	3	4	2	1
3	2	5	1	4

P42

3	4	2	1
4	3	1	2
2	1	3	4
1	2	4	3

P42

2	5	1	3	4
1	4	5	2	3
3	1	2	4	5
4	2	3	5	1
5	3	4	1	2

P43

2	1	4	3
4	3	2	1
3	4	1	2
1	2	3	4

P43

3	2	1
1	3	2
2	1	3

P43

3	2	1	4	5
1	4	5	3	2
5	3	2	1	4
2	1	4	5	3
4	5	3	2	1

P43

4	3	2	5	1
1	4	5	3	2
5	2	4	1	3
2	1	3	4	5
3	5	1	2	4

P43

2	3	1	4
4	1	3	2
3	2	4	1
1	4	2	3

P44

Allowing for reflections and reversals, here is one possible solution:

14	19	18
21	17	13
16	15	20

P44

2	11	5	16
13	8	10	3
12	1	15	6
7	14	4	9

P44

2	1	9
4	3	8
6	5	7

P44

Allowing for reflections and reversals, here is one possible solution:

12	21	15
19	16	13
17	11	20

P44

The numbers which have changed places are shown in bold type.

8	**1**	24	17	15
2	25	18	11	**9**
21	19	12	**10**	3
20	13	**6**	4	22
14	7	5	23	16

P45

Allowing for reflections and reversals, here is one possible solution:

3	9	3
5	5	5
7	1	7

P45

17	33	22
29	24	19
26	15	31

P45

The numbers which have changed places are shown in bold type.

23	24	8	**14**	19
9	15	**38**	19	7
20	9	12	25	22
15	17	20	17	**19**
21	**23**	10	13	21

P45

Allowing for reflections and reversals, here is one possible solution:

38	39	28
25	35	45
42	31	32

P45

Allowing for reflections and reversals, here is one possible solution:

7	2	9
8	6	4
3	10	5

P46

Allowing for reflections and reversals, here is one possible solution:

4	8	9
12	7	2
5	6	10

P46

57	27	24	26
17	33	39	45
31	40	22	41
29	34	49	22

P46

Allowing for reflections and reversals, here is one possible solution:

10	11	15
17	12	7
9	13	14

P46

13	10	13	29
27	15	18	5
19	12	20	14
6	28	14	17

P46

The numbers which have changed places are shown in bold type.

36	21	16	15	12
3	**6**	43	34	14
20	14	10	26	**30**
17	20	**27**	20	16
24	39	4	**5**	28

P47

2	24	16	26
28	14	22	4
30	12	20	6
8	18	10	32

The answers correspond to the questions when read from left to right, and from top to bottom

SOLUTIONS

P47

22	16	23	38
37	24	28	10
31	24	23	21
9	35	25	30

P47

The numbers which have changed places are shown in bold type.

15	6	14	27	**40**	11
32	**18**	17	7	23	16
29	25	18	**12**	13	16
12	25	23	24	14	**15**
9	28	**22**	31	3	20
16	11	19	12	20	35

P47

Allowing for reflections and reversals, here is one possible solution:

3	18	9
16	10	4
11	2	17

P47

Allowing for reflections and reversals, here is one possible solution:

6	1	8
7	5	3
2	9	4

P48

Allowing for reflections and reversals, here is one possible solution:

3	7	8
11	6	1
4	5	9

P48

18	15	17	12
20	9	17	16
14	23	13	12
10	15	15	22

P48

Allowing for reflections and reversals, here is one possible solution:

8	9	4
3	7	11
10	5	6

P48

8	6	7	4
6	6	3	1
9	5	0	2
7	5	2	9

P48

The numbers which have changed places are shown in bold type.

20	**13**	17	17	25	42
37	22	13	**17**	24	21
34	29	22	18	12	19
15	39	**24**	26	10	20
12	10	26	34	32	**20**
16	21	32	22	**31**	12

P49

1	12	8	13
14	7	11	2
15	6	10	3
4	9	5	16

P49

26	28	31	14
13	34	27	25
19	17	21	42
41	20	20	18

P49

Allowing for reflections and reversals, here is one possible solution:

4	18	8
14	10	6
12	2	16

P49

The numbers which have changed places are shown in bold type.

13	5	14	31	44	15
30	**20**	21	9	22	20
36	29	20	10	6	**21**
6	30	22	30	**17**	17
10	26	23	**29**	12	22
27	12	**22**	13	21	27

P49

4	2	7	8
9	3	3	2
0	9	5	6
6	1	2	5

P50

26	21	24	12
12	22	23	26
18	21	17	27
27	19	19	18

P50

18	9	12	7
13	6	19	8
11	16	5	14
4	15	10	17

P50

16	2	8	5
2	11	6	12
7	14	0	10
6	4	17	4

P50

20	8	11	4
10	6	13	14
4	17	7	15
9	12	12	10

P50

The numbers which have changed places are shown in bold type.

29	28	21	17	15	4	**17**
27	18	17	22	**14**	16	17
30	11	**16**	16	20	20	18
4	17	12	7	36	**38**	17
1	19	18	**33**	18	26	16
5	18	41	10	14	20	23
35	**20**	6	26	14	7	23

P51

14	9	4	16
13	7	13	10
14	12	11	6
2	15	15	11

P51

14	11	13	12
7	18	14	11
13	8	10	19
16	13	13	8

P51

The numbers which have changed places are shown in bold type.

31	**8**	10	13	14	32	15
6	21	**20**	22	30	17	7
17	30	17	24	17	11	**7**
12	22	33	13	15	17	11
14	16	21	**19**	13	11	29
16	13	3	19	12	**17**	43
27	13	19	13	**22**	18	11

P51

22	18	3	10	14
5	5	35	21	1
19	7	5	19	17
7	13	21	13	13
14	24	3	4	22

P51

21	8	16	6
10	12	15	14
3	13	11	24
17	18	9	7

P52

34	11	14	18
21	11	25	20
18	30	11	18
4	25	27	21

P52

32	29	4	1	24	21
30	31	2	3	22	23
12	9	17	20	28	25
10	11	18	19	26	27
13	16	36	33	5	8
14	15	34	35	6	7

P52

2	9	3
4	5	6
8	1	7

P52

The numbers which have changed places are shown in bold type.

16	16	**3**	9	14
6	9	29	13	1
15	5	6	**17**	15
7	**11**	17	11	12
14	17	3	8	**16**

P52

27	16	25	9	18
14	23	37	16	5
1	5	19	33	37
33	22	1	15	24
20	29	13	22	11

P53

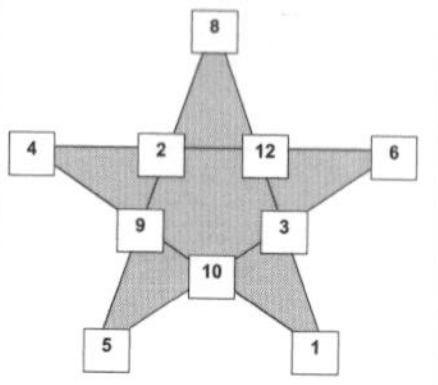

P53

The numbers which have changed places are shown in bold type.

20	10	21	1	**18**
19	14	**5**	18	14
3	19	4	**39**	5
12	14	23	10	11
16	**13**	17	2	22

P53

Allowing for reflections and reversals, here is one possible solution:

8	16	3
4	9	14
15	2	10

P53

5	13	16	24	23
21	28	6	9	18
12	14	23	25	9
28	7	13	16	20
19	22	25	8	11

P53

The numbers which have changed places are shown in bold type.

20	26	**6**	11	20
11	18	28	14	**12**
18	**7**	13	25	20
14	16	22	**16**	15
20	16	14	17	16

P54

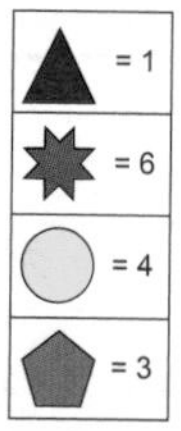

P54

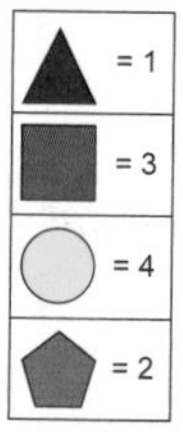

 The answers correspond to the questions when read from left to right, and from top to bottom

SOLUTIONS

The answers correspond to the questions when read from left to right, and from top to bottom

SOLUTIONS

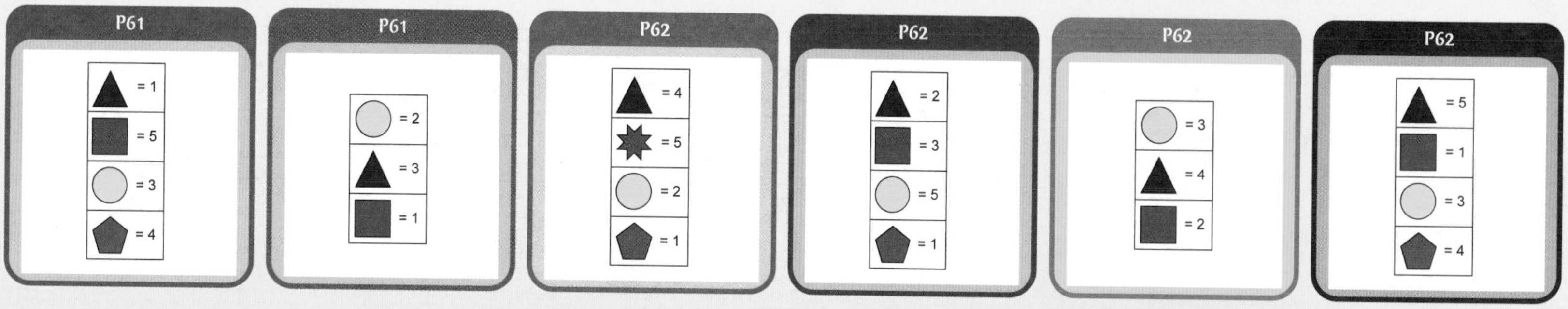

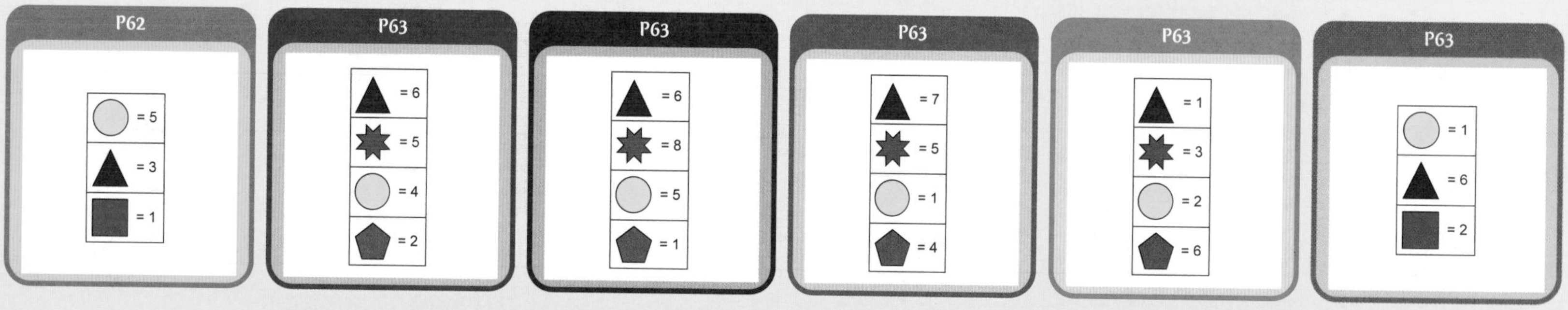

The answers correspond to the questions when read from left to right, and from top to bottom

SOLUTIONS

P68

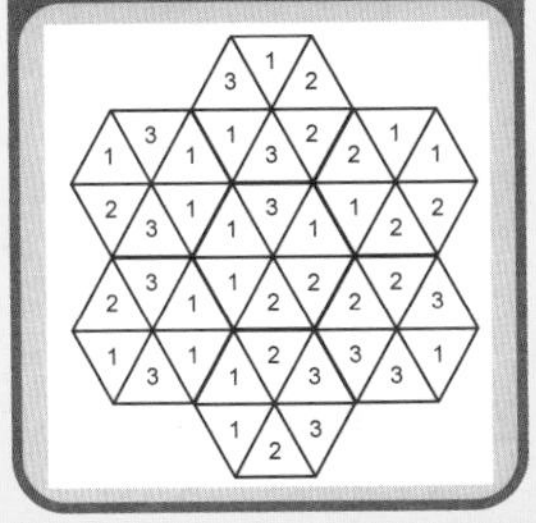

P69

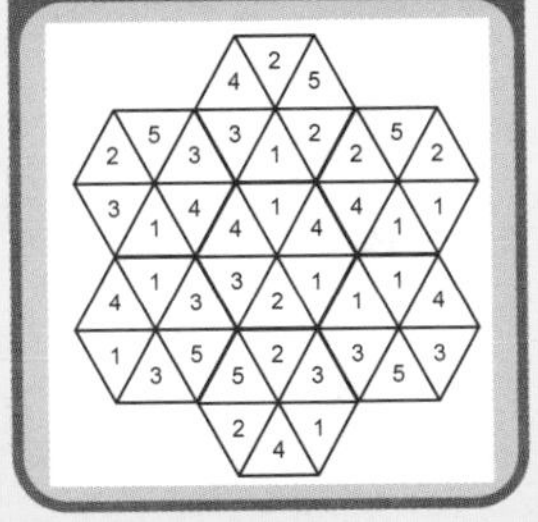

P69

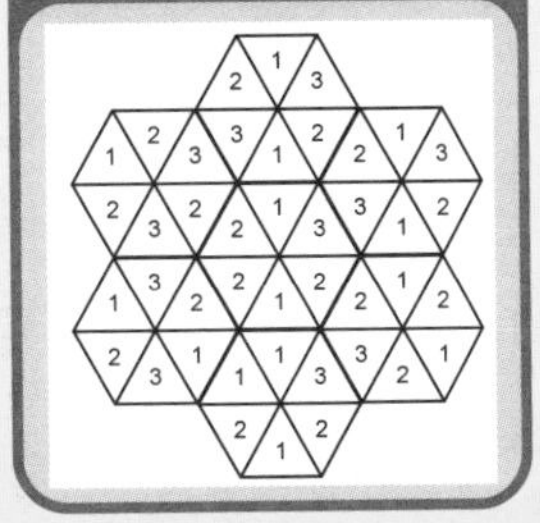

P69

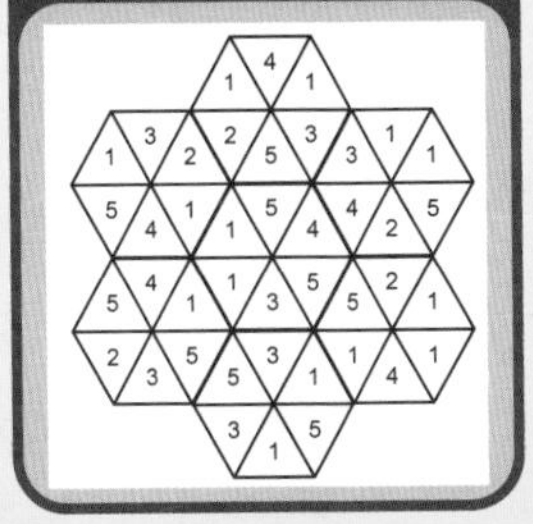

P69

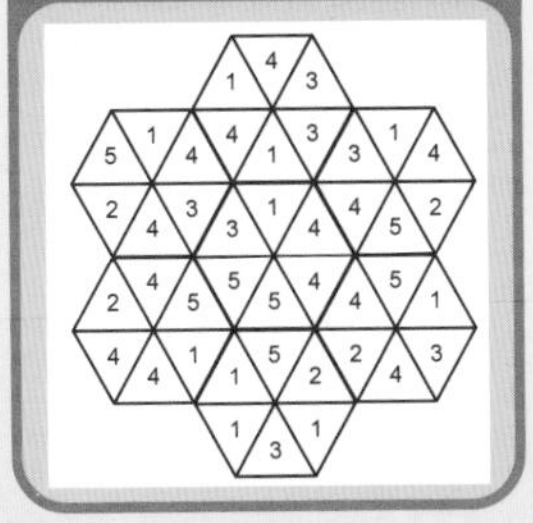

P69

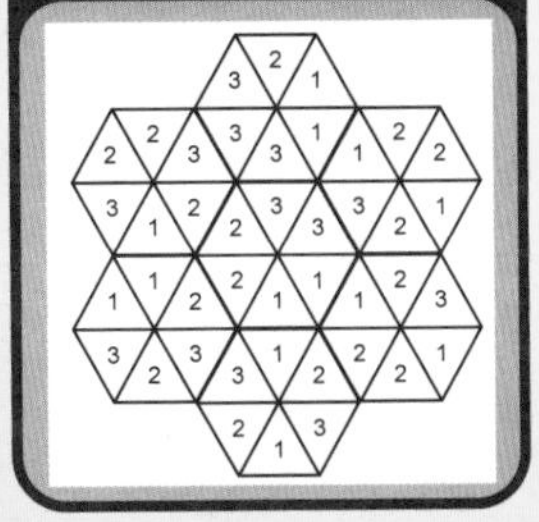

P70

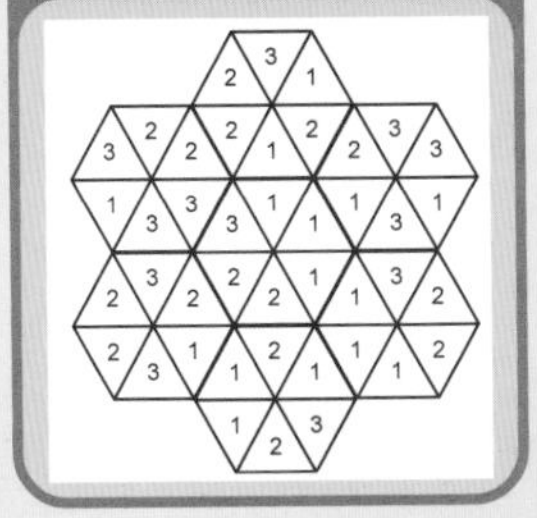

P70

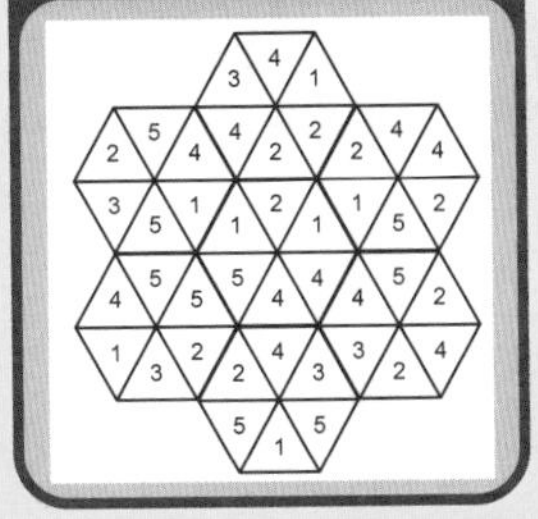

P70

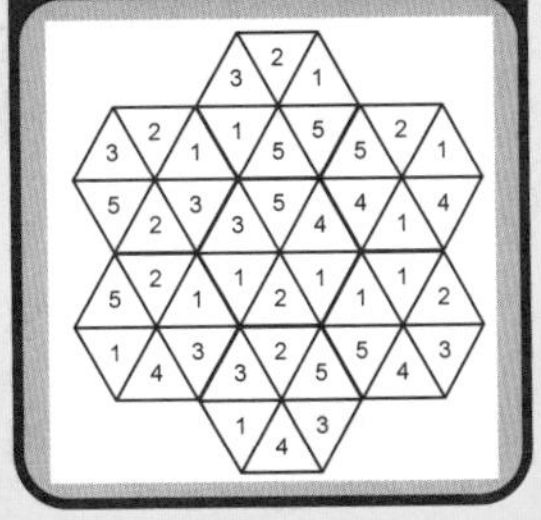

P70

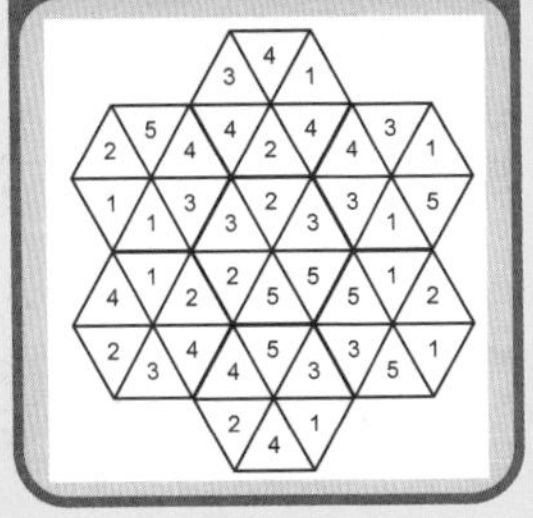

P70

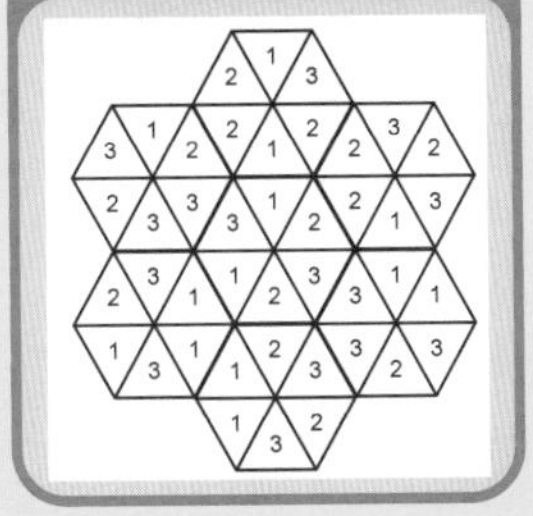

P71

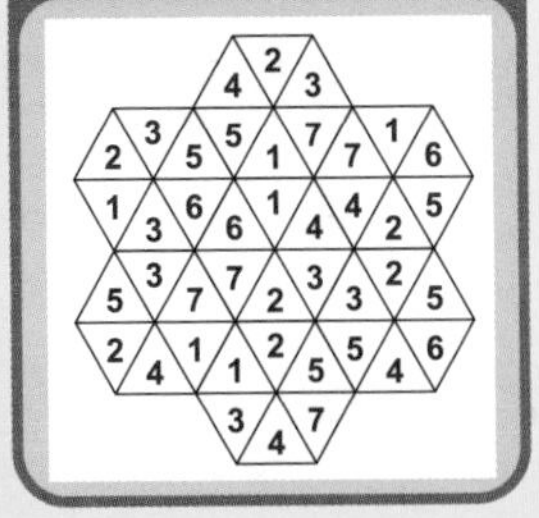

P71

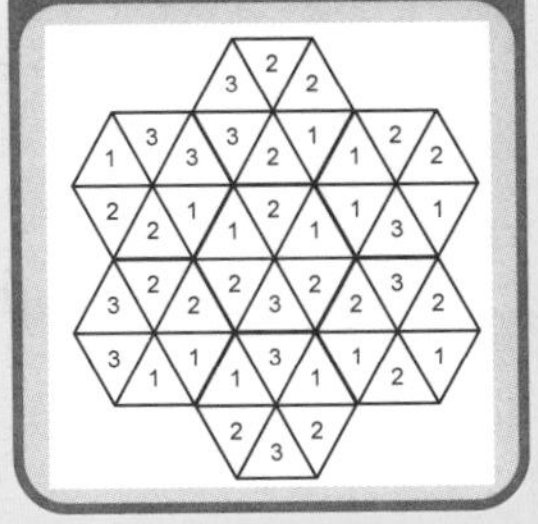

P71

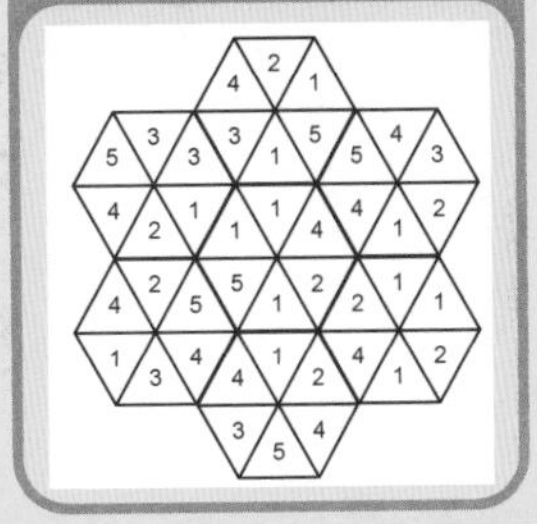

P71

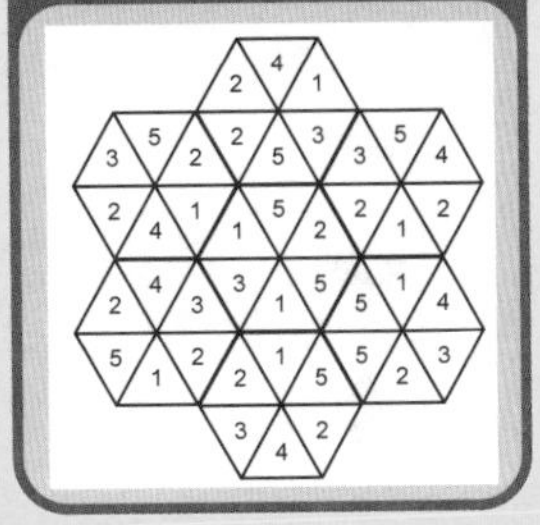

P71

P72

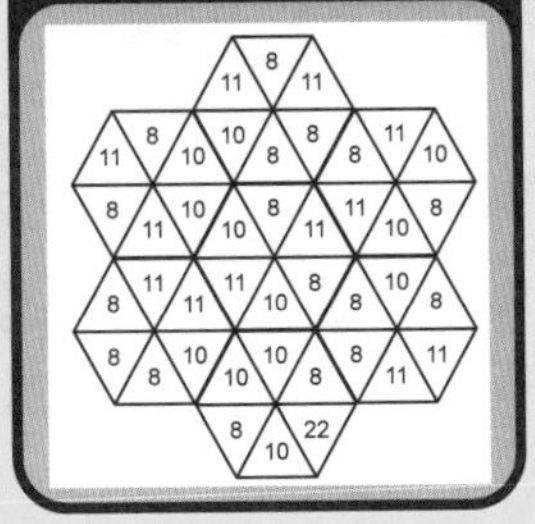

P72

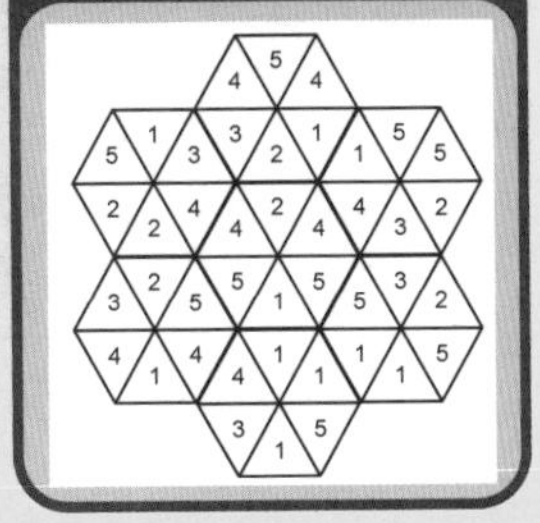

P72

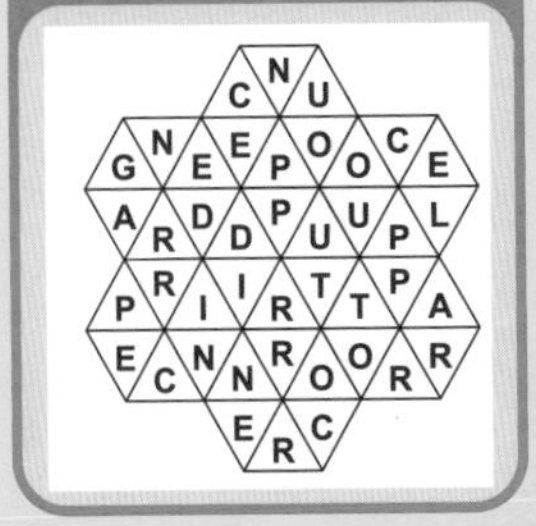

P72

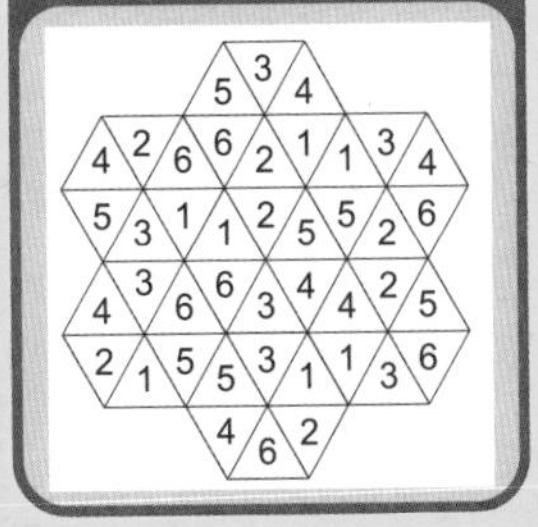

P72

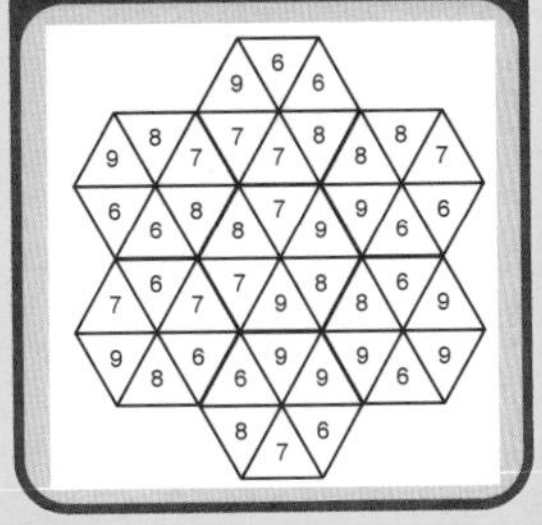

P73

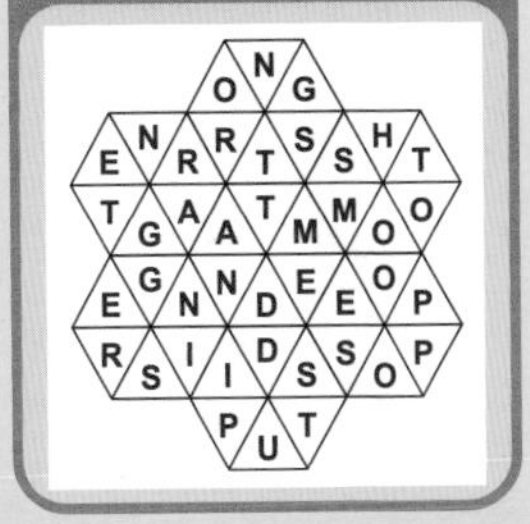

P73

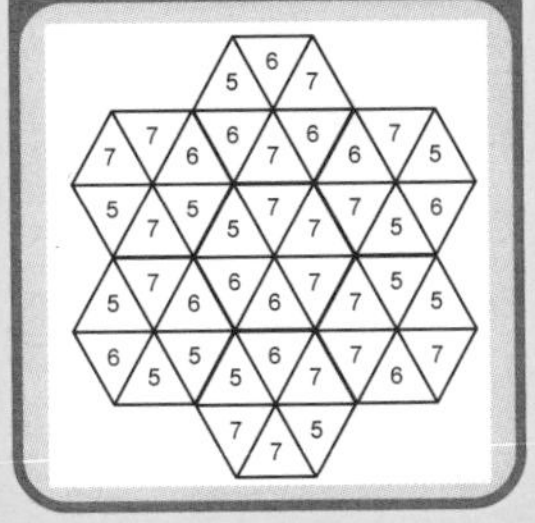

P73

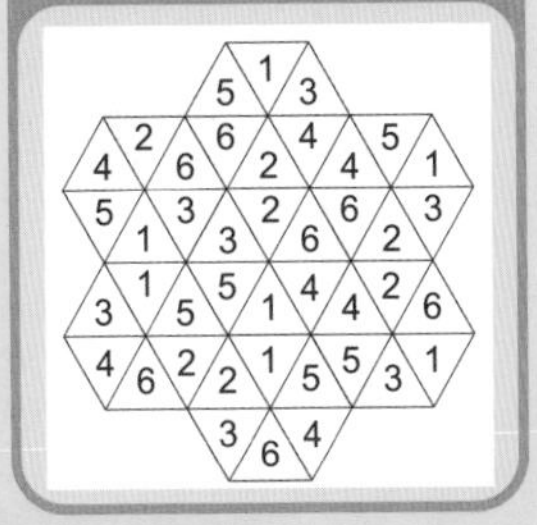

P73

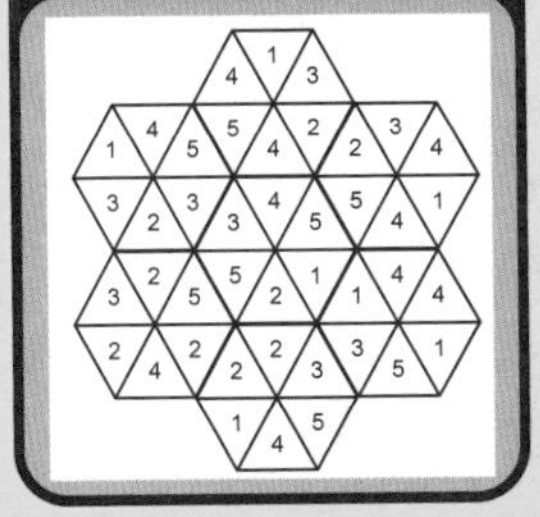

P73

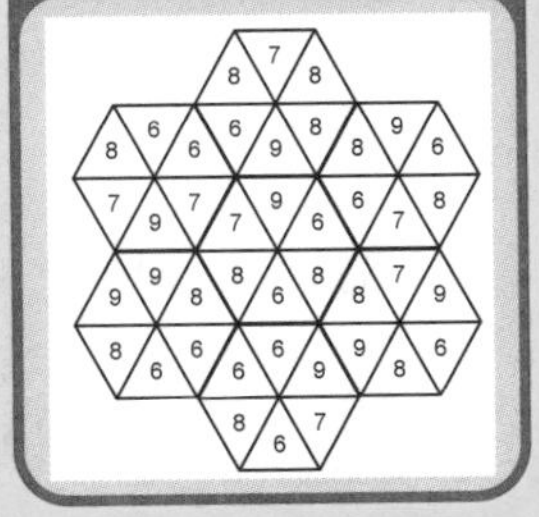

P74

	A	D
♠ =	3	3
♥ =	2	4
♦ =	1	1

P74

	A	D
♠ =	4	4
♥ =	2	5
♦ =	3	3
♣ =	1	1

P74

	A	D
♠ =	6	6
♥ =	8	8
♦ =	2	4
♣ =	7	7

P74

	A	D
♠ =	5	3
♥ =	4	4
♦ =	1	1
♣ =	2	2

P74

	A	D
♠ =	2	2
♥ =	3	1
♦ =	1	3

P75

	A	D
♠ =	2	1
♥ =	1	4
♦ =	3	3

P75

	A	D
♠ =	2	2
♥ =	5	3
♦ =	4	4
♣ =	3	1

P75

	A	D
♠ =	9	9
♥ =	13	6
♦ =	7	7
♣ =	12	12

P75

	A	D
♠ =	4	4
♥ =	1	2
♦ =	2	1

P75

	A	D
♠ =	9	8
♥ =	20	20
♦ =	7	7
♣ =	12	10

The answers correspond to the questions when read from left to right, and from top to bottom

SOLUTIONS

P76

	A	D
♠ =	3	2
♥ =	4	4
♦ =	1	1

P76

	A	D
♠ =	5	4
♥ =	1	1
♦ =	6	3
♣ =	2	2

P76

	A	D
♠ =	9	9
♥ =	1	11
♦ =	4	5
♣ =	10	10

P76

	A	D
♠ =	4	1
♥ =	1	3
♦ =	5	5
♣ =	2	2

P76

	A	D
♠ =	2	2
♥ =	4	4
♦ =	3	3

P77

	A	D
♠ =	1	1
♥ =	4	2
♦ =	2	3

P77

	A	D
♠ =	2	6
♥ =	6	2
♦ =	4	5
♣ =	3	3

P77

	A	D
♠ =	7	7
♥ =	18	1
♦ =	11	11
♣ =	3	13

P77

	A	D
♠ =	4	1
♥ =	3	3
♦ =	2	2

P77

	A	D
♠ =	13	4
♥ =	11	11
♦ =	8	7
♣ =	10	10

P78

	A	D
♠ =	1	4
♥ =	3	3
♦ =	4	2

P78

	A	D
♠ =	3	4
♥ =	1	1
♦ =	2	3
♣ =	4	2

P78

	A	D
♠ =	6	6
♥ =	8	8
♦ =	4	4
♣ =	9	7

P78

	A	D
♠ =	6	5
♥ =	1	4
♦ =	3	3
♣ =	2	2

P78

	A	D
♠ =	4	3
♥ =	2	2
♦ =	1	1

P79

	A	D
♠ =	1	3
♥ =	2	1
♦ =	4	4

P79

	A	D
♠ =	1	1
♥ =	2	2
♦ =	3	6
♣ =	6	3

P79

	A	D
♠ =	15	13
♥ =	9	9
♦ =	11	11
♣ =	19	19

P79

	A	D
♠ =	2	4
♥ =	1	1
♦ =	4	3

P79

	A	D
♠ =	12	12
♥ =	8	7
♦ =	9	9
♣ =	5	6

P80

	A	D
♠ =	1	3
♥ =	2	1
♦ =	4	4

P80

	A	D
♠ =	5	5
♥ =	3	3
♦ =	1	4
♣ =	2	2

P80

	A	D
♠ =	12	12
♥ =	8	11
♦ =	14	10
♣ =	15	15

P80

	A	D
♠ =	6	1
♥ =	4	4
♦ =	2	6
♣ =	1	2

P80

	A	D
♠ =	4	4
♥ =	1	3
♦ =	3	2

P81

	A	D
♠ =	3	3
♥ =	4	1
♦ =	2	2

P81

	A	D
♠ =	1	2
♥ =	2	3
♦ =	4	5
♣ =	3	1

P81

	A	D
♠ =	19	6
♥ =	6	7
♦ =	14	14
♣ =	8	8

P81

	A	D
♠ =	3	4
♥ =	1	1
♦ =	2	2

P81

	A	D
♠ =	3	3
♥ =	1	6
♦ =	4	4
♣ =	2	2

P82

	A	D
♠ =	4	4
♥ =	2	2
♦ =	3	1

P82

	A	D
♠ =	1	2
♥ =	2	3
♦ =	4	5
♣ =	3	1

P82

	A	D
♠ =	9	9
♥ =	6	6
♦ =	11	10
♣ =	17	8

P82

	A	D
♠ =	6	7
♥ =	4	4
♦ =	7	6
♣ =	2	3

P82

	A	D
♠ =	3	3
♥ =	1	6
♦ =	4	4
♣ =	2	2

P83

	A	D
♠ =	1	2
♥ =	2	3
♦ =	4	5
♣ =	3	1

The answers correspond to the questions when read from left to right, and from top to bottom

SOLUTIONS

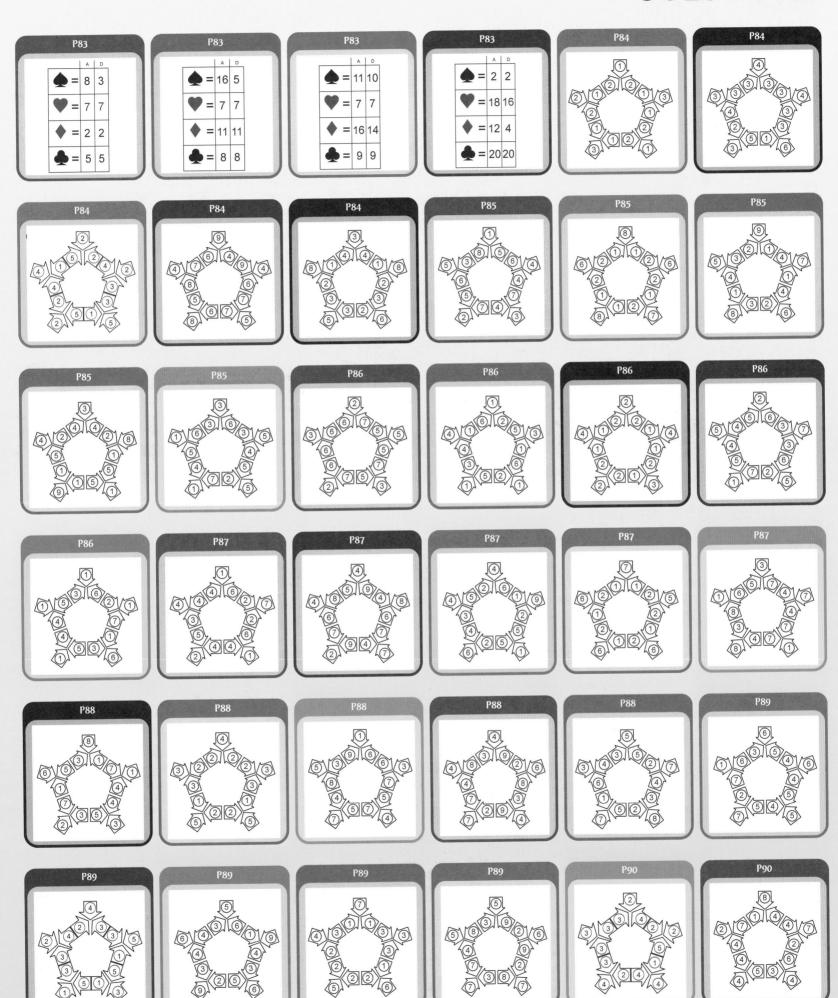

P83

	A	D
♠ =	8	3
♥ =	7	7
♦ =	2	2
♣ =	5	5

P83

	A	D
♠ =	16	5
♥ =	7	7
♦ =	11	11
♣ =	8	8

P83

	A	D
♠ =	11	10
♥ =	7	7
♦ =	16	14
♣ =	9	9

P83

	A	D
♠ =	2	2
♥ =	18	16
♦ =	12	4
♣ =	20	20

P84

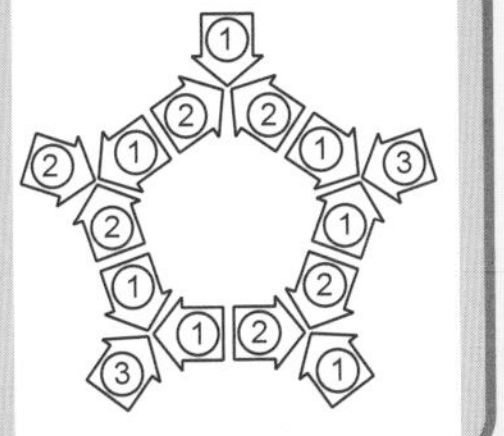

P84

P84

P84

P84

P85

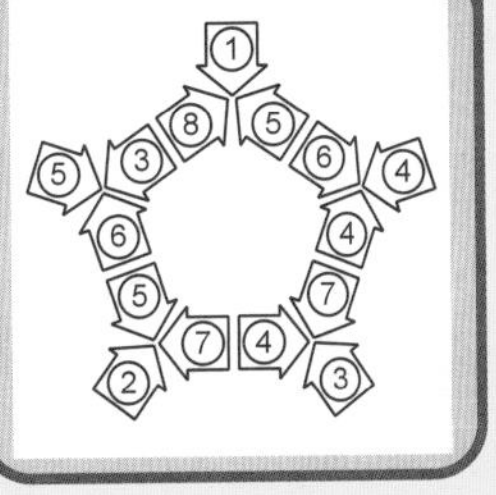

P85

P85

P85

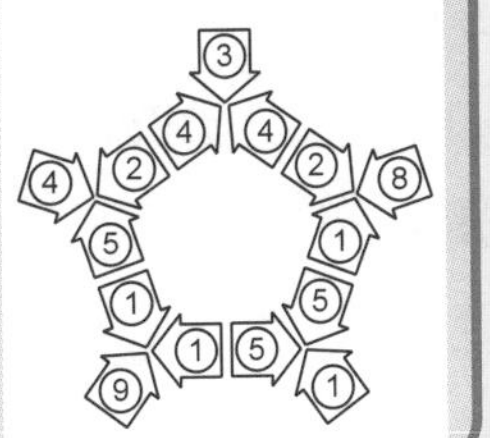

P85

P86

P86

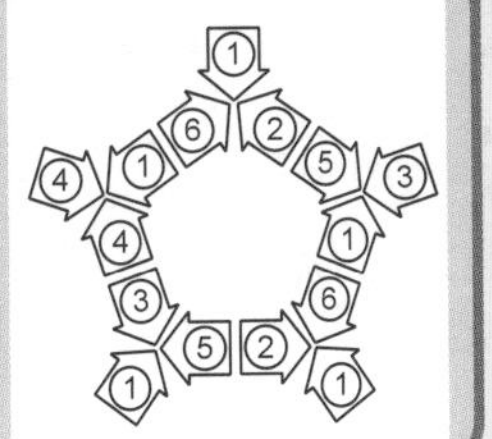

P86

P86

P86

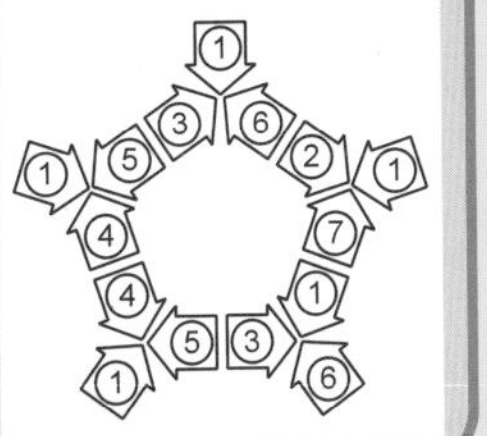

P87

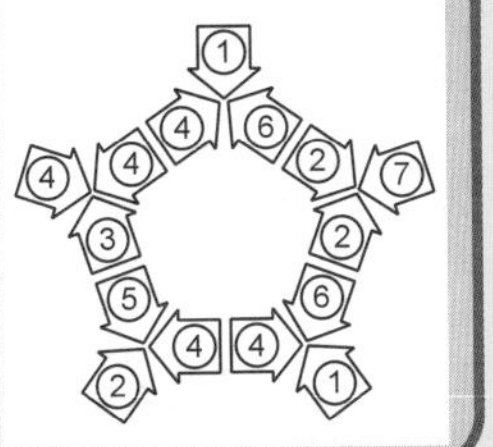

P87

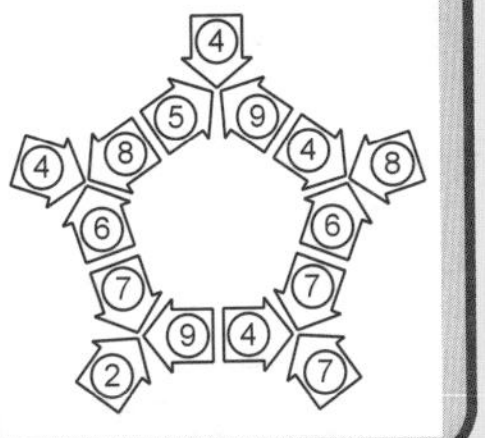

P87

P87

P87

P88

P88

P88

P88

P88

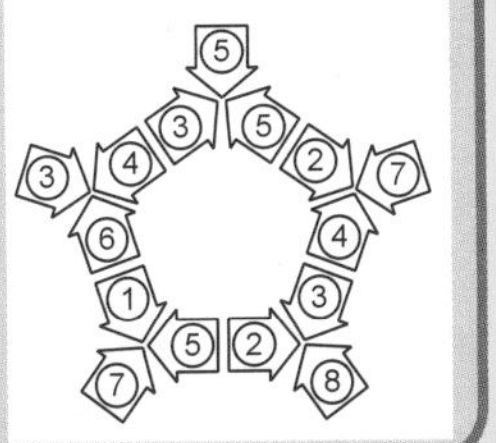

P89

P89

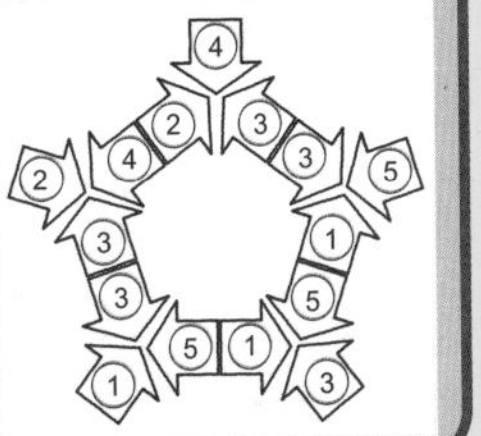

P89

P89

P89

P90

P90

The answers correspond to the questions when read from left to right, and from top to bottom

SOLUTIONS

P90

P90

P90

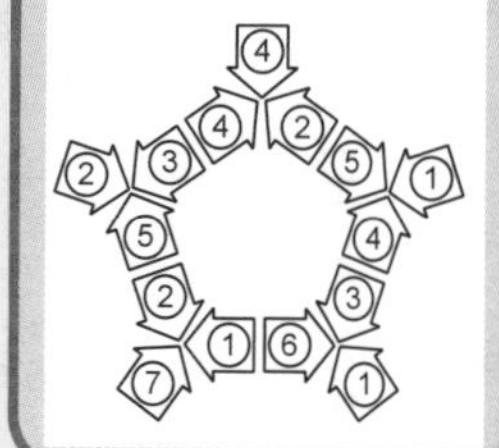

P91

P91

P91

P91

P91

P92

P92

P92

P92

P92

P93

P93

P93

P93

P93

P94

3	2	1
1	3	2
2	1	3

P94

1	2	4	3
3	1	2	4
4	3	1	2
2	4	3	1

P94

4	3	2	1
2	4	1	3
1	2	3	4
3	1	4	2

P94

2	1	3
1	3	2
3	2	1

P94

3	5	1	4	2
5	1	2	3	4
2	4	3	5	1
4	2	5	1	3
1	3	4	2	5

P95

2	4	5	1	3
1	3	4	2	5
5	2	1	3	4
3	5	2	4	1
4	1	3	5	2

P95

3	1	2
2	3	1
1	2	3

P95

3	4	1	3
3	1	2	4
4	2	3	1
1	3	4	2

P95

5	3	2	4	1
2	5	4	1	3
1	4	3	5	2
4	2	1	3	5
3	1	5	2	4

P95

2	1	3
3	2	1
1	3	2

P96

2	3	1
3	1	2
1	2	3

P96

1	3	2	4
3	2	4	1
4	1	3	2
2	4	1	3

P96

2	1	3	4
4	3	1	2
1	4	2	3
3	2	4	1

P96

1	3	2
3	2	1
2	1	3

P96

4	1	5	2	3
3	5	2	4	1
2	4	1	3	5
1	3	4	5	2
5	2	3	1	4

P97

3	5	2	1	4
4	1	5	3	2
2	4	3	5	1
5	2	1	4	3
1	3	4	2	5

P97

1	2	3
2	3	1
3	1	2

P97

3	1	4	2
2	4	3	1
4	2	1	3
1	3	2	4

 The answers correspond to the questions when read from left to right, and from top to bottom

SOLUTIONS

P97

5	2	1	3	4
4	5	3	2	1
1	3	2	4	5
2	4	5	1	3
3	1	4	5	2

P97

2	1	3
1	3	2
3	2	1

P98

3	2	1
2	1	3
1	3	2

P98

4	2	3	1
1	3	4	2
2	4	1	3
3	1	2	4

P98

3	2	4	1
4	1	2	3
2	3	1	4
1	4	3	2

P98

3	1	2
1	2	3
2	3	1

P98

2	4	3	5	1
1	3	2	4	5
3	5	4	1	2
4	1	5	2	3
5	2	1	3	4

P99

1	5	2	3	4
4	3	5	2	1
2	4	1	5	3
5	1	3	4	2
3	2	4	1	5

P99

1	3	2
2	1	3
3	2	1

P99

3	4	1	2
1	3	2	4
2	1	4	3
4	2	3	1

P99

5	1	3	4	2
1	2	5	3	4
2	3	4	5	1
3	4	1	2	5
4	5	2	1	3

P99

2	3	1
1	2	3
3	1	2

P100

1	2	3
3	1	2
2	3	1

P100

1	3	2	4
2	4	1	3
4	2	3	1
3	1	4	2

P100

2	1	3	4
1	2	4	3
3	4	2	1
4	3	1	2

P100

3	2	1
2	1	3
1	3	2

P100

2	5	4	1	3
3	2	1	5	4
4	1	2	3	5
1	3	5	4	2
5	4	3	2	1

P101

4	3	1	2	5
1	2	5	4	3
5	4	3	1	2
3	1	2	5	4
2	5	4	3	1

P101

3	1	2
2	3	1
1	2	3

P101

4	3	1	2
3	2	4	1
2	1	3	4
1	4	2	3

P101

3	4	5	1	2
4	5	2	3	1
5	2	1	4	3
1	3	4	2	5
2	1	3	5	4

P101

1	2	3
2	3	1
3	1	2

P102

1	2	5	4	3
5	1	3	2	4
3	4	2	1	5
4	3	1	5	2
2	5	4	3	1

P102

2	3	1	4
4	1	2	3
1	4	3	2
3	2	4	1

P102

4	1	3	2
2	3	1	4
3	4	2	1
1	2	4	3

P102

3	1	4	2	5
2	5	3	1	4
5	2	1	4	3
1	4	5	3	2
4	3	2	5	1

P102

5	3	1	4	2
4	2	5	1	3
2	4	3	5	1
1	5	2	3	4
3	1	4	2	5

P103

1	5	4	3	2
3	2	1	4	5
5	3	2	1	4
4	1	5	2	3
2	4	3	5	1

P103

4	1	2	6	3	5
3	6	5	4	2	1
2	3	4	1	5	6
1	2	6	5	4	3
6	5	3	2	1	4
5	4	1	3	6	2

P103

1	4	3	2
2	1	4	3
4	3	2	1
3	2	1	4

P103

2	3	4	1
3	2	1	4
4	1	2	3
1	4	3	2

P103

6	5	3	1	4	2
3	4	2	5	1	6
2	1	4	6	3	5
1	2	5	3	6	4
5	6	1	4	2	3
4	3	6	2	5	1

P104

4	8	5	6	3	1	9	7	2
9	6	1	7	2	8	3	4	5
3	2	7	9	5	4	1	6	8
8	9	2	3	4	7	5	1	6
5	1	6	2	8	9	4	3	7
7	4	3	5	1	6	8	2	9
2	3	8	1	7	5	6	9	4
6	7	4	8	9	3	2	5	1
1	5	9	4	6	2	7	8	3

P104

6	1	3	4	5	2	7	9	8
2	8	5	3	7	9	1	6	4
9	7	4	8	6	1	2	3	5
1	5	7	9	2	4	3	8	6
4	3	6	5	8	7	9	1	2
8	2	9	1	3	6	5	4	7
3	4	8	7	9	5	6	2	1
5	9	2	6	1	8	4	7	3
7	6	1	2	4	3	8	5	9

P104

5	3	1	9	7	4	6	8	2
4	7	2	1	6	8	5	9	3
9	6	8	2	3	5	1	4	7
6	8	7	5	2	9	3	1	4
1	4	9	3	8	7	2	6	5
3	2	5	4	1	6	8	7	9
2	1	4	6	9	3	7	5	8
7	5	3	8	4	1	9	2	6
8	9	6	7	5	2	4	3	1

P104

4	9	6	7	1	3	2	8	5
2	1	7	8	9	5	6	3	4
8	3	5	4	2	6	7	1	9
9	8	3	5	6	4	1	7	2
6	2	4	3	7	1	5	9	8
7	5	1	2	8	9	4	6	3
3	6	2	9	5	7	8	4	1
5	7	9	1	4	8	3	2	6
1	4	8	6	3	2	9	5	7

The answers correspond to the questions when read from left to right, and from top to bottom

SOLUTIONS

P104

8	4	6	1	5	2	7	3	9
2	5	1	3	7	9	8	6	4
7	9	3	4	6	8	5	1	2
1	6	8	9	2	4	3	7	5
4	7	9	5	3	6	1	2	8
5	3	2	8	1	7	4	9	6
9	2	4	7	8	1	6	5	3
6	1	5	2	4	3	9	8	7
3	8	7	6	9	5	2	4	1

P104

3	2	7	6	5	4	8	1	9
4	6	1	2	9	8	7	3	5
8	9	5	7	1	3	4	6	2
6	7	9	3	4	2	1	5	8
5	8	4	1	6	7	2	9	3
2	1	3	9	8	5	6	7	4
9	3	6	4	2	1	5	8	7
1	5	2	8	7	9	3	4	6
7	4	8	5	3	6	9	2	1

P104

7	4	5	2	8	3	1	9	6
2	1	3	9	6	7	5	4	8
8	6	9	5	1	4	7	3	2
1	2	6	3	4	5	8	7	9
3	9	7	8	2	1	6	5	4
5	8	4	7	9	6	3	2	1
6	7	2	1	5	9	4	8	3
9	5	1	4	3	8	2	6	7
4	3	8	6	7	2	9	1	5

P105

8	3	9	5	1	4	7	6	2
2	7	4	3	8	6	1	9	5
6	5	1	9	7	2	3	4	8
7	9	2	4	6	3	8	5	1
4	6	3	8	5	1	2	7	9
5	1	8	7	2	9	4	3	6
3	4	6	2	9	8	5	1	7
1	8	5	6	3	7	9	2	4
9	2	7	1	4	5	6	8	3

P105

6	1	9	2	4	8	5	3	7
2	7	4	5	3	1	8	9	6
3	5	8	7	9	6	1	2	4
4	3	2	8	6	5	7	1	9
9	6	5	1	7	4	3	8	2
1	8	7	9	2	3	4	6	5
5	2	3	6	8	7	9	4	1
7	4	6	3	1	9	2	5	8
8	9	1	4	5	2	6	7	3

P105

1	4	3	2	6	8	5	7	9
9	8	5	4	3	7	2	1	6
7	6	2	1	9	5	4	8	3
6	1	9	5	2	3	7	4	8
2	3	4	7	8	9	6	5	1
8	5	7	6	1	4	3	9	2
4	2	8	9	5	6	1	3	7
5	9	1	3	7	2	8	6	4
3	7	6	8	4	1	9	2	5

P105

6	1	4	3	9	2	5	8	7
2	8	9	5	4	7	6	3	1
7	5	3	6	1	8	4	2	9
1	3	8	9	6	4	2	7	5
4	7	6	2	5	1	8	9	3
5	9	2	7	8	3	1	6	4
3	4	1	8	2	9	7	5	6
8	6	7	1	3	5	9	4	2
9	2	5	4	7	6	3	1	8

P105

4	3	1	6	5	2	8	9	7
8	5	9	4	7	3	6	2	1
7	6	2	8	1	9	4	3	5
3	8	5	9	6	1	7	4	2
9	4	6	2	8	7	5	1	3
2	1	7	3	4	5	9	8	6
6	2	8	7	3	4	1	5	9
1	7	3	5	9	8	2	6	4
5	9	4	1	2	6	3	7	8

P105

7	5	6	1	3	8	2	4	9
4	8	9	7	2	5	6	1	3
2	1	3	9	6	4	5	8	7
6	2	1	4	7	9	3	5	8
9	4	5	3	8	2	1	7	6
3	7	8	6	5	1	9	2	4
8	6	4	5	1	3	7	9	2
1	9	7	2	4	6	8	3	5
5	3	2	8	9	7	4	6	1

P105

7	8	9	1	3	5	4	2	6
4	3	6	8	9	2	7	1	5
1	2	5	6	4	7	9	8	3
2	7	3	5	1	8	6	4	9
6	4	8	9	2	3	1	5	7
9	5	1	7	6	4	8	3	2
8	6	7	3	5	1	2	9	4
3	9	4	2	8	6	5	7	1
5	1	2	4	7	9	3	6	8

P106

1	8	4	6	3	5	7	2	9
6	3	2	7	4	9	5	8	1
7	5	9	2	8	1	3	6	4
8	1	5	9	7	2	4	3	6
2	4	6	5	1	3	9	7	8
3	9	7	8	6	4	1	5	2
5	7	8	4	9	6	2	1	3
9	2	3	1	5	8	6	4	7
4	6	1	3	2	7	8	9	5

P106

8	6	4	7	9	2	1	3	5
5	9	1	4	3	6	2	7	8
3	2	7	1	5	8	9	4	6
4	3	6	8	7	1	5	9	2
7	5	9	2	6	3	8	1	4
1	8	2	5	4	9	7	6	3
2	7	8	3	1	4	6	5	9
9	4	5	6	2	7	3	8	1
6	1	3	9	8	5	4	2	7

P106

1	3	5	2	9	6	7	4	8
8	6	2	1	7	4	5	3	9
7	9	4	8	5	3	1	6	2
3	2	6	7	4	5	8	9	1
4	7	9	6	8	1	3	2	5
5	1	8	9	3	2	6	7	4
9	4	7	5	6	8	2	1	3
6	5	1	3	2	9	4	8	7
2	8	3	4	1	7	9	5	6

P106

3	5	6	2	1	4	8	7	9
1	9	2	7	5	8	6	3	4
4	8	7	9	6	3	1	2	5
7	6	5	4	3	1	2	9	8
9	3	8	5	2	6	7	4	1
2	1	4	8	9	7	5	6	3
5	4	1	6	7	9	3	8	2
6	2	9	3	8	5	4	1	7
8	7	3	1	4	2	9	5	6

P106

7	9	6	2	4	3	8	5	1
8	5	2	1	9	7	3	6	4
3	4	1	5	6	8	2	7	9
2	1	4	8	7	6	9	3	5
6	8	5	3	1	9	7	4	2
9	3	7	4	2	5	6	1	8
1	2	9	7	3	4	5	8	6
4	7	8	6	5	2	1	9	3
5	6	3	9	8	1	4	2	7

P106

2	3	8	9	7	1	4	5	6
1	4	5	8	3	6	2	9	7
6	7	9	4	2	5	1	8	3
9	8	1	6	4	2	7	3	5
3	5	6	7	1	9	8	4	2
7	2	4	3	5	8	9	6	1
5	6	2	1	8	4	3	7	9
4	1	7	5	9	3	6	2	8
8	9	3	2	6	7	5	1	4

P106

9	1	5	8	6	3	4	7	2
7	4	8	5	9	2	3	6	1
3	2	6	1	4	7	9	5	8
4	7	9	3	8	5	2	1	6
6	5	1	7	2	4	8	9	3
8	3	2	6	1	9	7	4	5
1	6	7	9	3	8	5	2	4
5	8	4	2	7	6	1	3	9
2	9	3	4	5	1	6	8	7

P107

7	9	2	3	6	4	5	1	8
5	3	4	9	8	1	2	6	7
6	8	1	7	5	2	3	9	4
9	7	8	6	1	3	4	2	5
3	4	6	2	7	5	9	8	1
2	1	5	8	4	9	7	3	6
8	6	9	5	3	7	1	4	2
4	2	7	1	9	6	8	5	3
1	5	3	4	2	8	6	7	9

P107

4	1	7	8	3	5	2	6	9
9	2	3	4	7	6	5	1	8
5	6	8	2	1	9	3	7	4
8	3	4	9	2	1	7	5	6
1	5	6	3	8	7	4	9	2
2	7	9	6	5	4	8	3	1
3	8	1	5	6	2	9	4	7
7	9	2	1	4	3	6	8	5
6	4	5	7	9	8	1	2	3

P107

6	5	7	9	4	3	1	8	2
1	8	9	2	5	6	3	7	4
3	4	2	8	7	1	9	6	5
5	3	6	4	9	8	7	2	1
7	1	8	3	2	5	6	4	9
9	2	4	1	6	7	5	3	8
2	9	5	6	3	4	8	1	7
4	6	1	7	8	9	2	5	3
8	7	3	5	1	2	4	9	6

P107

9	5	2	4	3	6	8	1	7
4	1	6	8	7	2	9	5	3
7	8	3	9	5	1	2	4	6
8	7	1	3	4	5	6	9	2
3	4	9	6	2	8	1	7	5
6	2	5	1	9	7	4	3	8
2	3	8	7	1	9	5	6	4
5	9	7	2	6	4	3	8	1
1	6	4	5	8	3	7	2	9

P107

2	1	4	5	3	9	6	8	7
8	9	6	4	1	7	2	5	3
3	5	7	2	6	8	4	9	1
1	3	5	7	2	4	8	6	9
7	6	8	9	5	1	3	2	4
9	4	2	3	8	6	7	1	5
6	8	3	1	7	5	9	4	2
4	2	1	6	9	3	5	7	8
5	7	9	8	4	2	1	3	6

P107

8	5	6	2	3	4	1	9	7
7	4	2	9	5	1	6	8	3
9	1	3	8	7	6	4	2	5
4	7	5	6	8	3	9	1	2
1	2	8	4	9	7	5	3	6
6	3	9	1	2	5	8	7	4
5	6	7	3	1	9	2	4	8
2	9	4	7	6	8	3	5	1
3	8	1	5	4	2	7	6	9

P107

7	1	8	5	6	9	3	4	2
9	3	6	4	2	1	5	8	7
2	5	4	7	8	3	1	9	6
6	9	3	8	7	2	4	1	5
8	4	1	3	5	6	2	7	9
5	2	7	1	9	4	6	3	8
1	7	5	6	3	8	9	2	4
4	6	9	2	1	7	8	5	3
3	8	2	9	4	5	7	6	1

P108

1	5	9	4	2	3	7	6	8
4	6	2	8	5	7	1	9	3
3	8	7	6	9	1	4	5	2
2	7	6	5	3	8	9	4	1
8	9	1	2	4	6	5	3	7
5	4	3	7	1	9	2	8	6
6	1	4	3	7	5	8	2	9
9	3	5	1	8	2	6	7	4
7	2	8	9	6	4	3	1	5

P108

2	5	7	1	3	8	4	6	9
4	6	8	7	5	9	1	3	2
1	3	9	6	2	4	8	5	7
3	7	6	4	1	2	5	9	8
5	8	1	9	7	3	2	4	6
9	4	2	5	8	6	7	1	3
6	2	3	8	4	5	9	7	1
8	1	5	3	9	7	6	2	4
7	9	4	2	6	1	3	8	5

P108

7	4	6	8	3	5	9	2	1
9	5	2	1	6	7	4	3	8
3	1	8	4	9	2	5	7	6
2	8	9	6	4	3	7	1	5
1	7	3	2	5	9	8	6	4
5	6	4	7	1	8	2	9	3
8	9	5	3	7	1	6	4	2
6	2	1	9	8	4	3	5	7
4	3	7	5	2	6	1	8	9

P108

3	8	4	6	9	2	1	7	5
7	6	9	1	8	5	4	3	2
1	2	5	3	4	7	6	8	9
9	3	8	2	1	6	5	4	7
5	1	6	4	7	3	9	2	8
4	7	2	9	5	8	3	1	6
8	9	7	5	3	1	2	6	4
2	5	1	8	6	4	7	9	3
6	4	3	7	2	9	8	5	1

P108

2	7	4	6	1	9	3	8	5
3	9	6	2	8	5	1	7	4
8	1	5	3	7	4	9	2	6
4	5	7	9	6	3	2	1	8
9	2	8	1	4	7	5	6	3
1	6	3	8	5	2	4	9	7
5	4	9	7	2	6	8	3	1
7	3	1	4	9	8	6	5	2
6	8	2	5	3	1	7	4	9

P108

4	5	6	8	1	3	7	9	2
3	9	2	6	5	7	4	8	1
1	7	8	4	2	9	3	5	6
5	8	1	2	9	4	6	7	3
6	3	7	5	8	1	2	4	9
9	2	4	3	7	6	8	1	5
7	6	3	9	4	5	1	2	8
8	1	5	7	6	2	9	3	4
2	4	9	1	3	8	5	6	7

P108

6	2	7	1	9	4	8	3	5
5	1	9	7	8	3	6	2	4
3	8	4	5	6	2	9	1	7
4	9	6	8	2	1	5	7	3
8	3	2	9	5	7	4	6	1
1	7	5	3	4	6	2	8	9
7	6	8	4	3	5	1	9	2
9	4	1	2	7	8	3	5	6
2	5	3	6	1	9	7	4	8

P109

1	7	6	9	3	5	2	4	8
8	5	4	2	7	6	1	9	3
2	9	3	4	8	1	7	5	6
7	3	1	8	2	4	9	6	5
6	4	9	1	5	7	8	3	2
5	8	2	3	6	9	4	7	1
3	1	7	5	9	2	6	8	4
4	6	8	7	1	3	5	2	9
9	2	5	6	4	8	3	1	7

P109

7	5	8	9	2	4	3	6	1
3	1	9	8	7	6	2	4	5
2	6	4	3	5	1	7	8	9
5	7	6	2	1	8	4	9	3
1	4	2	7	9	3	8	5	6
9	8	3	4	6	5	1	7	2
8	2	7	5	3	9	6	1	4
6	3	5	1	4	7	9	2	8
4	9	1	6	8	2	5	3	7

P109

7	3	8	5	2	6	1	9	4
6	1	4	3	8	9	2	7	5
2	5	9	7	1	4	3	6	8
5	2	1	4	9	3	7	8	6
4	8	6	2	7	5	9	3	1
3	9	7	1	6	8	5	4	2
9	4	2	8	5	7	6	1	3
1	7	3	6	4	2	8	5	9
8	6	5	9	3	1	4	2	7

P109

7	8	9	2	4	5	1	6	3
6	2	3	1	8	9	4	7	5
5	1	4	7	3	6	2	8	9
4	5	6	3	9	2	7	1	8
3	9	8	4	7	1	5	2	6
2	7	1	5	6	8	9	3	4
9	3	5	8	1	7	6	4	2
1	4	2	6	5	3	8	9	7
8	6	7	9	2	4	3	5	1

P109

7	8	9	6	5	2	1	3	4
4	1	2	3	9	8	6	5	7
5	6	3	7	1	4	9	2	8
1	3	5	8	2	9	7	4	6
8	4	6	5	7	3	2	9	1
9	2	7	4	6	1	3	8	5
2	7	4	9	8	6	5	1	3
3	5	1	2	4	7	8	6	9
6	9	8	1	3	5	4	7	2

The answers correspond to the questions when read from left to right, and from top to bottom

SOLUTIONS

P109

5	6	7	4	3	1	8	9	2
3	8	1	9	5	2	7	6	4
4	2	9	7	8	6	1	5	3
7	9	3	8	6	5	2	4	1
8	1	5	2	4	3	9	7	6
6	4	2	1	9	7	5	3	8
1	3	8	5	7	4	6	2	9
2	5	6	3	1	9	4	8	7
9	7	4	6	2	8	3	1	5

P109

6	8	9	1	3	2	4	5	7
3	4	7	9	5	6	8	2	1
5	2	1	7	4	8	3	9	6
4	6	2	8	1	9	7	3	5
1	7	3	6	2	5	9	4	8
9	5	8	3	7	4	1	6	2
8	3	5	4	6	7	2	1	9
2	9	4	5	8	1	6	7	3
7	1	6	2	9	3	5	8	4

P110

6	8	4	2	5	3	7	9	1
2	5	9	7	1	4	3	8	6
7	1	3	9	8	6	5	4	2
4	3	7	6	2	1	9	5	8
5	9	6	4	3	8	1	2	7
1	2	8	5	9	7	6	3	4
9	4	1	8	6	5	2	7	3
3	7	5	1	4	2	8	6	9
8	6	2	3	7	9	4	1	5

P110

1	8	9	2	4	7	6	5	3
5	7	2	6	8	3	1	4	9
3	4	6	5	1	9	2	7	8
2	1	7	3	9	4	8	6	5
8	9	4	1	6	5	7	3	2
6	3	5	8	7	2	9	1	4
4	6	1	9	5	8	3	2	7
7	2	8	4	3	6	5	9	1
9	5	3	7	2	1	4	8	6

P110

2	6	3	5	8	1	4	7	9
8	4	5	9	7	3	6	2	1
1	9	7	2	4	6	5	8	3
5	3	2	8	6	7	9	1	4
9	7	8	1	5	4	3	6	2
6	1	4	3	2	9	7	5	8
7	5	1	4	9	2	8	3	6
3	8	9	6	1	5	2	4	7
4	2	6	7	3	8	1	9	5

P110

3	6	7	9	2	5	4	1	8
2	5	9	1	8	4	6	7	3
8	4	1	7	3	6	5	9	2
5	7	2	8	4	9	1	3	6
6	1	3	2	5	7	9	8	4
4	9	8	3	6	1	7	2	5
7	3	5	4	9	2	8	6	1
9	2	4	6	1	8	3	5	7
1	8	6	5	7	3	2	4	9

P110

9	2	8	5	1	6	7	4	3
1	5	6	3	4	7	2	9	8
4	7	3	2	9	8	6	1	5
6	3	5	9	2	4	8	7	1
7	9	1	8	6	3	5	2	4
8	4	2	1	7	5	9	3	6
3	6	9	7	5	1	4	8	2
5	8	7	4	3	2	1	6	9
2	1	4	6	8	9	3	5	7

P110

5	9	3	6	2	1	4	7	8
8	7	4	5	3	9	6	1	2
1	6	2	8	4	7	9	3	5
3	5	1	4	7	2	8	9	6
4	2	6	9	8	3	1	5	7
7	8	9	1	6	5	3	2	4
9	1	8	2	5	6	7	4	3
6	3	5	7	9	4	2	8	1
2	4	7	3	1	8	5	6	9

P110

8	2	5	3	4	7	6	1	9
9	7	1	8	6	5	4	3	2
4	3	6	2	9	1	7	5	8
7	9	2	1	3	4	8	6	5
5	6	8	9	7	2	3	4	1
1	4	3	6	5	8	2	9	7
6	8	7	5	1	3	9	2	4
2	1	9	4	8	6	5	7	3
3	5	4	7	2	9	1	8	6

P110

5	7	4	3	9	6	8	1	2
9	1	2	4	7	8	5	3	6
6	8	3	2	5	1	7	9	4
3	9	8	5	4	7	2	6	1
2	4	5	6	1	9	3	7	8
7	6	1	8	2	3	4	5	9
4	2	6	1	3	5	9	8	7
8	5	9	7	6	4	1	2	3
1	3	7	9	8	2	6	4	5

P111

P111

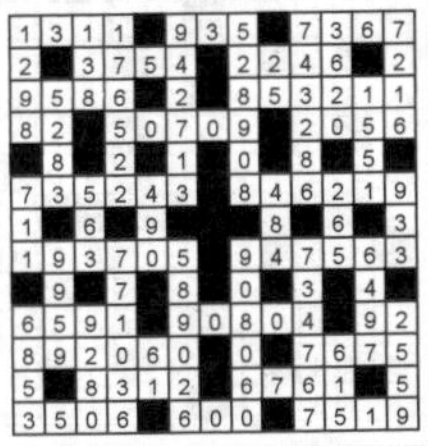

P112

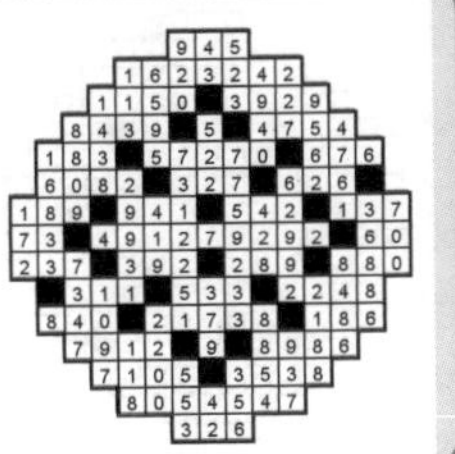

P112

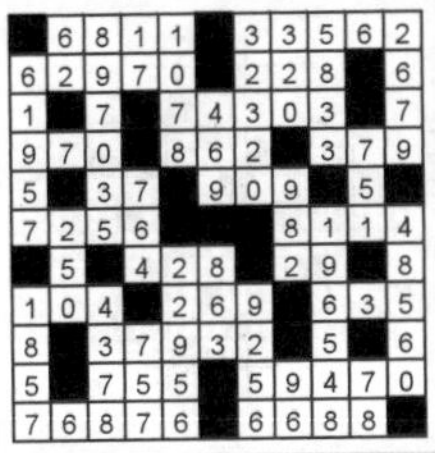

P112

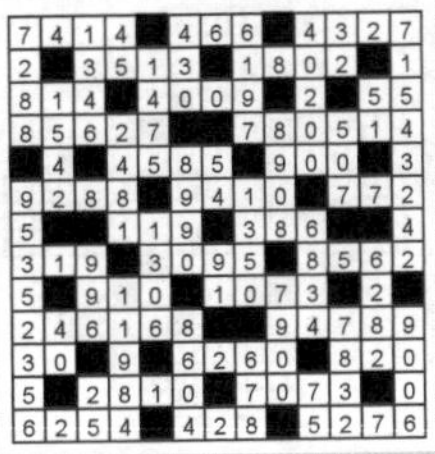

P112

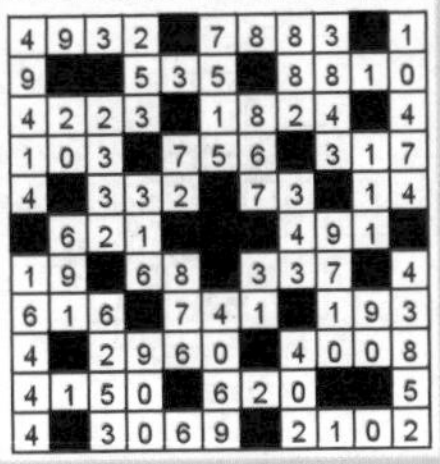

P113

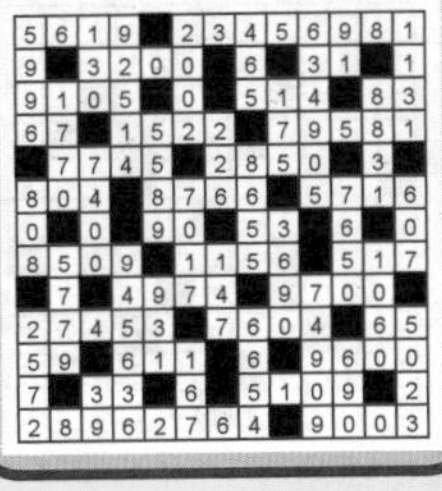

P113

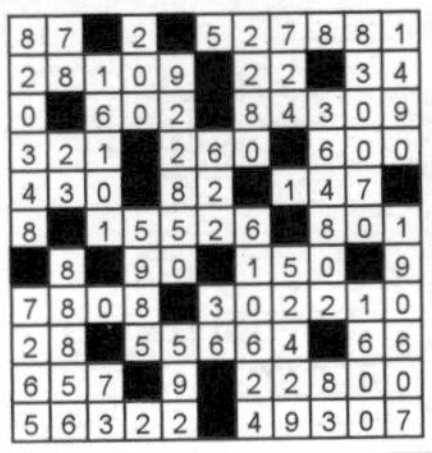

P113

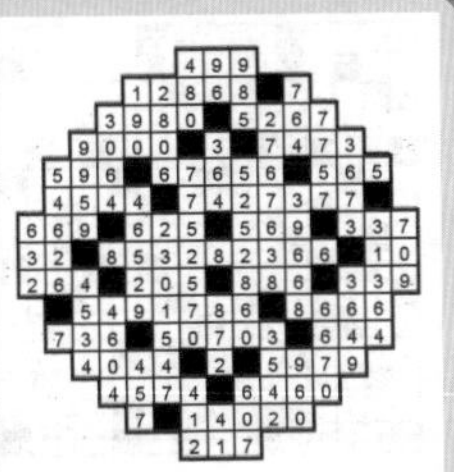

P113

P114

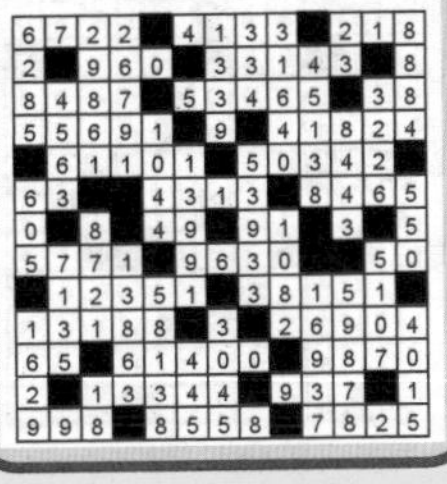

P114

P114

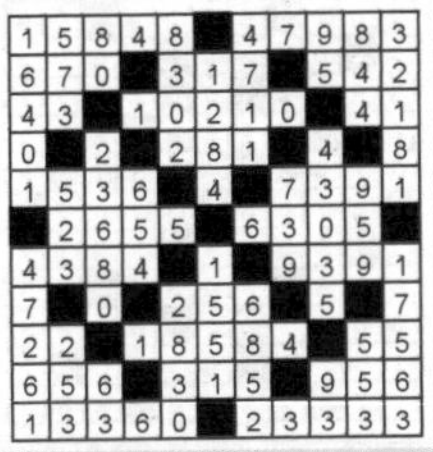

P114

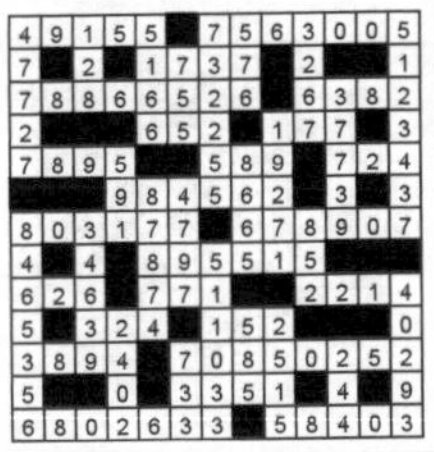

P115

P115

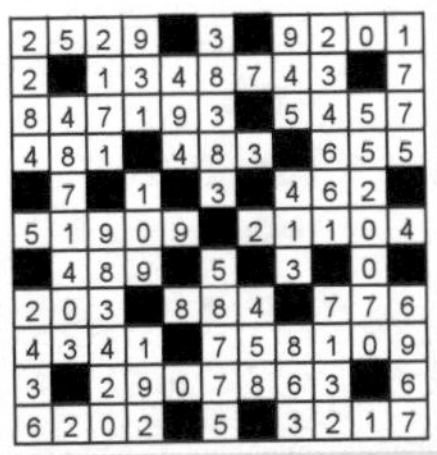

P115

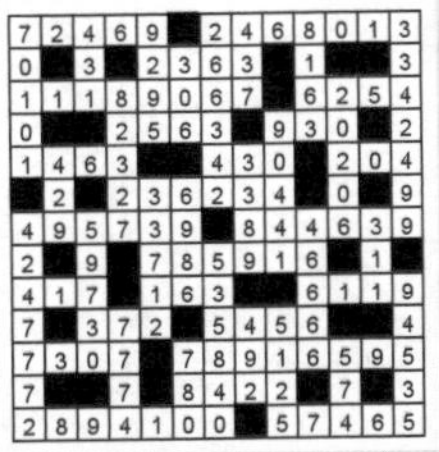

P115

P116

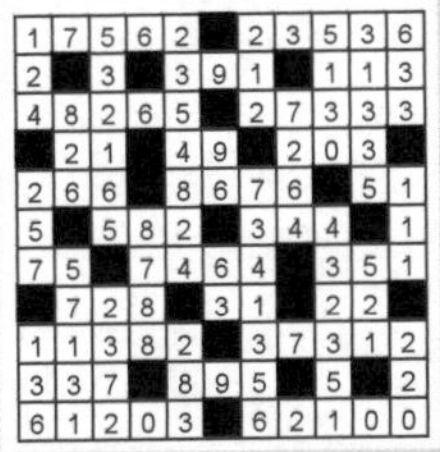

P116

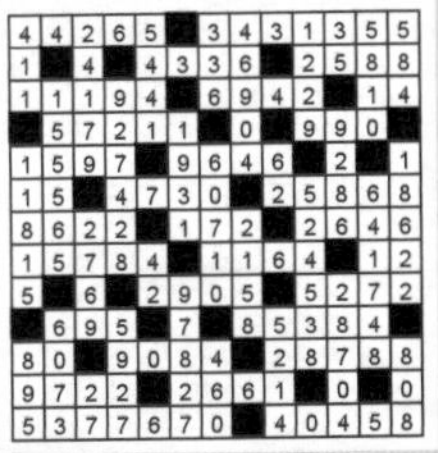

P116

P116

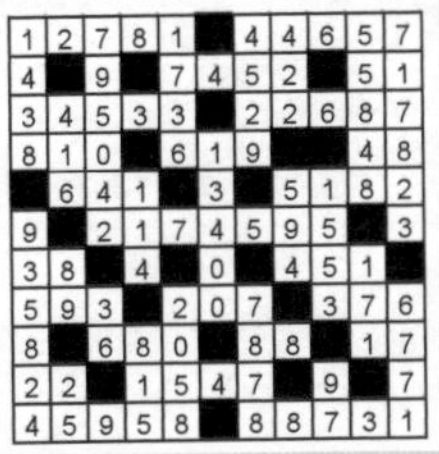

P117

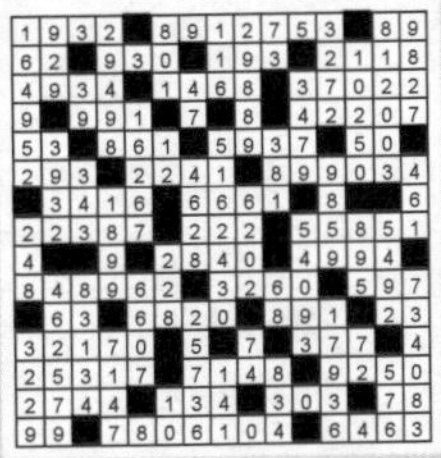

P117

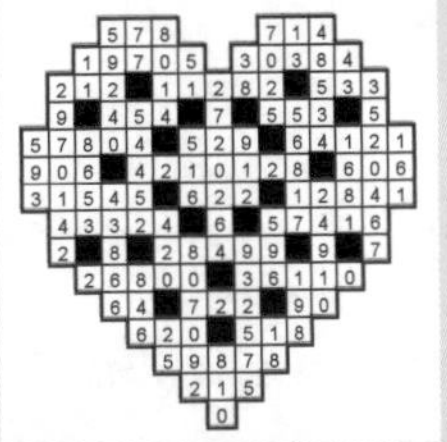

P117

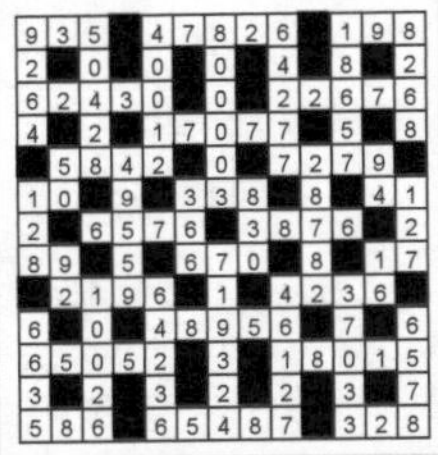

P117

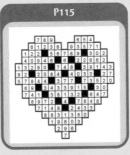

SOLUTIONS

P118
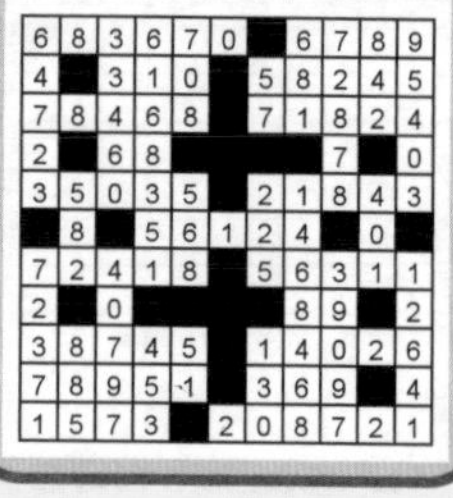

P118

P118

P118

P119

P119
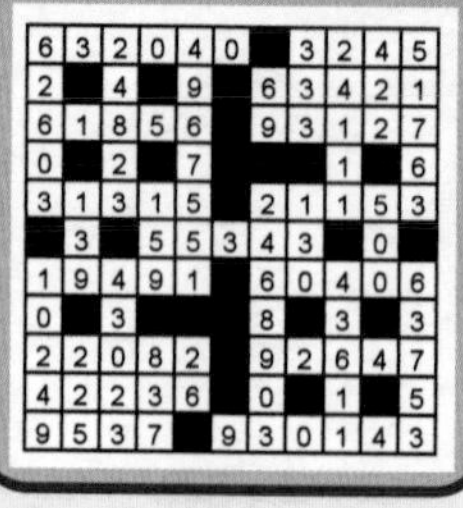

P119
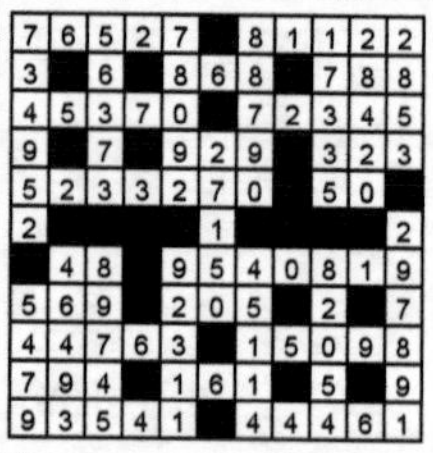

P119

P120
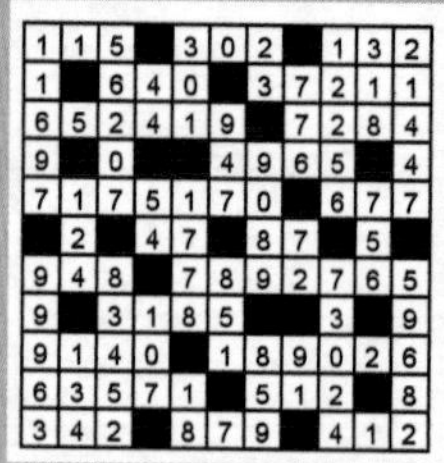

P120

P120
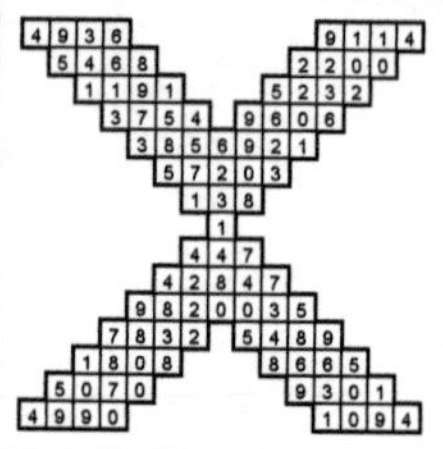

P120
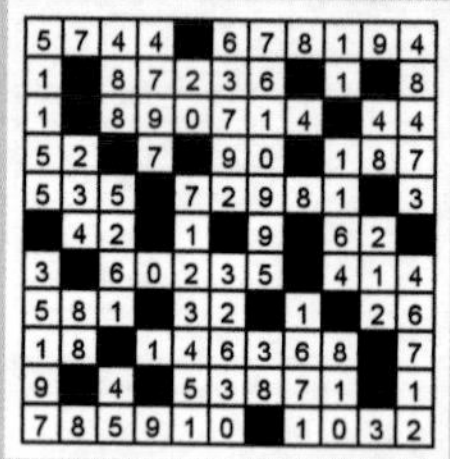

P121
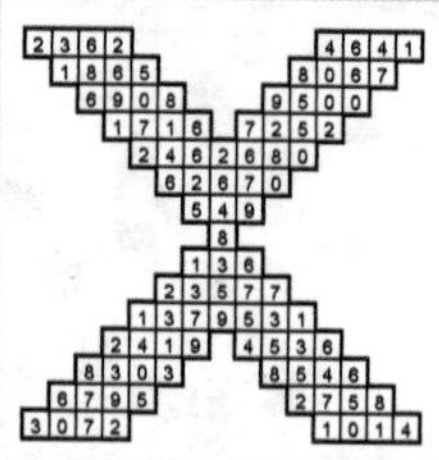

P121
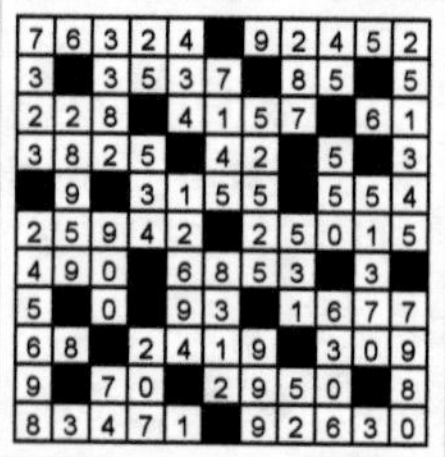

P121

P121
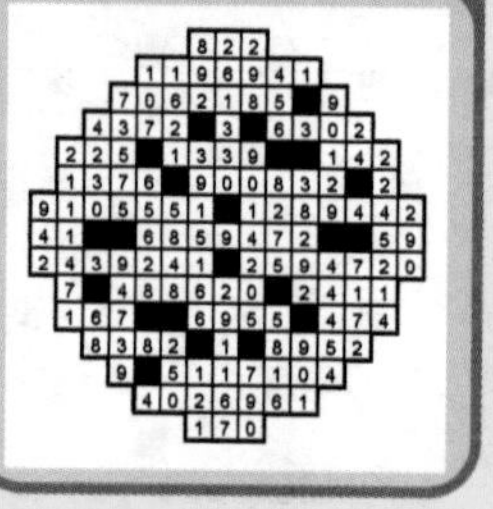

P122

P122
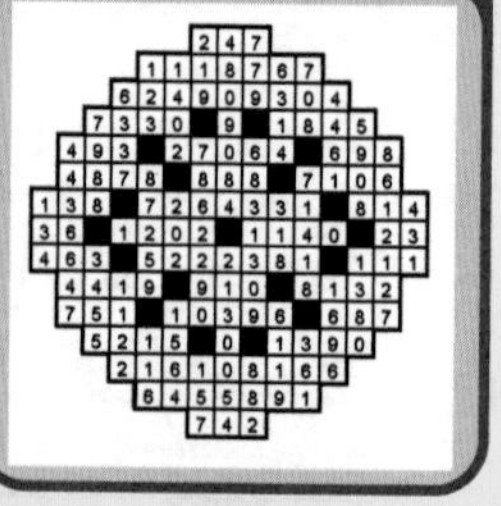

P122

P122
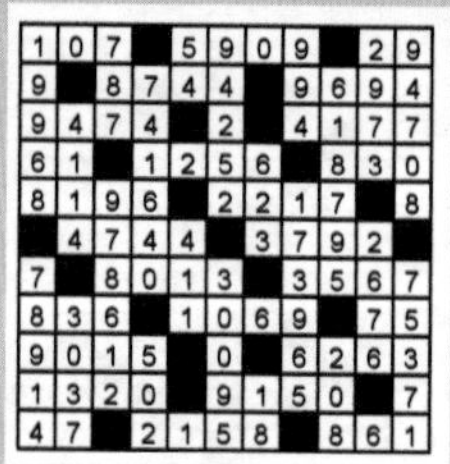

P123

P123
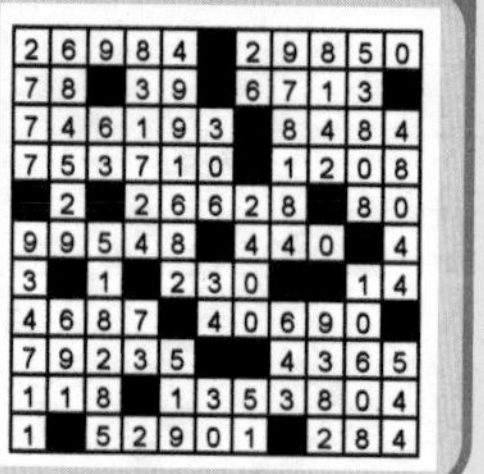

P123

P123
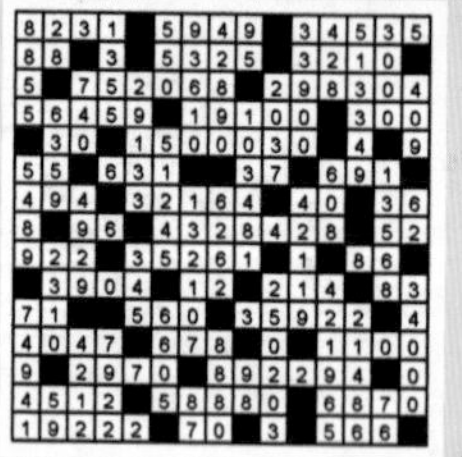

P124

26
14 12
7 7 5
3 4 3 2
1 2 2 1 1

P124

78
38 40
20 18 22
12 8 10 12
9 3 5 5 7
8 1 2 3 2 5

P124

456
227 229
109 118 111
52 57 61 50
25 27 30 31 19
12 13 14 16 15 4

P124

31
15 16
7 8 8
3 4 4 4
1 2 2 2 2

P124

84
44 40
23 21 19
13 10 11 8
9 4 6 5 3
7 2 2 4 1 2

P125

90
50 40
28 22 18
16 12 10 8
10 6 6 4 4
7 3 3 3 1 3

P125

93
34 59
13 21 38
6 7 14 24
4 2 5 9 15
3 1 1 4 5 10

P125

43
18 25
10 8 17
6 4 4 13
3 3 1 3 10

P125

543
256 287
128 128 159
70 58 70 89
38 32 26 44 45
18 20 12 14 30 15

P125

429
205 224
97 108 116
48 49 59 57
29 19 30 29 28
21 8 11 19 10 18

P126

64
40 24
28 12 12
21 7 5 7
17 4 3 2 5
15 2 2 1 1 4

P126

55
26 29
12 14 15
5 7 7 8
3 2 5 2 6

 The answers correspond to the questions when read from left to right, and from top to bottom

SOLUTIONS

P126

715
365 350
177 188 162
80 97 91 71
36 44 53 38 33
20 16 28 25 13 20

P126

431
225 206
126 99 107
77 49 50 57
48 29 20 30 27
30 18 11 9 21 6

P126

67
32 35
17 15 20
9 8 7 13
5 4 4 3 10
4 1 3 1 2 8

P127

106
60 46
40 20 26
29 11 9 17
22 7 4 5 12
18 4 3 1 4 8

P127

47
27 20
15 12 8
8 7 5 3
4 4 3 2 1

P127

665
345 320
176 169 151
91 85 84 67
49 42 43 41 26
26 23 19 24 17 9

P127

563
291 272
144 147 125
70 74 73 52
35 35 39 34 18
15 20 15 24 10 8

P127

29
16 13
9 7 6
5 4 3 3
3 2 2 1 2

P128

36
16 20
7 9 11
3 4 5 6
2 1 3 2 4

P128

99
49 50
23 26 24
11 12 14 10
7 4 8 6 4
6 1 3 5 1 3

P128

516
256 260
128 128 132
63 65 63 69
28 35 30 33 36
7 21 14 16 17 19

P128

111
51 60
26 25 35
15 11 14 21
9 6 5 9 12
6 3 3 2 7 5

P128

23
11 12
5 6 6
2 3 3 3
1 1 2 1 2

P129

115
45 70
18 27 43
8 10 17 26
4 4 6 11 15
2 2 2 4 7 8

P129

753
348 305
142 206 199
49 93 113 86
15 34 59 54 32
8 7 27 32 22 10

P129

34
16 18
9 7 11
5 4 3 8
3 2 2 1 7

P129

596
306 290
161 145 145
86 75 70 75
44 42 33 37 38
6 38 4 29 8 30

P129

136
57 79
38 19 60
31 7 12 48
27 4 3 9 39
25 2 2 1 8 31

P130

147
70 77
50 20 57
42 8 12 45
37 5 3 9 36
33 4 1 2 7 29

P130

404
203 201
119 84 117
83 36 48 69
67 16 20 28 41
60 7 9 11 17 24

P130

41
19 22
8 11 11
3 5 6 5
2 1 4 2 3

P130

649
324 325
161 163 162
80 81 82 80
40 40 41 41 39
21 19 21 20 21 18

P130

54
30 24
18 12 12
11 7 5 7
6 5 2 3 4
2 4 1 1 2 2

P131

159
69 90
28 41 49
12 16 25 24
6 6 10 15 9
3 3 3 7 8 1

P131

166
101 65
66 35 30
47 19 16 14
37 10 9 7 7
33 4 6 3 4 3

P131

656
304 352
140 164 188
64 76 88 100
29 35 41 47 53
13 16 19 22 25 28

P131

658
327 331
167 160 171
89 78 82 89
51 38 40 42 47
30 21 17 23 19 28

P131

49
30 19
18 12 7
10 8 4 3
4 6 2 2 1

P132

181
90 91
40 50 41
13 27 23 18
2 11 16 7 11
1 1 10 6 1 10

P132

52
21 31
13 8 23
11 2 6 17
10 1 1 5 12

P132

838
460 378
254 206 172
131 123 83 89
56 75 48 35 54
22 34 41 7 28 26

P132

79
42 37
21 21 16
9 12 9 7
3 6 6 3 4
2 1 5 1 2 2

P132

174
96 78
52 44 34
28 24 20 14
15 13 11 9 5
8 7 6 5 4 1

P133

68
34 34
16 18 16
7 9 9 7
3 4 5 4 3
2 1 3 2 2 1

P133

144
70 74
34 36 38
18 16 20 18
11 7 9 11 7
6 5 2 7 4 3

P133

638
393 245
251 142 103
157 94 48 55
80 77 17 31 24
9 71 6 11 20 4

SOLUTIONS

P133

683
347 336
175 172 164
89 86 86 78
49 40 46 40 38
26 23 17 29 21 17

P133

58
40 18
32 8 10
27 5 3 7
24 3 2 1 6

P134

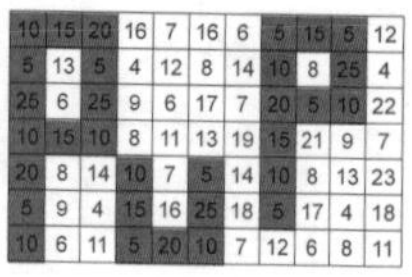

P134

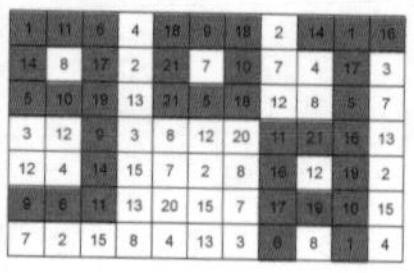

P134

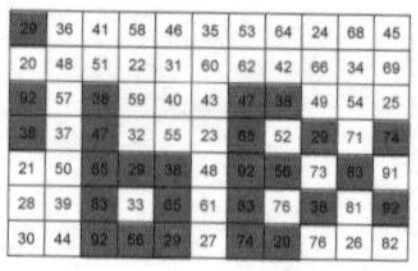

P134

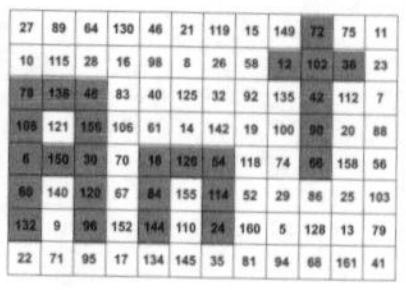

P134

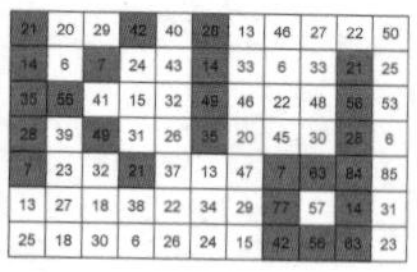

P135

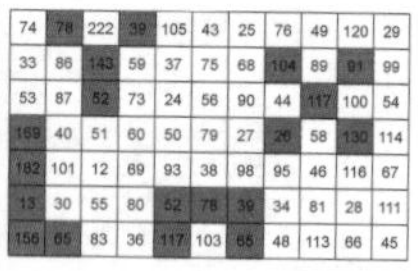

P135

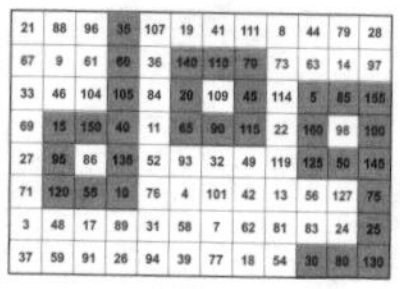

P135

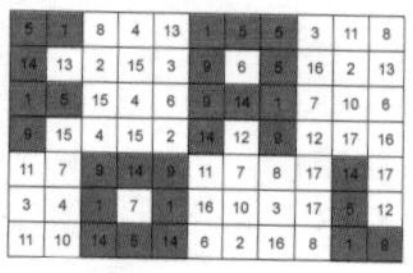

P135

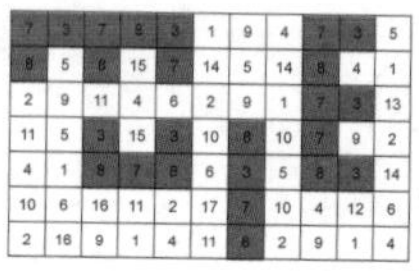

P135

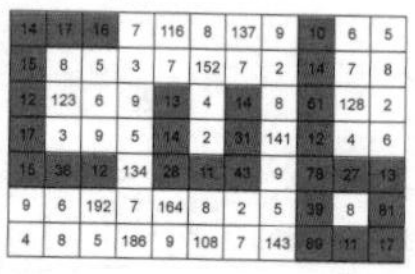

P136

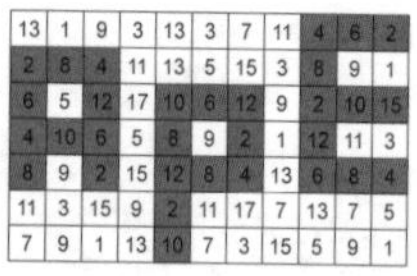

P136

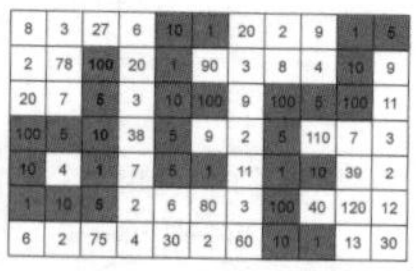

P136

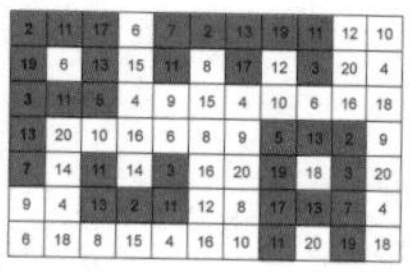

P136

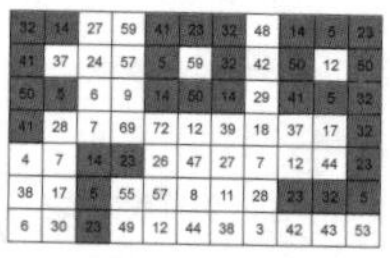

P136

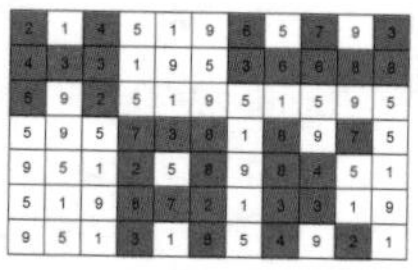

P137

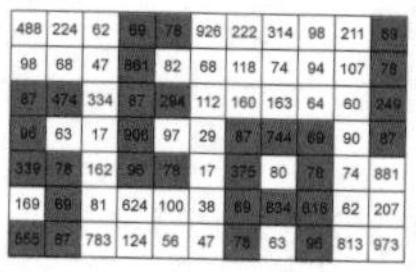

P137

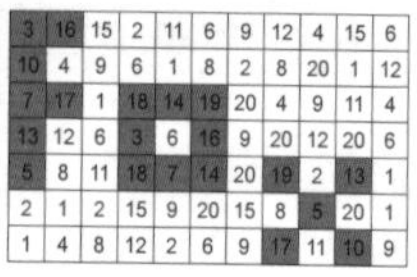

P137

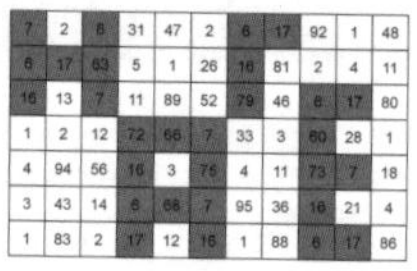

P137

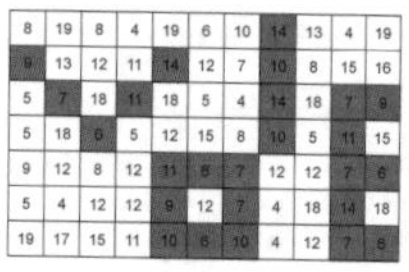

P137

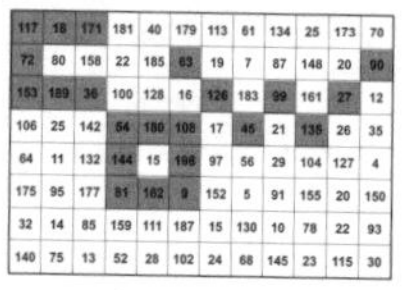

P138

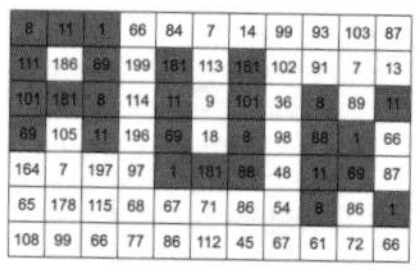

P138

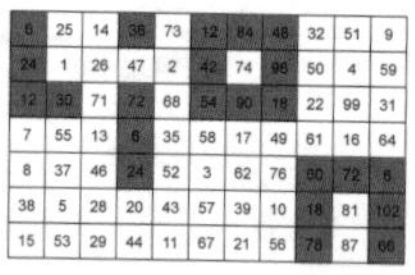

P138

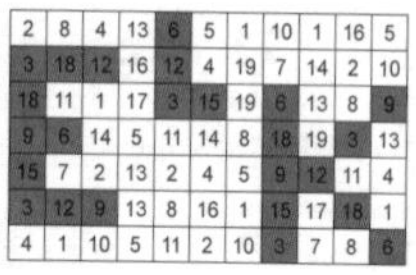

P138

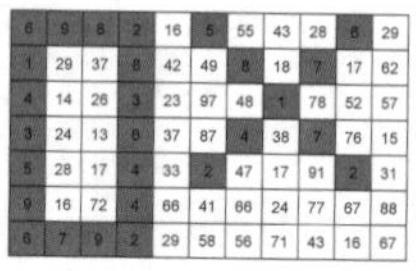

P138

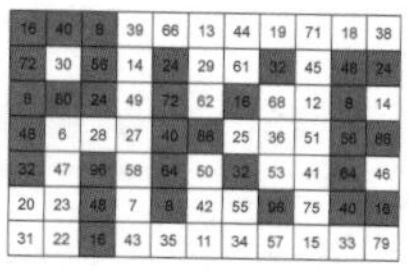

P139

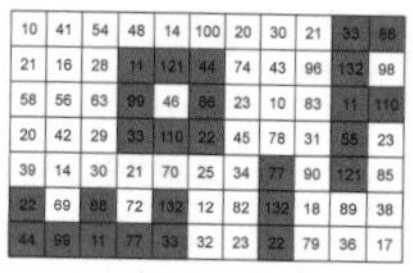

P139

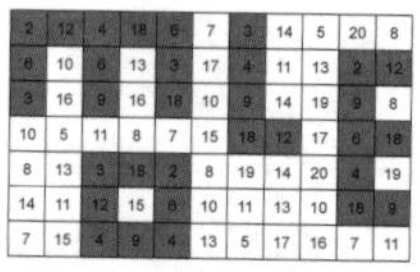

P139

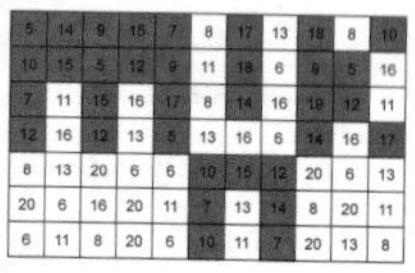

P139

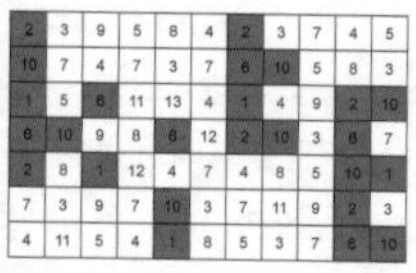

P139

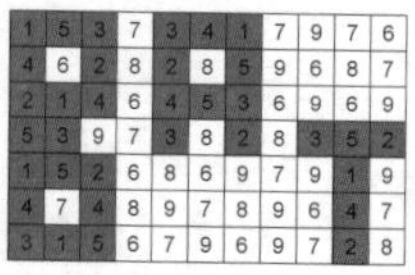

P140

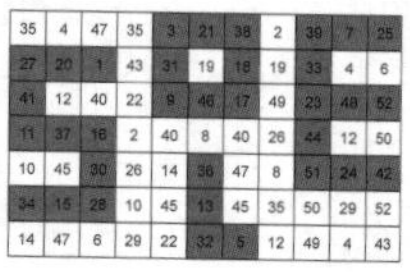

P140

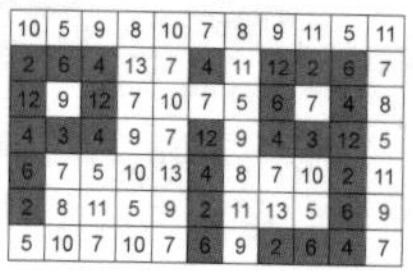

P140

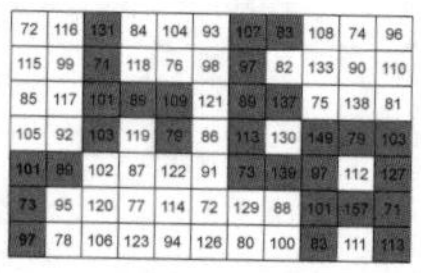

P140

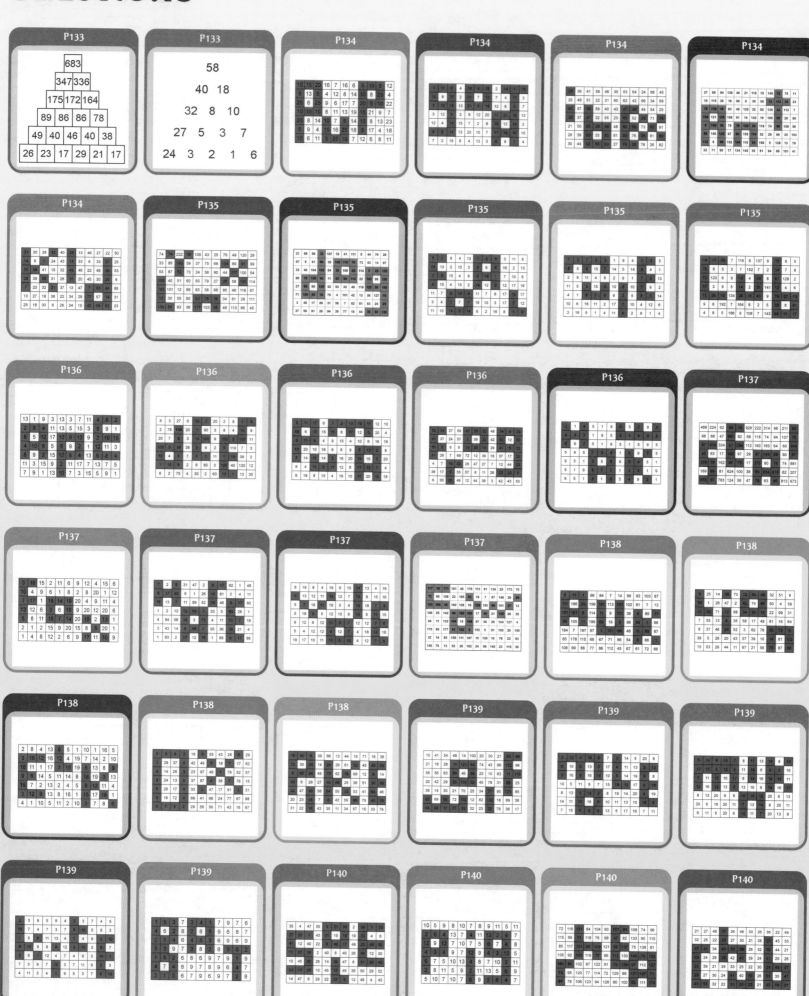

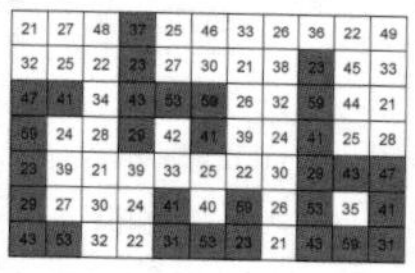

The answers correspond to the questions when read from left to right, and from top to bottom

SOLUTIONS

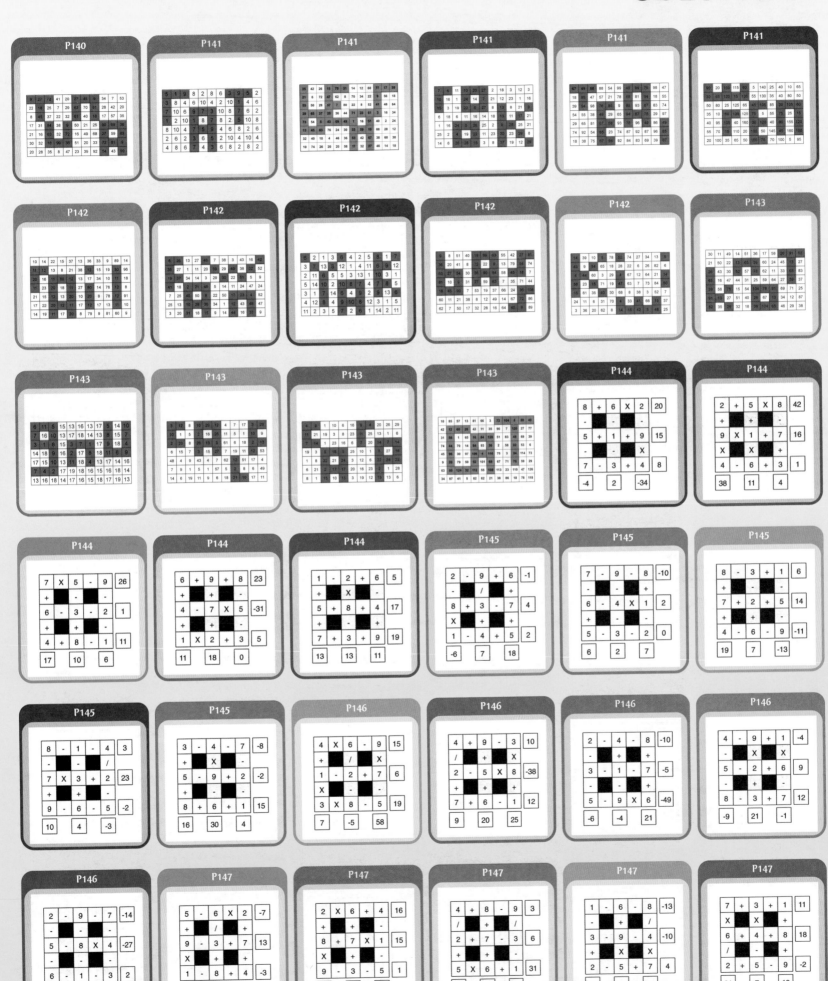

P140

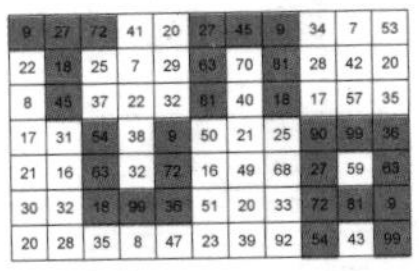

P141

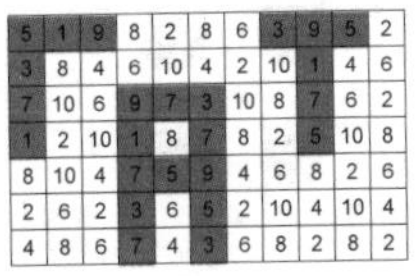

P141

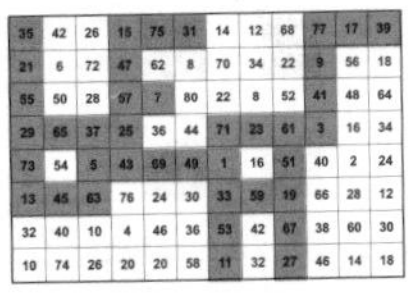

P141

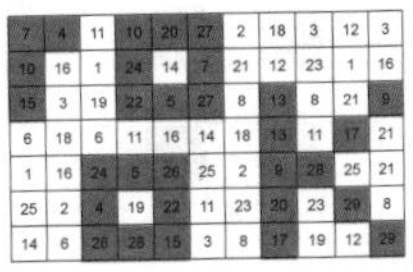

P141

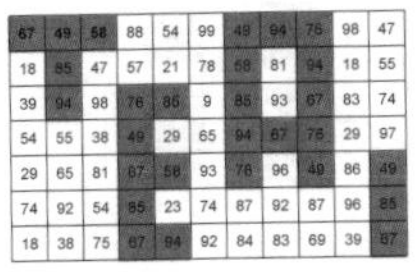

P141

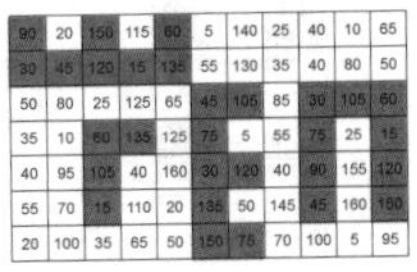

P142

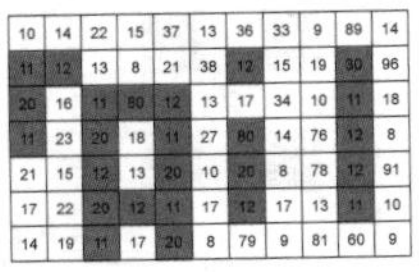

P142

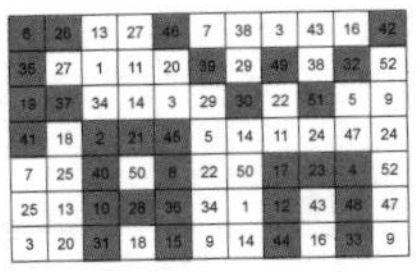

P142

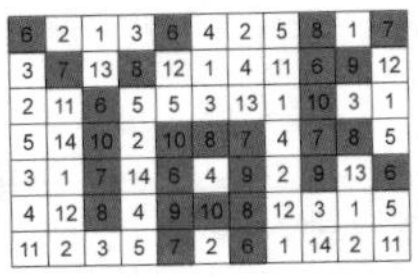

P142

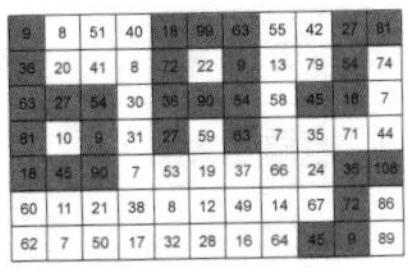

P142

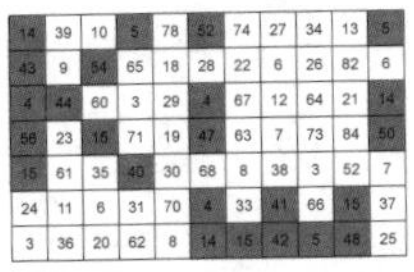

P143

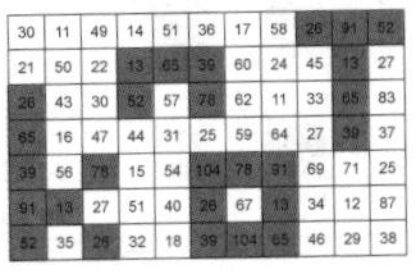

P143

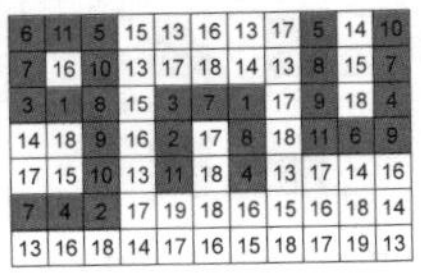

P143

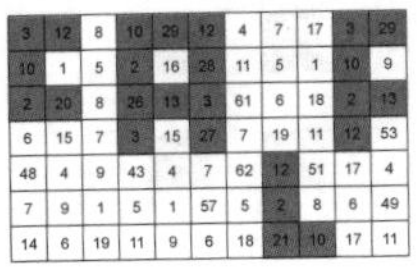

P143

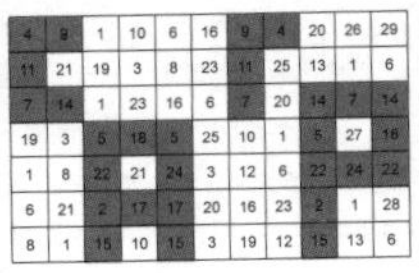

P143

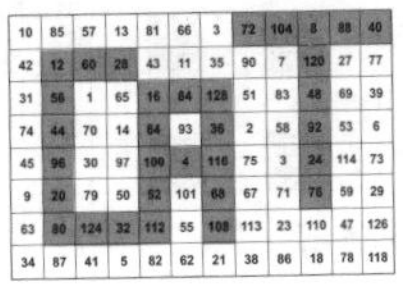

P144

8	+	6	X	2	20
-	■	-	■	-	
5	+	1	+	9	15
-	■	-	■	X	
7	-	3	+	4	8
-4		2		-34	

P144

2	+	5	X	8	42
+	■	+	■	-	
9	X	1	+	7	16
X	■	X	■	+	
4	-	6	+	3	1
38		11		4	

P144

7	X	5	-	9	26
+	■	-	■	-	
6	-	3	-	2	1
+	■	+	■	-	
4	+	8	-	1	11
17		10		6	

P144

6	+	9	+	8	23
+	■	+	■	-	
4	-	7	X	5	-31
+	■	+	■	-	
1	X	2	+	3	5
11		18		0	

P144

1	-	2	+	6	5
+	■	X	■	-	
5	+	8	+	4	17
+	■	-	■	+	
7	+	3	+	9	19
13		13		11	

P145

2	-	9	+	6	-1
-	■	/	■	+	
8	+	3	-	7	4
X	■	+	■	+	
1	-	4	+	5	2
-6		7		18	

P145

7	-	9	-	8	-10
-	■	-	■	+	
6	-	4	X	1	2
+	■	-	■	-	
5	-	3	-	2	0
6		2		7	

P145

8	-	3	+	1	6
+	■	-	■	-	
7	+	2	+	5	14
+	■	+	■	-	
4	-	6	-	9	-11
19		7		-13	

P145

8	-	1	-	4	3
-	■	-	■	/	
7	X	3	+	2	23
+	■	+	■	-	
9	-	6	-	5	-2
10		4		-3	

P145

3	-	4	-	7	-8
+	■	X	■	-	
5	-	9	+	2	-2
+	■	-	■	-	
8	+	6	+	1	15
16		30		4	

P146

4	X	6	-	9	15
+	■	/	■	X	
1	-	2	+	7	6
X	■	-	■	-	
3	X	8	-	5	19
7		-5		58	

P146

4	+	9	-	3	10
/	■	+	■	X	
2	-	5	X	8	-38
+	■	+	■	+	
7	+	6	-	1	12
9		20		25	

P146

2	-	4	-	8	-10
-	■	+	■	+	
3	-	1	-	7	-5
-	■	-	■	+	
5	-	9	X	6	-49
-6		-4		21	

P146

4	-	9	+	1	-4
-	■	X	■	X	
5	-	2	+	6	9
-	■	+	■	-	
8	-	3	+	7	12
-9		21		-1	

P146

2	-	9	-	7	-14
-	■	-	■	-	
5	-	8	X	4	-27
-	■	-	■	-	
6	-	1	-	3	2
-9		0		0	

P147

5	-	6	X	2	-7
+	■	/	■	+	
9	-	3	+	7	13
X	■	+	■	+	
1	-	8	+	4	-3
14		10		13	

P147

2	X	6	+	4	16
+	■	+	■	-	
8	+	7	X	1	15
X	■	+	■	-	
9	-	3	-	5	1
74		16		-2	

P147

4	+	8	-	9	3
/	■	+	■	/	
2	+	7	-	3	6
+	■	+	■	-	
5	X	6	+	1	31
7		21		2	

P147

1	-	6	-	8	-13
-	■	+	■	/	
3	-	9	-	4	-10
+	■	X	■	X	
2	-	5	+	7	4
0		51		14	

P147

7	+	3	+	1	11
X	■	X	■	+	
6	+	4	+	8	18
/	■	-	■	+	
2	+	5	-	9	-2
21		7		18	

The answers correspond to the questions when read from left to right, and from top to bottom

SOLUTIONS

P148

5	+	8	X	4	37
+	■	X	■	+	
1	-	6	X	9	-53
+	■	/	■	-	
3	-	2	-	7	-6
9		24		6	

P148

2	X	7	-	6	8
+	■	-	■	+	
3	+	9	X	8	75
X	■	-	■	-	
4	-	5	-	1	-2
14		-7		13	

P148

8	+	6	+	7	21
+	■	+	■	+	
1	-	5	+	9	5
-	■	-	■	+	
3	-	4	-	2	-3
6		7		18	

P148

3	-	9	-	2	-8
+	■	+	■	-	
1	X	5	-	6	-1
+	■	+	■	X	
8	+	4	-	7	5
12		18		-40	

P148

6	-	9	-	8	-11
X	■	X	■	-	
7	-	4	+	3	6
-	■	+	■	+	
5	X	1	-	2	3
37		37		7	

P149

5	+	1	X	8	13
X	■	+	■	/	
3	+	6	+	2	11
+	■	-	■	+	
7	X	4	-	9	19
22		3		13	

P149

3	X	1	+	8	11
+	■	-	■	+	
6	X	7	+	5	47
/	■	-	■	+	
2	X	9	-	4	14
6		-15		17	

P149

6	-	2	+	1	5
X	■	X	■	+	
8	+	9	X	3	35
-	■	+	■	+	
7	-	5	X	4	-13
41		23		8	

P149

2	+	1	X	4	6
-	■	X	■	-	
5	+	8	+	3	16
X	■	+	■	-	
6	+	9	+	7	22
-28		17		-6	

P149

5	-	3	x	4	+	2	=10
+		+		+		+	
4	+	2	-	5	x	3	=3
-		x		-		-	
2	x	5	+	3	-	4	=9
x		-		x		x	
3	-	4	+	2	x	5	=5
=21		=21		=12		=5	

P150

2	+	5	x	1	-	7	=0
x		x		+		-	
1	x	7	+	2	-	5	=4
-		-		x		+	
7	-	1	+	5	x	2	=22
+		+		-		x	
5	x	2	-	7	+	1	=4
=0		=36		=8		=4	

P150

3	+	1	X	5	8
-	■	-	■	-	
2	-	9	-	8	-15
-	■	X	■	/	
6	+	7	-	4	9
-5		-62		3	

P150

3	-	9	+	5	-1
X	■	-	■	-	
2	X	4	-	8	0
+	■	+	■	-	
6	+	1	+	7	14
12		6		-10	

P150

7	-	2	-	6	-1
-	■	-	■	X	
4	+	3	+	9	16
-	■	-	■	+	
1	+	5	+	8	14
2		-6		62	

P150

8	X	7	-	3	53
+	■	-	■	-	
6	+	1	X	5	11
X	■	X	■	-	
9	+	4	-	2	11
62		3		-4	

P151

7	x	2	-	4	+	3	=13
+		x		-		+	
3	+	7	-	2	x	4	=32
-		+		+		x	
4	-	3	x	7	+	2	=9
x		-		x		-	
2	x	4	+	3	-	7	=4
=12		=13		=27		=7	

P151

6	+	4	+	7	17
X	■	+	■	-	
9	-	3	X	2	3
+	■	+	■	+	
8	+	1	+	5	14
62		8		10	

P151

9	-	2	+	7	14
/	■	+	■	+	
3	-	6	-	8	-11
-	■	+	■	+	
4	-	1	X	5	-1
-1		9		20	

P151

9	-	7	X	3	-12
+	■	-	■	-	
6	+	2	-	8	0
+	■	X	■	+	
4	X	5	+	1	21
19		-3		-4	

P151

6	+	1	x	5	-	7	=28
-		+		x		-	
1	x	5	-	7	+	6	=4
x		-		+		x	
7	-	6	+	1	x	5	=10
+		x		-		+	
5	+	7	-	6	x	1	=6
=40		=0		=30		=6	

P152

8	x	2	+	3	-	6	=13
-		+		+		-	
6	+	3	-	8	x	2	=2
x		x		-		x	
2	x	8	+	6	-	3	=19
+		-		x		+	
3	+	6	x	2	-	8	=10
=7		=34		=10		=20	

P152

8	-	2	X	7	-6
-	■	+	■	X	
3	-	5	X	4	-17
+	■	+	■	+	
1	+	9	+	6	16
6		16		34	

P152

6	-	7	-	4	-5
+	■	+	■	+	
1	+	9	-	8	2
-	■	-	■	/	
3	-	5	-	2	-4
4		11		8	

P152

9	+	2	-	5	x	7	=42
-		x		+		-	
7	-	5	x	9	+	2	=20
x		-		-		x	
2	x	9	+	7	-	5	=20
+		+		x		+	
5	+	7	x	2	-	9	=15
=9		=8		=14		=34	

P152

5	+	4	-	8	1
-	■	-	■	+	
2	X	7	+	3	17
+	■	+	■	-	
9	+	6	+	1	16
12		3		10	

P153

6	x	3	+	2	-	4	=16
-		x		+		-	
2	+	6	x	4	-	3	=29
x		-		-		x	
4	+	2	-	3	x	6	=18
+		+		x		+	
3	x	4	+	6	-	2	=16
=19		=20		=18		=8	

P153

2	+	1	+	3	6
X	■	-	■	X	
7	+	4	-	6	5
+	■	X	■	+	
5	-	8	-	9	-12
19		-31		27	

P153

2	+	7	+	3	12
-	■	+	■	X	
9	X	6	-	8	46
+	■	+	■	+	
5	-	4	-	1	0
-2		17		25	

P153

2	-	4	+	7	5
+	■	X	■	+	
9	+	8	X	3	33
+	■	-	■	+	
5	+	1	+	6	12
16		31		16	

P153

3	x	4	+	7	-	1	=18
+		x		+		+	
7	-	1	x	3	+	4	=22
-		+		x		-	
1	+	7	x	4	-	3	=29
x		-		-		x	
4	-	3	+	1	x	7	=14
=36		=8		=39		=14	

P154

1	3	2
2	1	3
3	2	1

P154

5	3	4	5	1
4	2	1	2	4
1	3	5	1	3
2	1	4	3	5
5	3	2	4	2

P154

4	2	3	1
2	1	2	3
4	2	4	1
3	4	1	3

P154

2	4	3	2
1	2	4	1
3	1	3	4
2	4	1	3

P154

2	2	1
2	3	3
1	1	3

P155

3	1	2	1	4
2	5	4	3	1
3	1	2	5	4
5	4	1	2	5
2	3	5	4	3

The answers correspond to the questions when read from left to right, and from top to bottom

SOLUTIONS

P155

3	2	1
2	1	2
3	1	3

P155

1	3	1	2	4
5	2	4	5	3
2	1	3	4	5
4	2	5	2	1
5	3	4	1	3

P155

3	1	3	2
1	4	2	4
2	1	4	3
4	2	3	1

P155

3	1	1
3	2	2
3	2	1

P156

2	1	2
3	2	3
1	3	1

P156

2	4	1	5	1
5	3	5	4	2
3	2	4	1	3
4	5	2	5	1
1	3	4	2	3

P156

4	1	2	3
2	4	3	4
3	1	2	1
1	2	4	3

P156

2	3	4	1
1	4	3	4
2	1	2	1
3	2	4	3

P156

1	2	1
3	1	2
2	3	3

P157

4	2	3	2	1
3	1	5	4	3
2	5	1	5	4
4	2	4	2	1
1	3	5	3	5

P157

3	3	2
1	2	1
3	1	2

P157

3	5	4	1	2
1	2	5	3	4
5	3	4	2	1
3	1	5	1	4
2	5	4	2	3

P157

3	1	3	4
2	4	2	3
4	1	4	2
1	3	2	1

P157

3	2	3
1	1	2
3	2	1

P158

1	2	3
2	3	1
2	3	1

P158

3	2	4	2	5
1	5	3	1	3
5	4	1	5	4
2	3	4	2	1
1	4	2	3	5

P158

1	4	1	2
2	3	2	4
1	4	1	3
3	2	3	4

P158

1	3	2	3
2	4	1	4
4	1	2	1
3	4	3	2

P158

2	2	2
3	1	3
1	1	3

P159

2	1	5	3	4
4	3	2	1	3
5	2	1	4	5
1	4	2	3	1
5	3	5	4	2

P159

3	2	2
2	1	1
3	3	1

P159

4	3	4	2	3
1	5	1	5	1
2	3	2	4	3
5	1	5	3	2
4	2	1	4	5

P159

3	4	1	3
1	2	3	4
4	3	2	1
2	1	4	2

P159

2	3	3
1	3	2
2	1	1

P160

2	1	3
2	2	3
1	1	3

P160

1	2	5	3	4
4	1	2	5	2
3	4	3	4	1
1	5	2	1	5
3	2	5	3	4

P160

2	1	2	1
4	2	3	4
3	4	2	1
4	3	1	3

P160

4	3	1	3
2	1	2	1
3	4	1	2
4	2	4	3

P160

3	1	2
2	3	3
1	1	2

P161

5	2	3	4	3
3	1	5	2	1
2	4	2	4	3
4	1	5	2	5
1	5	3	4	1

P161

3	2	2
1	1	1
2	3	3

P161

2	1	5	1	5
4	5	2	3	4
2	4	3	5	3
3	2	1	4	2
1	4	5	3	1

P161

1	4	2	1
4	3	1	3
3	1	2	4
4	2	3	2

P161

2	1	1
2	3	2
3	1	3

P162

3	2	3	4
1	4	1	2
2	3	4	1
4	1	3	2

P162

1	4	3	4	5
2	1	5	2	3
1	5	2	4	2
3	1	4	3	4
1	3	5	2	5

The answers correspond to the questions when read from left to right, and from top to bottom

SOLUTIONS

P162

4	1	4	1
2	3	2	4
1	2	1	3
3	4	3	2

P162

1	2	3	1
4	1	4	2
2	3	2	3
3	4	1	4

P162

3	1	4	2	3
5	4	2	1	4
2	3	1	5	2
4	2	5	1	3
1	5	3	5	4

P163

4	2	3	5	1
1	5	2	4	5
2	4	3	2	3
1	5	2	4	1
4	3	1	5	3

P163

4	3	4	1
2	1	2	4
3	2	4	3
2	1	3	2

P163

3	5	1	2	4	6
1	2	6	4	8	3
3	6	5	2	4	7
7	3	1	5	7	9
9	1	8	2	9	8
5	4	7	6	8	9

P163

6	5	4	3	2	1
5	2	9	4	7	2
1	6	2	5	3	4
4	5	7	6	9	8
9	8	1	7	8	3
3	6	7	8	9	1

P163

5	7	3	1	9	8
4	1	4	2	3	5
3	4	5	6	7	8
1	9	6	8	6	2
2	5	7	3	1	7
6	9	8	2	4	9

P164

				19
2	10	4	4	20
9	8	4	1	22
4	7	3	10	24
4	9	7	8	28
19	34	18	23	21

P164

				27
5	8	1	4	18
7	8	6	3	24
10	8	10	8	36
9	5	1	1	16
31	29	18	16	24

P164

				16
1	3	7	5	16
4	9	1	9	23
4	6	3	8	21
4	6	8	1	19
13	24	19	23	14

P164

				27
10	3	6	5	24
2	6	6	10	24
4	10	2	6	22
6	7	6	4	23
22	26	20	25	22

P164

				17
9	10	5	3	27
8	8	7	4	27
1	2	5	8	16
5	8	10	4	27
23	28	27	19	26

P164

				17
9	7	2	9	27
1	5	3	2	11
6	2	1	4	13
3	8	4	4	19
19	22	10	19	19

P165

				22
5	7	5	9	26
9	9	8	7	33
7	2	6	2	17
3	7	3	8	21
24	25	22	26	28

P165

				21
5	4	3	8	20
2	8	5	3	18
3	2	7	2	14
6	4	10	6	26
16	18	25	19	26

P165

				22
5	7	8	7	27
3	4	6	5	18
7	3	1	1	12
6	1	1	5	13
21	15	16	18	15

P165

				19
2	9	4	6	21
8	8	4	4	24
1	2	3	5	11
7	9	7	10	33
18	28	18	25	23

P165

				12
10	8	3	5	26
6	8	3	4	21
1	1	5	2	9
3	5	2	1	11
20	22	13	12	24

P166

				14
4	7	8	3	22
9	3	6	3	21
9	4	10	5	28
1	4	5	7	17
23	18	29	18	24

P166

				17
6	1	9	3	19
8	6	7	10	31
6	1	10	8	25
6	6	4	1	17
26	14	30	22	23

P166

				16
7	8	5	2	22
2	9	1	7	19
5	6	3	5	19
7	4	3	8	22
21	27	12	22	27

P166

				12
1	7	10	3	21
1	6	3	3	13
5	2	5	6	18
4	1	3	6	14
11	16	21	18	18

P166

				28
7	6	2	9	24
1	1	5	10	17
9	10	1	1	21
4	8	1	5	18
21	25	9	25	14

P166

				17
7	7	2	6	22
5	9	4	3	21
9	1	2	8	20
6	5	3	4	18
27	22	11	21	22

P167

				19
1	4	4	7	16
7	6	6	4	23
6	1	2	7	16
5	7	5	8	25
19	18	17	26	17

P167

				26
6	7	7	2	22
2	10	7	9	28
8	8	1	4	21
9	6	6	9	30
25	31	21	24	26

P167

				26
7	7	1	7	22
2	8	2	5	17
6	8	8	3	25
9	4	8	6	27
24	27	19	21	29

P167

				27
6	4	6	6	22
1	5	9	10	25
8	7	4	5	24
5	5	3	9	22
20	21	22	30	24

P167

				29
4	5	1	7	17
10	8	8	1	27
2	8	2	6	18
6	6	10	3	25
22	27	21	17	17

P168

				29
2	6	9	10	27
10	6	6	1	23
2	8	10	2	22
5	8	5	10	28
19	28	30	23	28

P168

				29
4	1	6	5	16
9	3	5	4	21
9	9	7	10	35
10	5	3	4	22
32	18	21	23	18

P168

				23
3	1	1	8	13
6	7	6	4	23
5	5	4	6	20
4	1	8	5	18
18	14	19	23	19

P168

				16
5	5	7	4	21
10	8	1	8	27
7	2	8	5	22
9	6	1	9	25
31	21	17	26	30

P168

				24
8	5	10	3	26
4	10	10	7	31
9	4	8	3	24
7	8	2	9	26
28	27	30	22	35

P168

				22
2	5	5	8	20
3	7	1	9	20
2	4	9	7	22
9	4	9	8	30
16	20	24	32	26

The answers correspond to the questions when read from left to right, and from top to bottom

SOLUTIONS

P169

				27
4	4	3	5	16
4	3	9	9	25
10	5	4	2	21
8	5	4	5	22
26	17	20	21	16

P169

				18
4	7	7	9	27
8	4	3	8	23
8	5	2	2	17
1	5	7	7	20
21	21	19	26	17

P169

				20
2	1	8	8	19
1	6	5	4	16
8	5	7	3	23
2	2	7	5	16
13	14	27	20	20

P169

				18
2	2	9	9	22
2	3	2	6	13
3	1	10	4	18
6	2	1	4	13
13	8	22	23	19

P169

				24
4	2	2	8	16
1	9	5	4	19
6	4	5	7	22
7	7	8	1	23
18	22	20	20	19

P170

				10
2	5	2	3	12
10	2	5	2	19
10	1	3	9	23
1	3	6	4	14
23	11	16	18	11

P170

				28
9	10	2	9	30
10	6	5	5	26
2	8	5	9	24
6	8	10	4	28
27	32	22	27	24

P170

				11
3	4	3	3	13
5	9	1	6	21
4	2	9	7	22
5	8	8	9	30
17	23	21	25	30

P170

					12
4	2	2	4	3	15
3	2	5	1	5	16
1	2	4	3	1	11
4	1	2	1	1	9
3	4	1	5	5	18
15	11	14	14	15	16

P170

				25
10	8	4	7	29
7	6	5	8	26
2	7	9	5	23
6	9	7	8	30
25	30	25	28	33

P170

				27
2	6	8	9	25
5	3	3	6	17
3	8	6	8	25
7	2	8	7	24
17	19	25	30	18

P171

					41
6	10	9	10	8	43
9	10	7	9	6	41
10	10	7	6	7	40
10	7	6	8	6	37
10	7	9	7	10	43
45	44	38	40	37	41

P171

				21
9	1	6	10	26
5	10	1	2	18
7	2	10	7	26
8	4	10	1	23
29	17	27	20	30

P171

				21
4	3	3	1	11
9	1	8	4	22
6	8	9	5	28
4	8	5	3	20
23	20	25	13	17

P171

					42
9	9	10	6	8	42
9	7	7	8	6	37
8	6	10	6	8	38
10	10	10	6	10	46
6	9	8	8	7	38
42	41	45	34	39	39

P171

				22
9	4	5	10	28
6	3	3	7	19
6	4	2	3	15
5	10	7	4	26
26	21	17	24	18

P172

					42
6	6	8	7	10	37
6	7	8	9	8	38
6	6	6	6	10	34
6	7	10	7	10	40
10	6	10	7	10	43
34	32	42	36	48	36

P172

				12
9	4	7	1	21
7	5	6	9	27
7	4	3	1	15
1	10	2	1	14
24	23	18	12	18

P172

				29
6	5	6	9	26
8	2	8	5	23
8	4	1	5	18
8	4	3	3	18
30	15	18	22	12

P172

					42
8	7	10	9	7	41
9	9	9	10	10	47
7	9	8	10	9	43
10	8	10	9	8	45
9	10	6	7	8	40
43	43	43	45	42	42

P172

				23
5	1	8	1	15
7	7	8	2	24
9	7	8	3	27
7	7	8	3	25
28	22	32	9	23

P172

				28
7	6	1	9	23
6	9	9	4	28
2	2	3	8	15
8	4	5	1	18
23	21	18	22	20

P173 line 1 (left)

987.
NUMBER INCREASE BY 109 EACH TIME.

P173 line 1 (right)

23.
NUMBERS INCREASE BY 2, THEN 3, THEN 4 IN ROTATION.

P173 line 2 (left)

9.
THE NUMBERS INCREASE BY 1 THEN 2 ROTATING.

P173 line 2 (right)

32.
MULTIPLY THE PREVIOUS TWO NUMBERS.

P173 line 3 (left)

182.
NUMBERS INCREASE BY 15, THEN 25, 35 ETC.

P173 line 3 (right)

30.
NUMBERS INCREASE BY 2,3,5,7 ETC (THE PRIME NUMBER SEQUENCE).

P173 line 4 (left)

72.
SUBTRACT THE SUM OF THE DIGITS.

P173 line 4 (right)

1.
THE NUMBERS ARE DIVIDED BY 5 EACH TIME.

P173 line 5 (left)

31.
NUMBER OF DAYS IN EACH MONTH FROM FEBRUARY.

P173 line 5 (right)

13.
SEQUENCE OF PRIME NUMBERS.

P174 line 1 (left)

58.
THE NUMBERS INCREASE BY 11

P174 line 1 (right)

0.
TAKE AWAY 1 FROM THE FIRST DIGIT. ADD 2 TO THE SECOND. TAKE AWAY 3 FROM THE THIRD. ADD 4 TO THE FOURTH ETC.

P174 line 2 (left)

2.
THE DIGITS OF PI.

P174 line 2 (right)

152.
TAKE AWAY 99 EACH TIME.

The answers correspond to the questions when read from left to right, and from top to bottom

SOLUTIONS

P174 line 3 (left)
48.
THE NUMBERS ADVANCE BY 1, 2, 4, 8 ETC.

P174 line 3 (right)
11.
ALL THE NUMBERS ARE ODD STARTING FROM 1.

P174 line 4 (left)
44.
ADD THE PREVIOUS THREE NUMBERS.

P174 line 4 (right)
44.
ADD THE PREVIOUS TWO NUMBERS TOGETHER.

P174 line 5 (left)
1.
THE NUMBERS ARE HALVED EACH TIME.

P174 line 5 (right)
75.
THE NUMBERS DECREASE BY 25 EACH TIME.

P175 line 1 (left)
XII.
EVEN NUMBERS IN ROMAN NUMERALS.

P175 line 1 (right)
-140.
THE NUMBERS DECREASE BY 4, 16, 64, 256

P175 line 2 (left)
13.
FOLLOWS THE SEQUENCE OF PRIME NUMBERS.

P175 line 2 (right)
17.
THE NUMBERS GO DOWN BY 3 EACH TIME.

P175 line 3 (left)
610.
ADD THE PREVIOUS 2. THESE NUMBERS ARE IN THE FIBONACCI SERIES.

P175 line 3 (right)
46.
THE NUMBERS INCREASE BY 7, THEN 8, 9 ETC.

P175 line 4 (left)
15.
ADD 1 THEN 2 THEN 3 ETC.

P175 line 4 (right)
103.
DOUBLE THE PREVIOUS NUMBER THEN TAKE AWAY 1 ,THEN 2 , THEN 3 ,THEN 4 ,THEN ,THEN 5.

P175 line 5 (left)
21.
THE NUMBERS INCREASE BY 5, THEN 4 ETC.

P175 line 5 (right)
8.
NUMBERS OF THE LETTERS IN EACH DAY OF THE WEEK.

P176 line 1 (left)
20.
THE NUMBERS DECREASE BY 10 THEN 8, 6, 4 ETC.

P176 line 1 (right)
37.
THE NUMBERS INCREASE BY 7 EACH TIME.

P176 line 2 (left)
69.
DOUBLE AND THEN SUBTRACT 5.

P176 line 2 (right)
125.
CUBE OF THE NUMBERS 1, 2, 3 ETC.

P176 line 3 (left)
25.
THE NUMBERS DECREASE BY 9 EACH TIME.

P176 line 3 (right)
4.
SEQUENCE OF SUBTRACT 2, THEN ADD 1.

P176 line 4 (left)
41.
PRIME NUMBER FROM 19 ONWARDS.

P176 line 4 (right)
96.
THE NUMBERS DOUBLE EACH TIME.

P176 line 5 (left)
5.
ADD THE PREVIOUS TWO NUMBERS. THIS IS THE FIBONACCI SERIES

P176 line 5 (right)
50.
SQUARE EACH NUMBER THEN DOUBLE IT.

P177 line 1 (left)
987.
NUMBER INCREASE BY BY 109 EACH TIME.

P177 line 1 (right)
35.
SQUARE OF THE NUMBERS 1, 2, 3, 4, 5, 6 THEN SUBTRACT 1.

P177 line 2 (left)
33.
ADD 3 THEN 4 THEN 5 THEN 6 ETC.

P177 line 2 (right)
500.
THE NUMBERS INCREASE BY 125, THEN 100, THEN 75 ETC.

P177 line 3 (left)
12.
SUBTRACT 2 TO THE FIRST NUMBER THEN ADD SEVEN TO THE NEXT NUMBER IN ROTATION.

P177 line 3 (right)
0.
THE NUMBERS DECREASE BY 20 EACH TIME.

P177 line 4 (left)
49.
SQUARE EACH NUMBER FROM 2 ONWARDS.

P177 line 4 (right)
168.
SUBTRACT 4 THEN MULTIPLY BY 3.

P177 line 5 (left)
4.
THE NUMBER OF LETTERS IN THE WORDS TEN, NINE EIGHT ETC.

P177 line 5 (right)
12.
ALL THE NUMBERS ARE EVEN.

The answers correspond to the questions when read from left to right, and from top to bottom

SOLUTIONS

P178
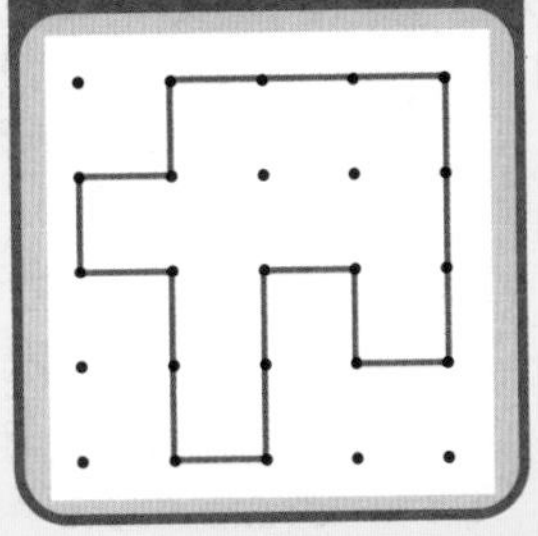
P178
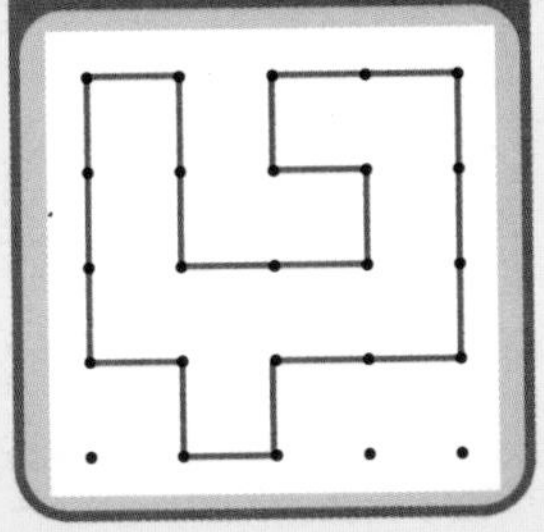
P178
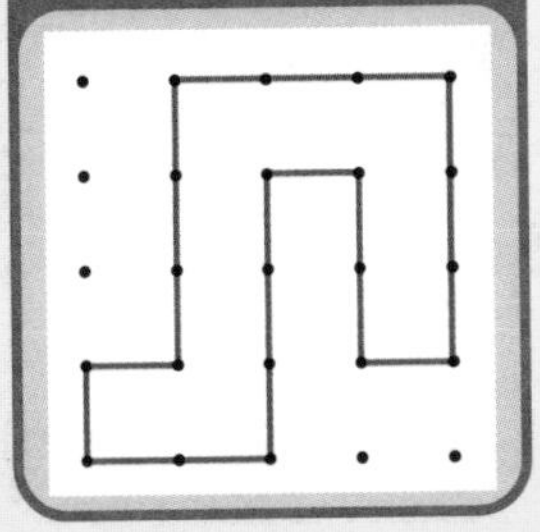
P178
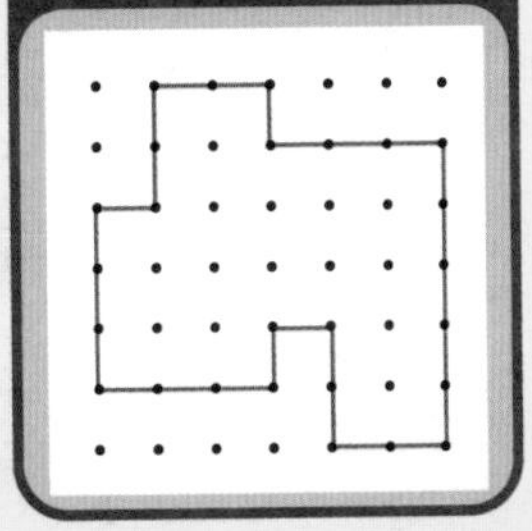
P178
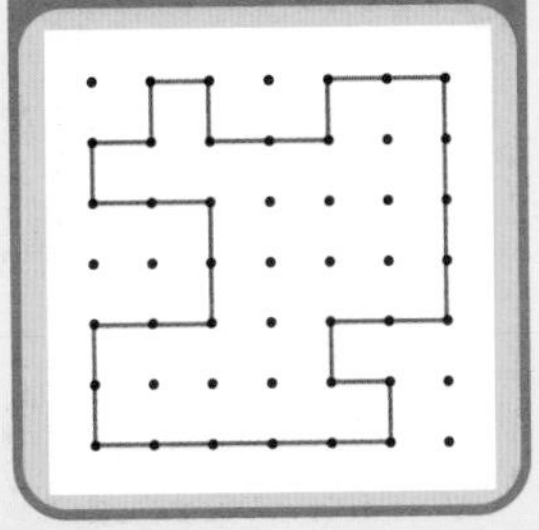
P178
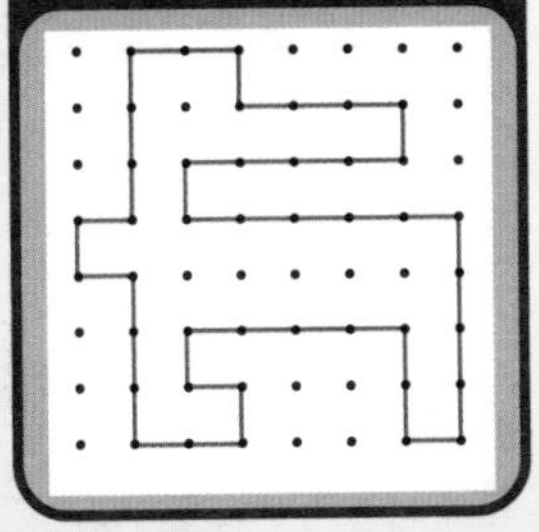
P178
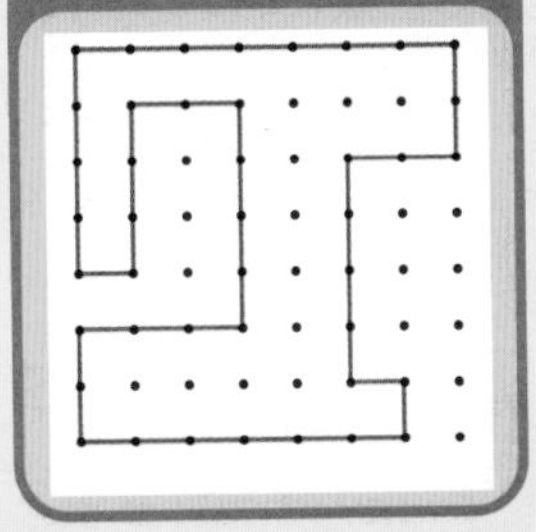
P179
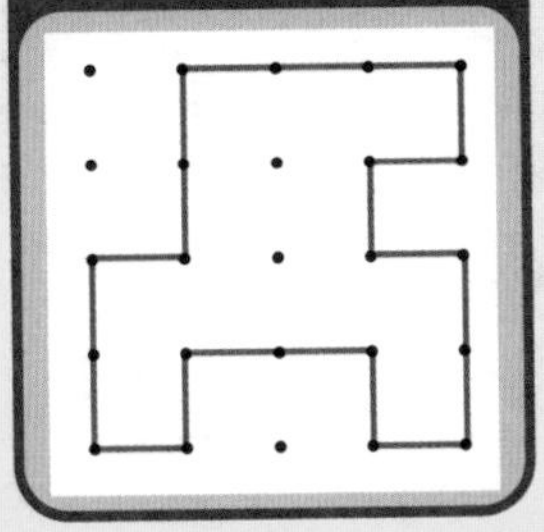
P179
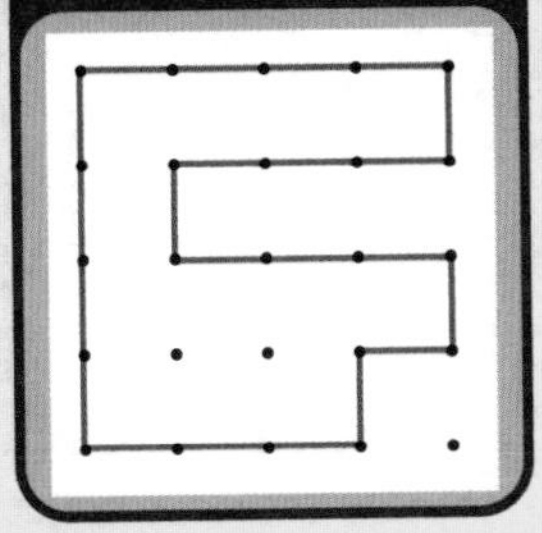
P179
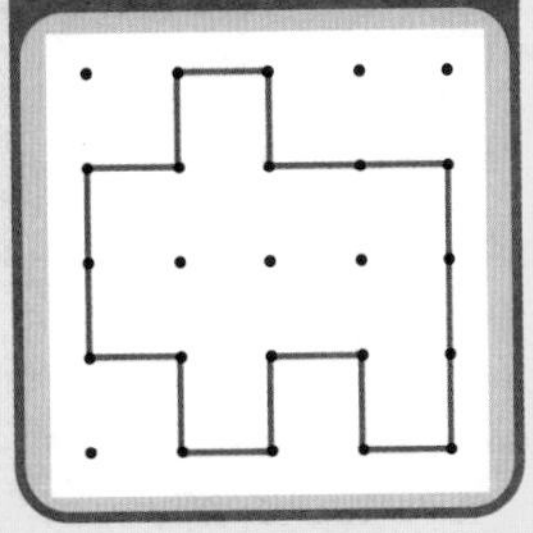
P179
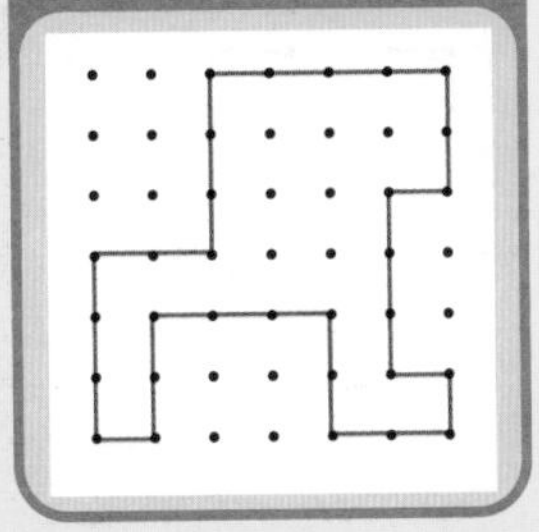
P179
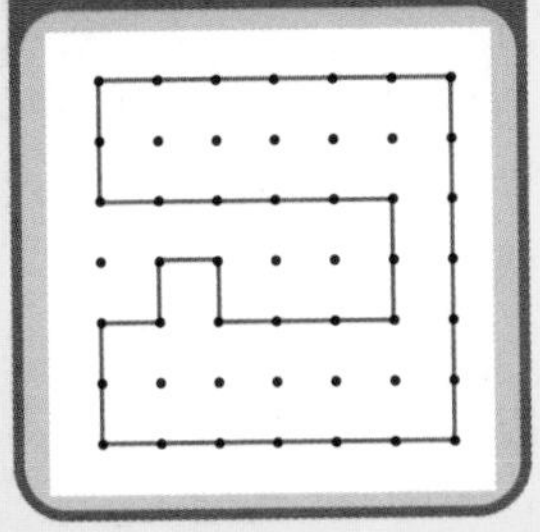
P179
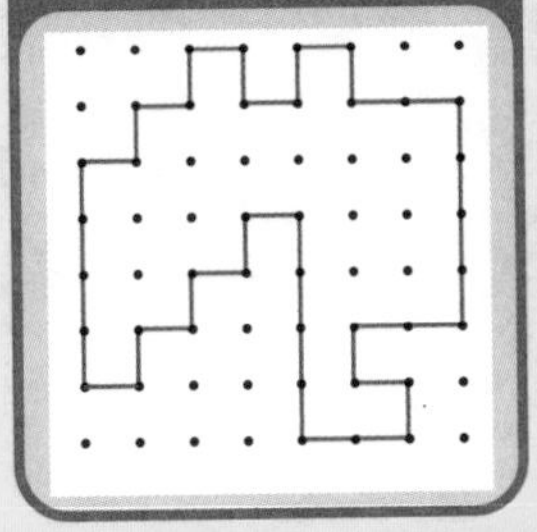
P179
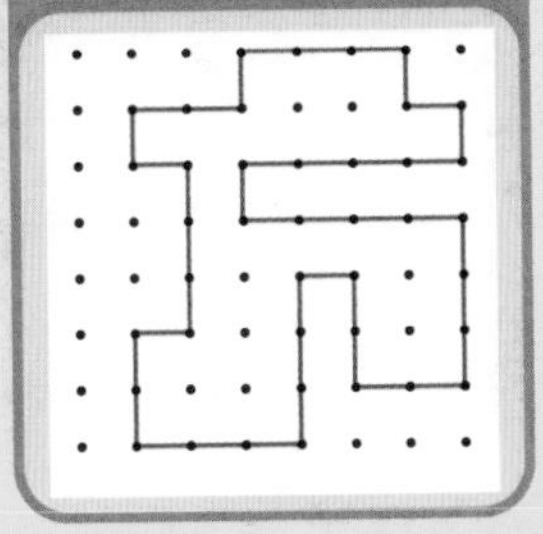
P180
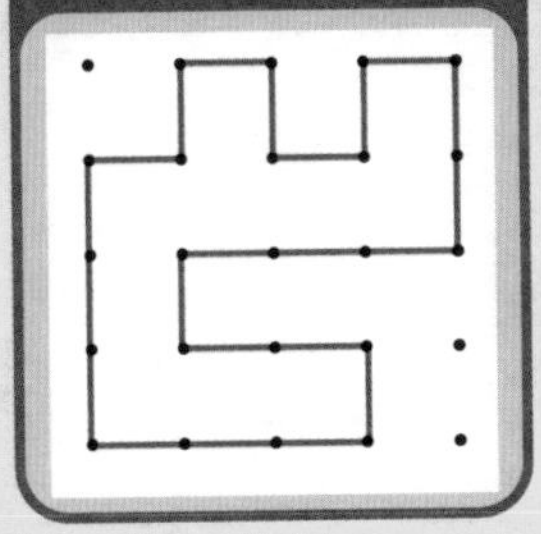
P180
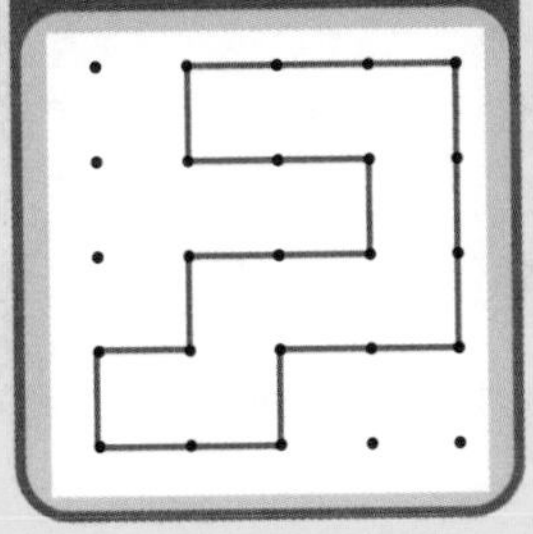
P180
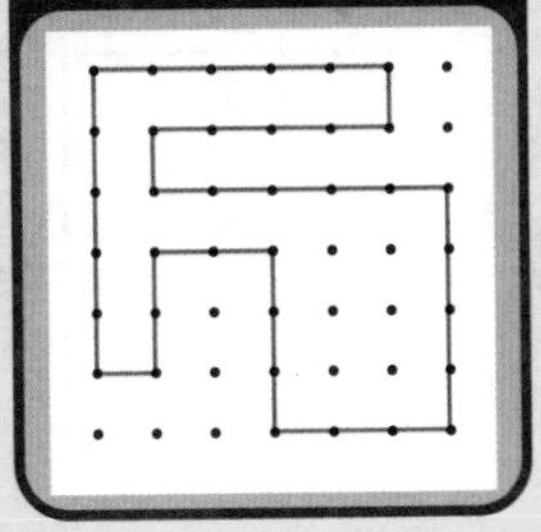
P180
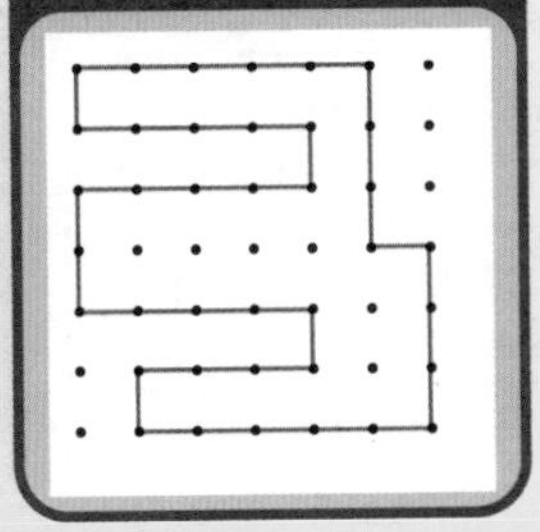
P180
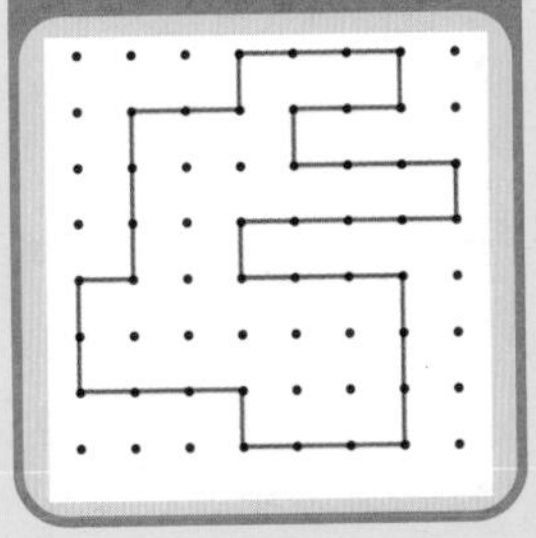
P180
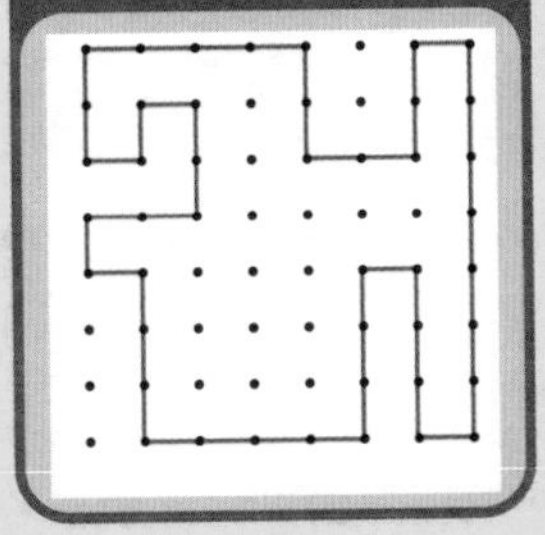
P181
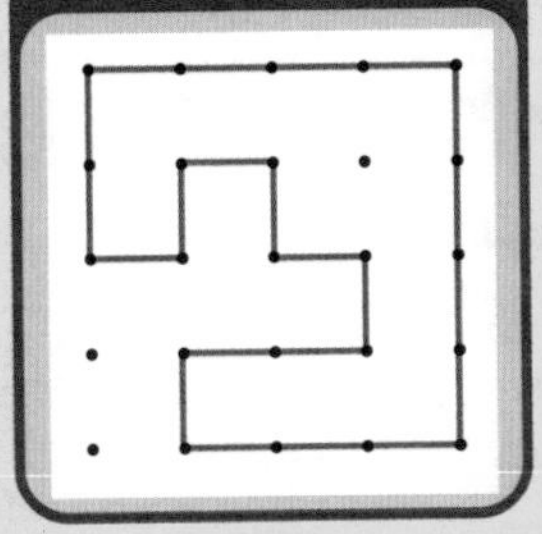
P181
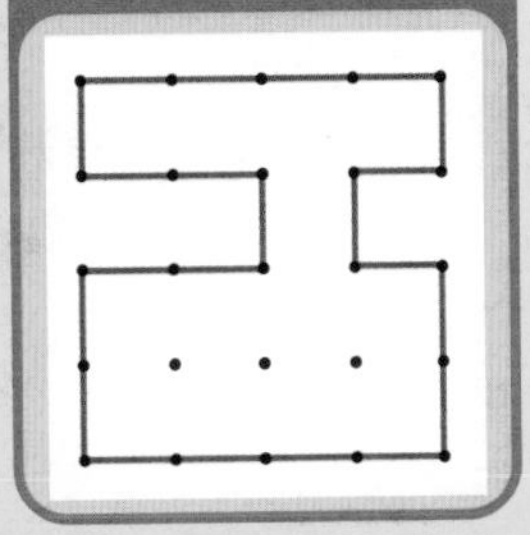
P181
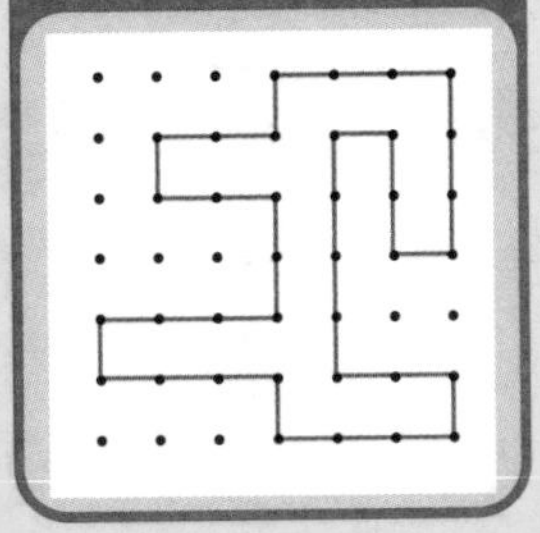
P181
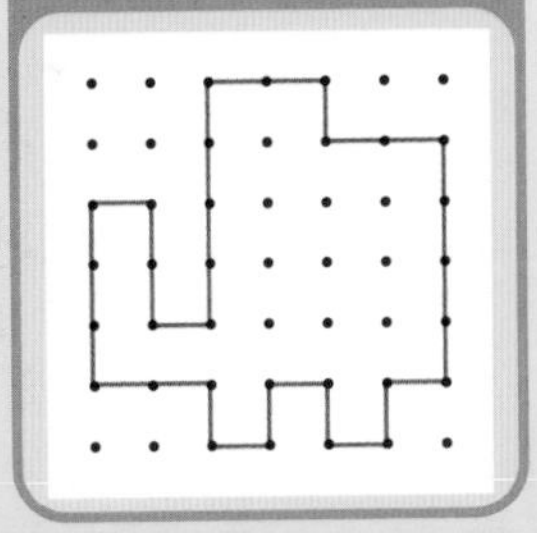
P181
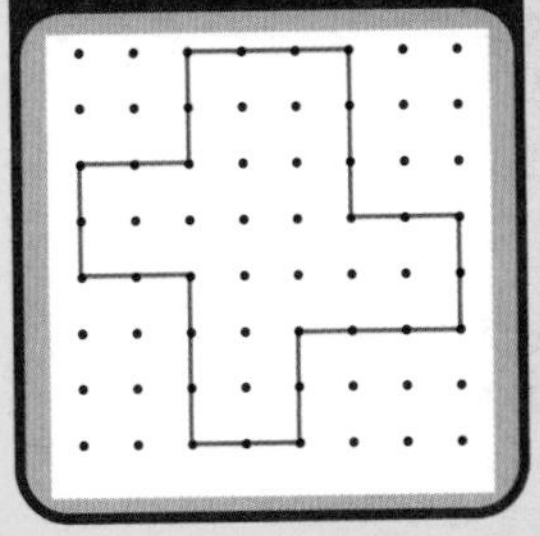
P181
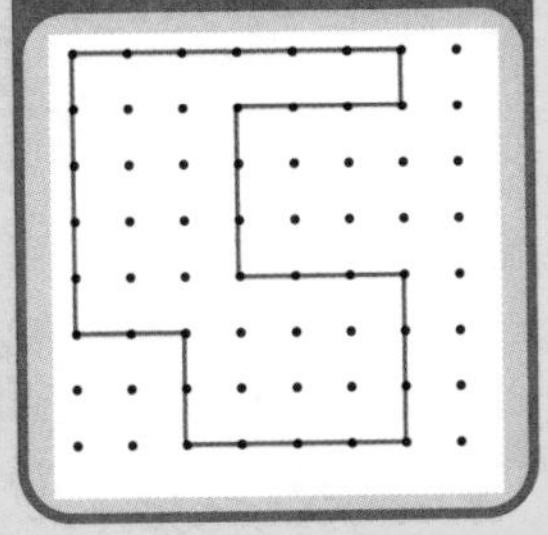
P182
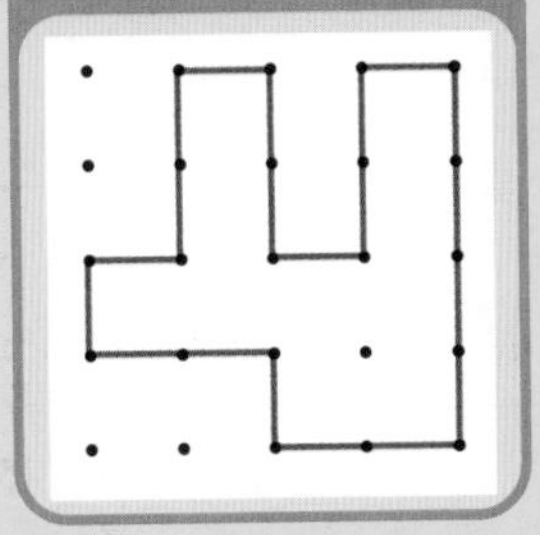
P182
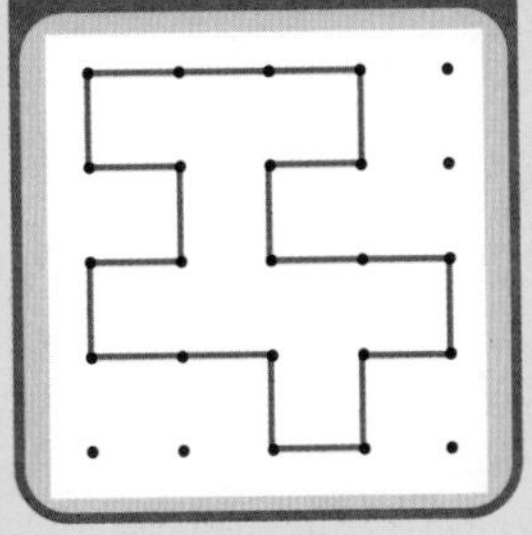
P182
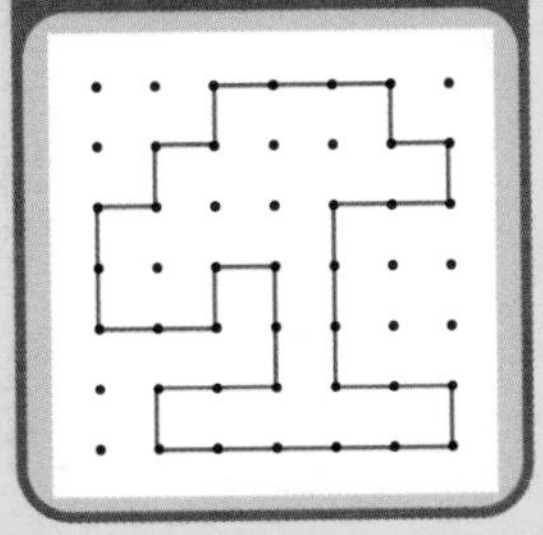
P182
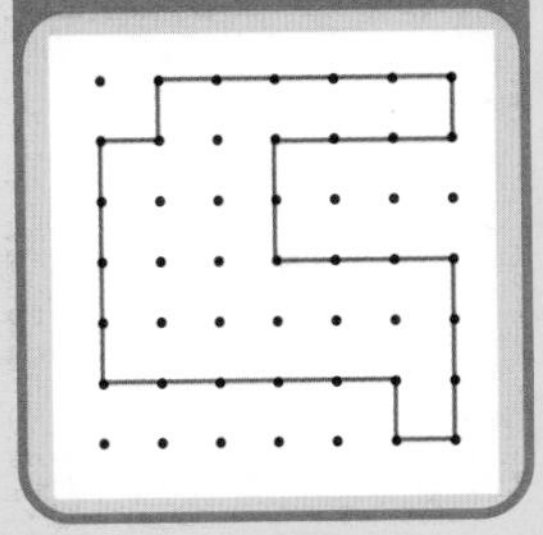
P182
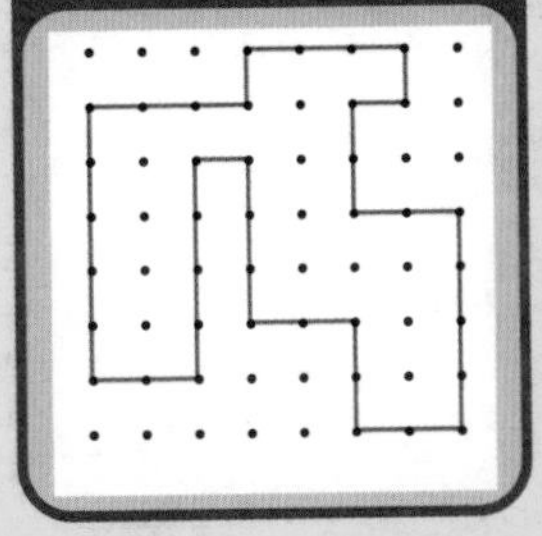
P182
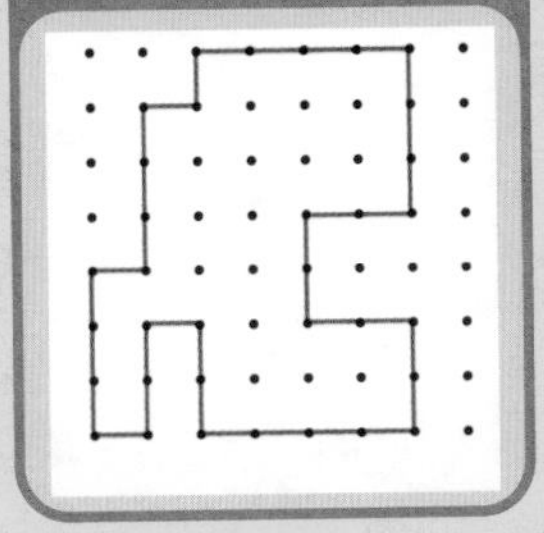
P183
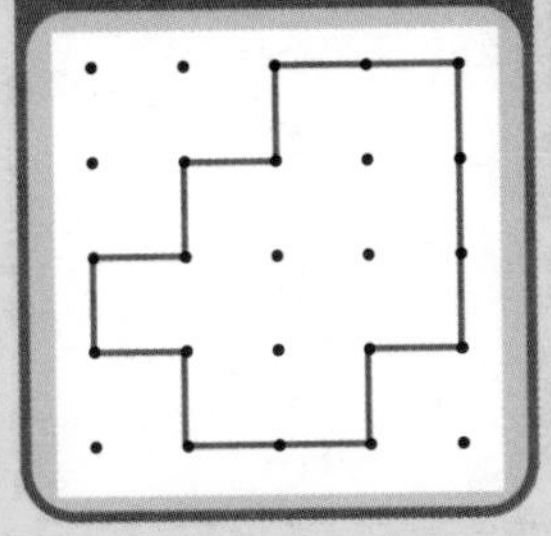
P183
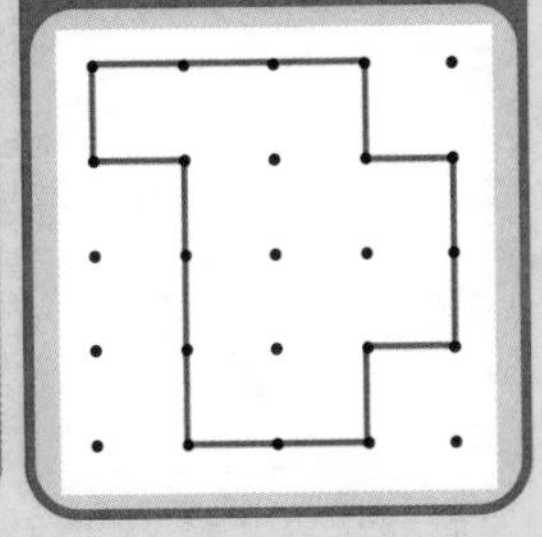
P183
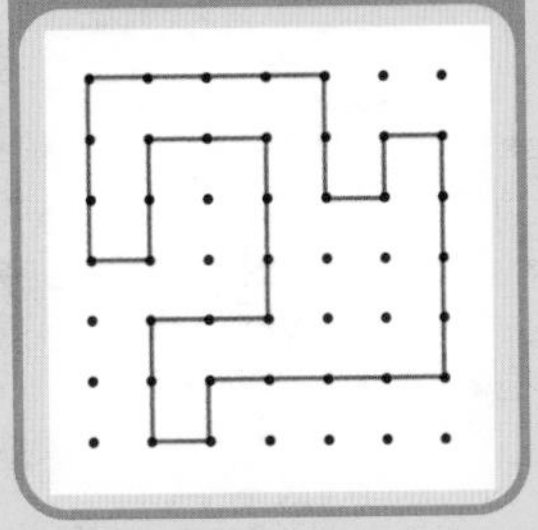
P183
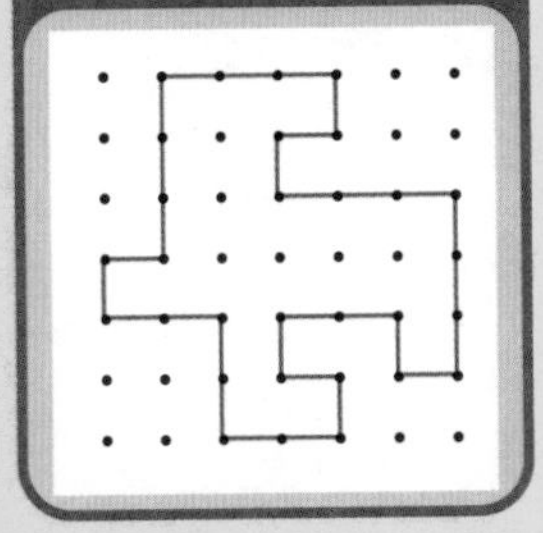

The answers correspond to the questions when read from left to right, and from top to bottom

SOLUTIONS

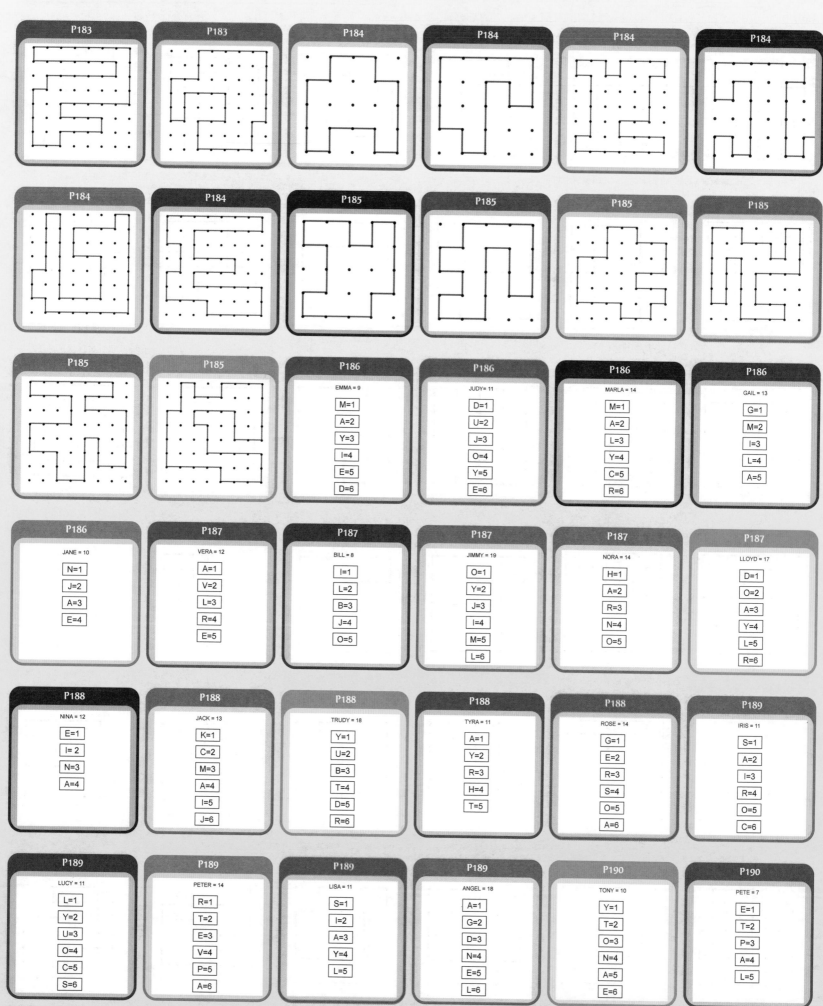

P183

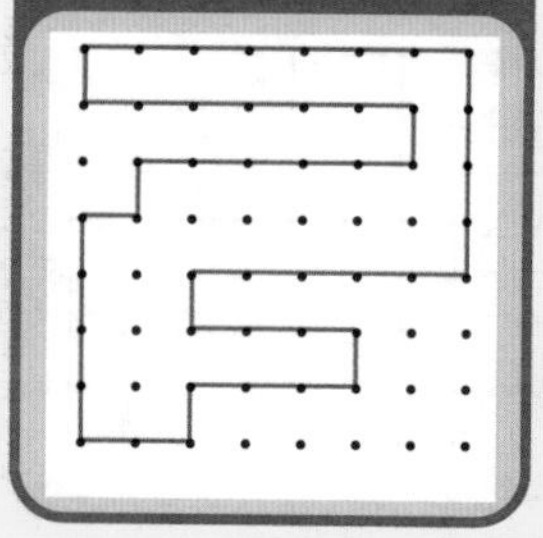

P183

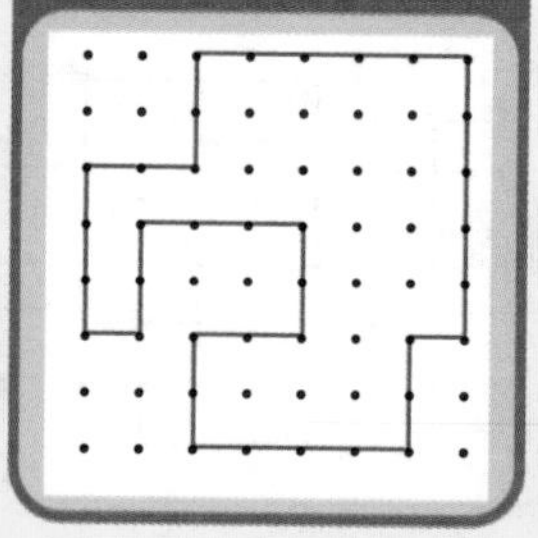

P184

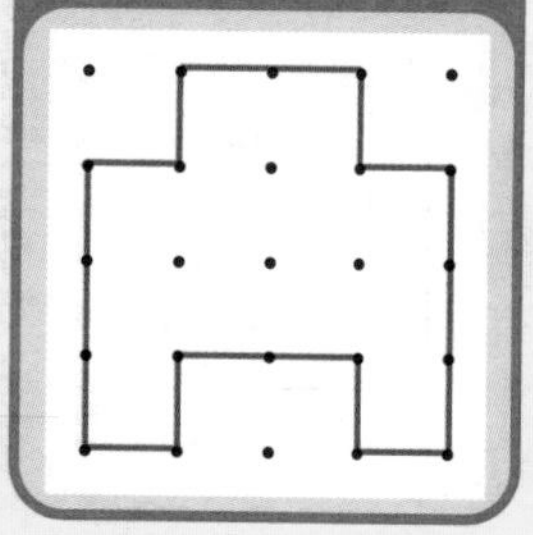

P184

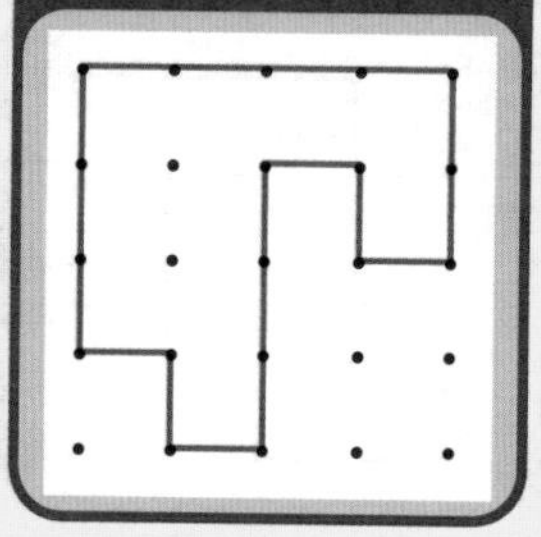

P184

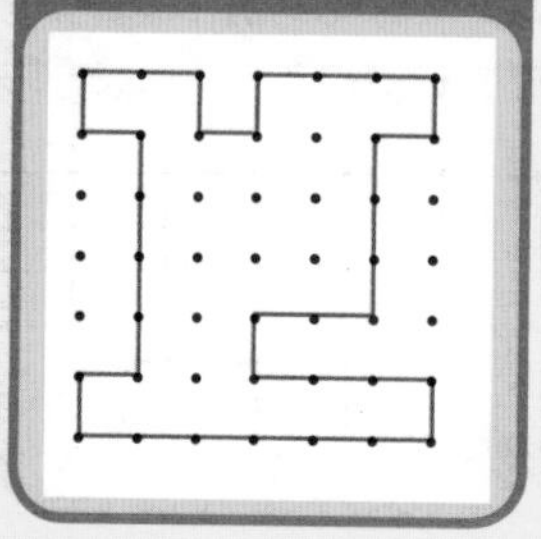

P184

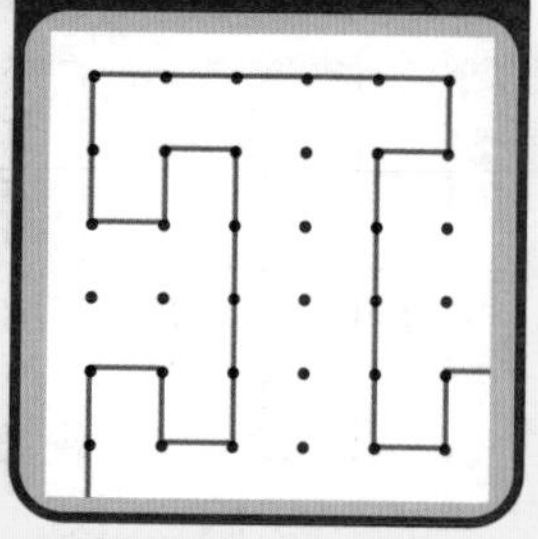

P184

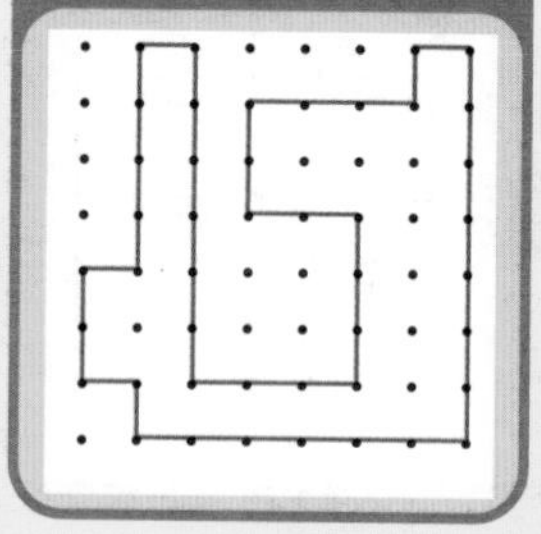

P184

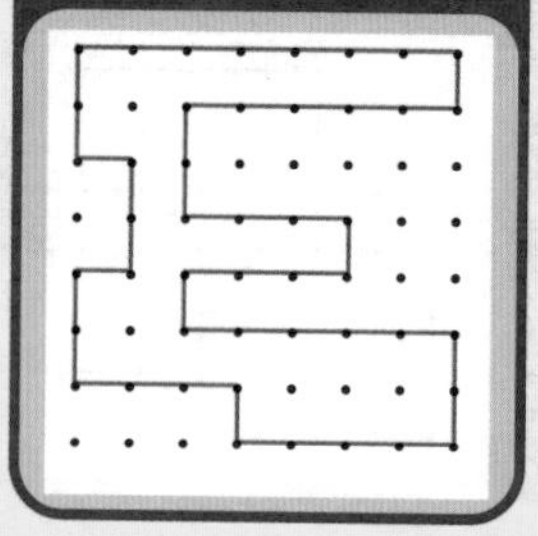

P185

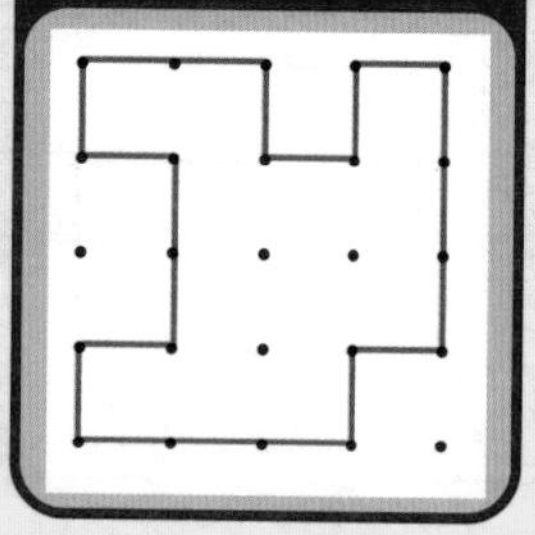

P185

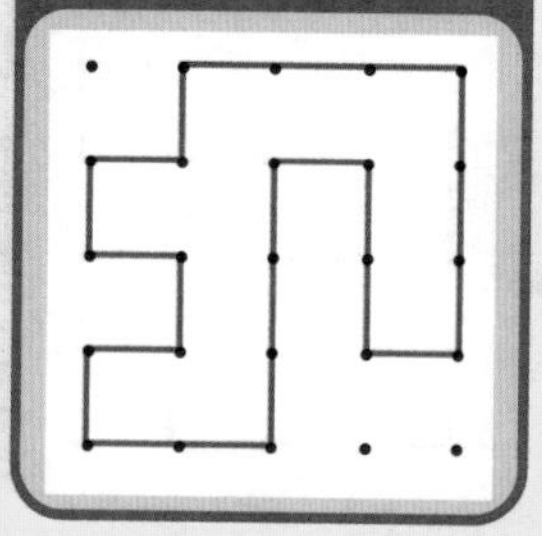

P185

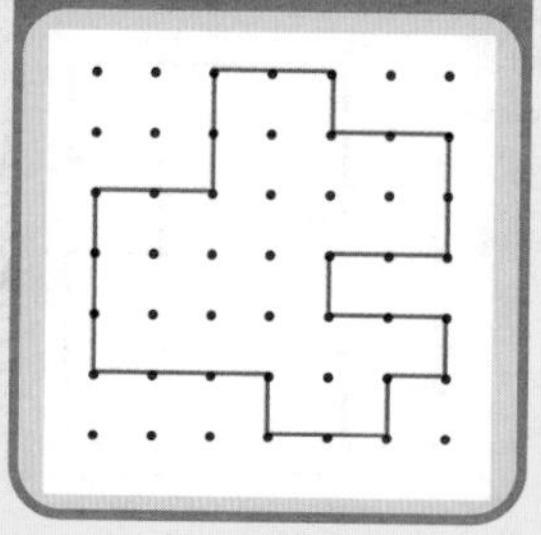

P185

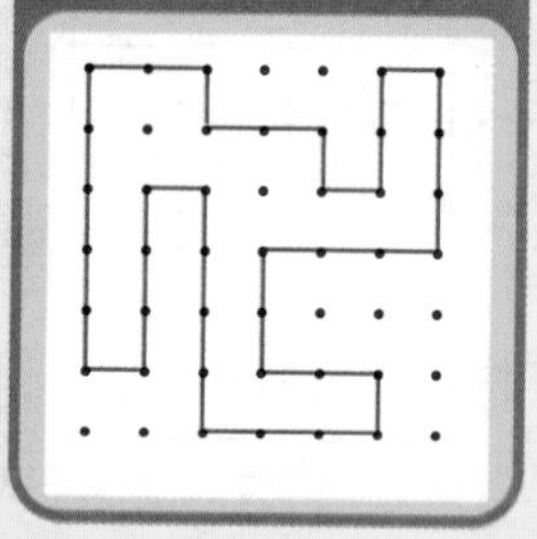

P185

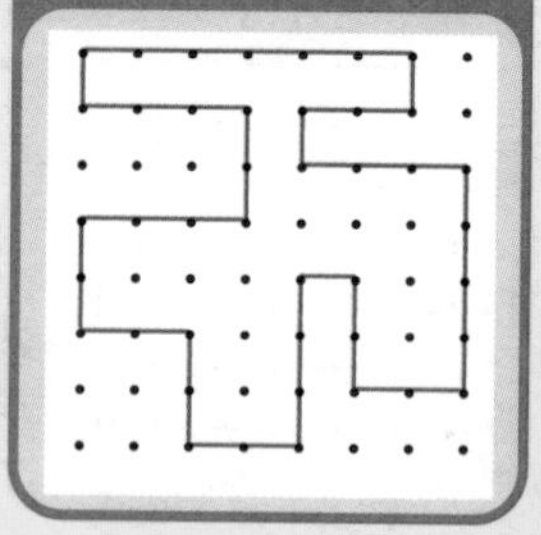

P185

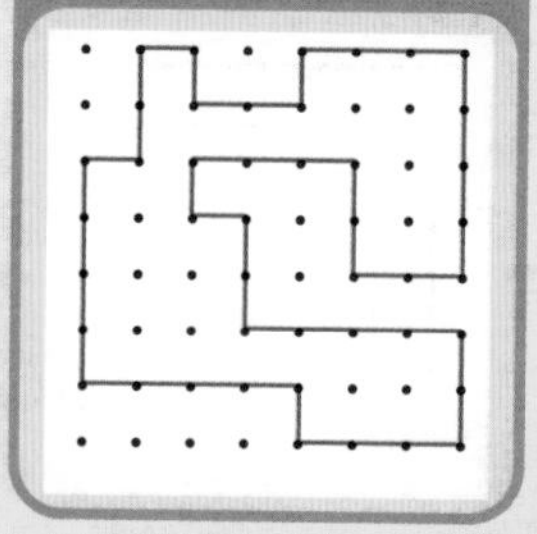

P186
EMMA = 9
M=1
A=2
Y=3
I=4
E=5
D=6

P186
JUDY= 11
D=1
U=2
J=3
O=4
Y=5
E=6

P186
MARLA = 14
M=1
A=2
L=3
Y=4
C=5
R=6

P186
GAIL = 13
G=1
M=2
I=3
L=4
A=5

P186
JANE = 10
N=1
J=2
A=3
E=4

P187
VERA = 12
A=1
V=2
L=3
R=4
E=5

P187
BILL = 8
I=1
L=2
B=3
J=4
O=5

P187
JIMMY = 19
O=1
Y=2
J=3
I=4
M=5
L=6

P187
NORA = 14
H=1
A=2
R=3
N=4
O=5

P187
LLOYD = 17
D=1
O=2
A=3
Y=4
L=5
R=6

P188
NINA = 12
E=1
I= 2
N=3
A=4

P188
JACK = 13
K=1
C=2
M=3
A=4
I=5
J=6

P188
TRUDY = 18
Y=1
U=2
B=3
T=4
D=5
R=6

P188
TYRA = 11
A=1
Y=2
R=3
H=4
T=5

P188
ROSE = 14
G=1
E=2
R=3
S=4
O=5
A=6

P189
IRIS = 11
S=1
A=2
I=3
R=4
O=5
C=6

P189
LUCY = 11
L=1
Y=2
U=3
O=4
C=5
S=6

P189
PETER = 14
R=1
T=2
E=3
V=4
P=5
A=6

P189
LISA = 11
S=1
I=2
A=3
Y=4
L=5

P189
ANGEL = 18
A=1
G=2
D=3
N=4
E=5
L=6

P190
TONY = 10
Y=1
T=2
O=3
N=4
A=5
E=6

P190
PETE = 7
E=1
T=2
P=3
A=4
L=5

The answers correspond to the questions when read from left to right, and from top to bottom

SOLUTIONS

P190

ORSON = 13

O=1 N=2 E=3 S=4 R=5 Y=6

P190

BART = 11

T=1 B=2 A=3 E=4 R=5

P190

DOUG = 14

T=1 U=2 O=3 D=4 G=5 S=6

P191

LANA = 13

S=1 L=2 A=3 M=4 N=5 I=6

P191

LEE = 7

L=1 N=2 E=3 K=4 A=5 I=6

P191

MILLIE = 17

I=1 E=2 M=3 S=4 L=5

P191

STAN = 14

I=1 A=2 T=3 S=4 N=5 U=6

P191

CELIA = 18

L=1 C=2 R=3 A=4 I=5 E=6

P192

MAUD = 13

U=1 T=2 M=3 A=4 D=5 N=6

P192

ANITA = 12

N=1 A=2 T=3 I=4

P192

ALISON = 21

A=1 I=2 N=3 L=4 S=5 O=6

P192

WILF = 10

I=1 F=2 W=3 L=4 N=5

P192

DALE = 10

L=1 A=2 E=3 D=4

P193

KERRY = 22

M=1 R=2 A=3 I=4 E=5 Y=6 K=7

P193

JOANNA = 22

J=1 R=2 O=3 A=4 N=5 Y=6

P193

BORIS = 16

I=1 S=2 O=3 B=4 Y=5 R=6 N=7

P193

LILY = 11

B=1 L=2 Y=3 I=4 O=5

P193

ROGER = 12

R=1 G=2 E=3 Y=4 O=5 A=6

P194

DEAN = 12

A=1 E=2 M=3 N=4 D=5

P194

DAVE = 10

V=1 D=2 E=3 A=4

P194

DENNIS = 17

N=1 D=2 S=3 I=4 A=5 E=6

P194

TINA = 11

A=1 N=2 T=3 H=4 I=5

P194

SUSAN = 19

E=1 N=2 S=3 L=4 A=5 U=6

P195

KATE = 12

T=1 A=2 I=3 K=4 E=5

P195

ZOLA = 13

L=1 R=2 Z=3 O=4 A=5

P195

VIVIAN = 21

D=1 V=2 A=3 N=4 I=5

P195

MAGGIE = 16

G=1 A=2 M=3 E=4 I=5 D=6

P195

JOLENE = 20

O=1 L=2 J=3 N=4 E=5 Y=6

Books in the series...

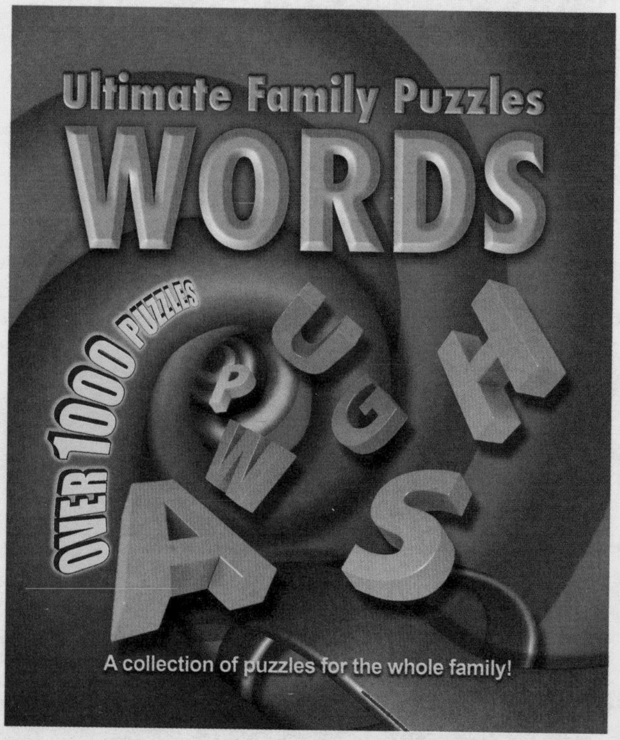